Dividing the Waters

A publication of the
Center for Self-Governance

DIVIDING THE WATERS

Governing Groundwater
in Southern California

William Blomquist

 PRESS

San Francisco, California

This book is a joint publication of the Center for Self-Governance and the International Center for Self-Governance, dedicated to promoting the self-governing and entrepreneurial way of life in the United States and around the world. Both centers are affiliated with the Institute for Contemporary Studies, a non-partisan, nonprofit public policy research organization. The analyses, conclusions, and opinions expressed in ICS Press publications are those of the authors and not necessarily those of the Institute for Contemporary Studies, or of the Institute's officers, directors, or others associated with, or funding, its work.

Publication of this book was funded in part by the U.S. Agency for International Development.

Inquiries, book orders, and catalog requests should be addressed to ICS Press, 243 Kearny Street, San Francisco, CA 94108. (415) 981-5353. Fax (415) 986-4878. For book orders and catalog requests call toll free in the contiguous United States: **(800) 326-0263.** Distributed to the trade by National Book Network, Lanham, Maryland.

Copyeditor: Vicky Macintyre
Proofreader: Eve Kushner
Indexer: Stephen R. Ingle

Library of Congress Cataloging-in-Publication Data

Blomquist, William A. (William Andrew), 1957-
  Dividing the waters : governing groundwater in southern California
  / William A. Blomquist.
    p.   cm.
  ''A publication of the Center for Self-Governance.''
  Includes bibliographical references and index.
  ISBN 1-55815-200-8 (cloth) : $44.95. — ISBN 1-55815-210-5 (paper)
  : 14.95
    1. Water-supply—Government policy—California, Southern.
  2. Water, Underground—Government policy—California, Southern.
  I. Title.
  HD1694.C2B55   1992
  333.91'04'097949—dc20
                                                92-24878
                                                  CIP

Contents

List of Maps   vii

List of Tables   viii

List of Abbreviations   ix

A Note from the Publisher   Robert B. Hawkins, Jr.   xi

Foreword   Elinor Ostrom   xiii

Preface   xv

Part One   They Prefer Chaos: Groundwater and Governance

1   Chaos or Order?   3
2   Groundwater Basins: Their Value and Characteristics   13
3   The Lay of the Land: Four Southern California   27
    Watersheds
4   Water Development and Water Law in Southern   43
    California

Part Two   Institutional Design and Development: Eight Cases

5   Raymond Basin: Constituting Self-Governance in a   73
    Groundwater Basin
6   West Basin: Simultaneous and Sequential Problem Solving   97
    in a Coastal Basin

7   Central Basin: Developing a Polycentric Public Enterprise   127
     System in the Middle of a Watershed

8   Main San Gabriel Basin: Adaptation, Innovation, and   159
     Learning

9   The San Fernando Valley: Institutional Adaptation under   189
     Constraint

10   The Mojave River Basins: High Desert Drama and   219
     Institutional Failure

11   Orange County: Governing by District, Managing by   245
     Incentives

12   Chino Basin: Basin Governance for Land Use Transition   271

Part Three   Why They Prefer "Chaos"

13   Evaluating Performance: Can "Chaos" Work?   301
14   Institutional Development and Human Action   319
15   Polycentricity, Entrepreneurship, and Performance   339

Appendix 1   An Integrated Chronology of the Eight Cases   365
Bibliography   377
Index   403
About the Author   415

List of Maps

Selected Southern California Groundwater Basins   xx–xxi
Raymond Groundwater Basin   74
West Coast Groundwater Basin   98
Central Groundwater Basin   128
Main San Gabriel Groundwater Basin   160
San Fernando Valley Groundwater Basin   190
Mojave River Groundwater Basins   220
Orange County Groundwater Basin   246
Chino Groundwater Basin   272

List of Tables

4.1 Population of Southern California Counties, 1860–1990   51

4.2 Developed Land Use, Coastal Los Angeles County, 1880–1960   57

5.1 Raymond Basin Parties' Decreed Rights, Extractions, and Total Water Use, 1945–1990   86

5.2 Cost of Raymond Basin Watermaster Services and Amount Paid by Parties, Fiscal Years 1945–1990   94

6.1 West Basin Water production and Total Water Use, 1933–1990   100

6.2 Amount of CWBWRD Pump Tax and Price of MWD Replenishment Water, 1961–1990   114

6.3 West Basin Watermaster Expenditures, 1956–1990   123

6.4 West Basin Parties to Watermaster Service, Adjudicated Rights, and Active Pumpers and Nonparties, 1956–1990   124

7.1 Water Spreading at Montebello Forebay, 1954–1990   133

7.2 San Gabriel River Watermaster Budget and Expenditures   143

7.3 Lower Area Annual Entitlement, Usable Water, and Makeup Water Received by Lower Area, and Accrued Credit or Debit of Upper Area, 1963–1964 through 1988–1989   145

7.4 Central Basin Parties to Watermaster Service, Agreed Pumping Allocation, and Active Pumpers and Nonparties, 1963–1990   149

7.5 Central Basin Water Production and Total Water Use, 1962–1990   155

7.6 Central Basin Watermaster Expenditures, 1963–1990   156

8.1 Groundwater Production and Overdraft in the Main San Gabriel Basin, 1934–1972   161

8.2 Main San Gabriel Watermaster Assessment Rates   176

8.3 Main San Gabriel Basin Operations under the Judgment   183

8.4 Main San Gabriel Basin Cyclic Storage   185

9.1 ULARA Groundwater Extractions by Subarea, 1969–1990   214

9.2 Water Imported into ULARA, 1969–1990   215

10.1 Annual Groundwater Extractions, 1950–1981   223

11.1 Orange County Water District Replenishment Assessment ("Pump Tax"), 1955–1990   256

11.2 Orange County Replenishment Water Purchase and Costs, 1950–1990   258

11.3 Orange County Groundwater Production and Total Water Obtained, 1953–1990   260

12.1 Assessments in Chino Basin, 1978–1989   283

12.2 Water Production and Replenishment in Chino Basin, 1975–1989   293

12.3 Chino Basin Production, Imports, and Total Water Use, 1975–1989   294

12.4 Chino Basin Watermaster Budget and Expenditures, 1978–1989   295

13.1 Amortized Adjudication Costs and Basin Management Costs of Groundwater Production, 1985   307

13.2 Comparisons of Water Costs with and without Management, 1985   311

List of Abbreviations

CBMWD	Central Basin Municipal Water District (Chap. 7)
CBMWD	Chino Basin Municipal Water District (Chap. 12)
CBWA	Central Basin Water Association (Chap. 7)
CBWA	Chino Basin Water Association (Chap. 12)
CWBWRD	Central and West Basin Water Replenishment District
DPW	Department of Public Works
DWR	Department of Water Resources
EPA	Environmental Protection Agency
LACFCD	Los Angeles County Flood Control District
LADWP	Los Angeles Department of Water and Power
LAFCo	Local Agency Formation Commission
MWA	Mojave Water Agency
MWD	Metropolitan Water District of Southern California
OCWD	Orange County Water District
SAWPA	Santa Ana Watershed Project Authority
SBVMWD	San Bernardino Valley Municipal Water District
SGVMWD	San Gabriel Valley Municipal Water District
SWRB	State Water Resources Board
TDS	total dissolved solids
ULARA	Upper Los Angeles River Area
USGS	U.S. Geological Survey
USGVMWD	Upper San Gabriel Valley Municipal Water District
USGVWA	Upper San Gabriel Valley Water Association
WATER	Water Association to Establish Rights
WBMWD	West Basin Municipal Water District
WBWA	West Basin Water Association
WMWD	Western Municipal Water District of Riverside County

A Note from the Publisher

You hold in your hands an extremely important book, one that contributes vitally to our understanding of successful public policy. William Blomquist explains how California water users were able to protect and allocate underground water supplies despite rapidly growing demand for scarce water resources. In telling this story, he demonstrates how people who are self-governing can solve complex and important environmental problems without the need for centralized direction—in this case, a "water czar" or statewide bureaucracy. All that is required, along with their own will, effort, and creativity, is an enabling institutional environment.

Dividing the Waters thus points out the fallacies underlying the views of public policy advocates and environmental activists who believe that central direction and control are required to cope with today's environmental challenges. As the southern California experience clearly shows, when citizens have the opportunity to engage in self-governing, collective action, and innovative, entrepreneurial solutions are encouraged, we need not have a "tragedy of the commons."

But the implications of *Dividing the Waters* extend well beyond even the contemporary debate over appropriate environmental policies. If self-governing men and women are able to successfully address issues as complex and vexing as those surrounding groundwater usage, might not their capacities in other areas of public life be just as great? Blomquist answers a powerful "Yes!"

By looking deeply into the political processes exemplified in his case studies, Blomquist illuminates the underlying principles that make possible a free and innovative society. Such a society may well be based on a polycentric order, rather than the centralized order that now prevails in most areas of our lives. Such a society holds out to all citizens the opportunity to play creative and vital roles in addressing the many challenges confronting public life. *Dividing the Waters* shows convincingly that the principles of self-governance that so impressed Alexis de Tocqueville in Jacksonian America remain no less powerful and empowering today.

Robert B. Hawkins, Jr.
President
Institute for Contemporary Studies

Foreword

It is a substantial pleasure to write a foreword for William Blomquist's *Dividing the Waters.* I feel more than a little responsible for Bill's interest in this topic as I encouraged him to undertake a dissertation that examined the stability of the institutions devised by groundwater pumpers in Raymond, West, and Central basins and Orange County, California. I first became aware of these intriguing forms of self-governance in the early 1960s when Louis Weschler and I wrote dissertations focusing on several of these basins. In his dissertation, Bill undertook a comparative study of four basins and how they have evolved over time. Bill and I then initiated a research project funded by the U.S. Geological Survey that enabled Bill to add four more cases and continue to study the four initially covered in his dissertation. As part of this project, Bill prepared a series of basin-specific reports that have been the empirical foundation for this book. While I may have been the instigator of this project, Bill has carried it much further than I dreamt was possible. Further, I have now learned more from Bill's work than I was able to teach him in the first place.

This volume illustrates the process of learning about collective-action problems in complex settings involving large numbers of participants. The complexity of these settings is far greater than we can begin to approximate in more formal theoretical representations of collective-action problems. In their efforts to reduce the adverse consequences of their interdependence with one another, participants frequently had to invent new concepts and propose rules that no one previously had used. The reader will gain substantial insight about how individuals far from the limelight of the evening news tackled tough problems affecting millions of people and vast sums of property value. And, in many instances, these individuals crafted new institutions that have performed effectively over several decades with many efficiently enhancing properties. But Blomquist's book is not only about success. It also helps us understand why some efforts to solve collective-action problems fail. For the theory of collective action to evolve still further we need to understand both successes and failures in settings that are relatively similar to one another.

This book will be of major value to many readers. Let me recommend it first to those interested in learning more about how self-governing societies work. The analysis of how individuals identify problems and set about the tasks of public entrepreneurship to solve problems is crucial to an understanding of self-goverance. Second, let me recommend it to political economists and institutional analysts interested in empirical work related to some of the toughest theoretical questions. The volume helps us understand where our current theories are sufficient and where further work is needed. Let me also recommend it to students interested in the history of the West and how it was "conquered." Part of that story has to do with the courage and fortitude of the first pioneers. But without the fortitude and vision of many of the individuals who participated in the crafting of groundwater institutions in southern California, urban populations facing the recent major droughts would have suffered far more than they did.

Elinor Ostrom
Codirector, Workshop in Political Theory
and Policy Analysis, and Arthur F. Bentley
Professor of Political Science, Indiana University

Preface

Groundwater has been referred to as the "unseen resource" and the "hidden resource." It seems appropriate, then, to use case studies involving groundwater in order to study institutional development. In many ways, institutional development is the "unseen process," perhaps even the "hidden process."

Social scientists in general, and political scientists in particular, talk and write about institutions all the time. We refer to "institutional imperatives," "institutional limits," "institutional gaps," "institutional performance," and so on. We much less often talk about the processes by which institutional arrangements come into being.

When the origins and purposes of institutions are discussed at all, they are often discussed retrospectively, with motivations imputed to the designers after the fact. Thus we find institutions characterized as congealed preferences or instruments of domination or mechanisms for the implementation of policies decided somewhere else by someone else. Sometimes, explanations of this sort can be compelling; at other times, they seem wide of the mark. In any event, there is a difference between retrospective interpretations of the origin and purpose of already-existing institutions and a conscious examination and analysis of the processes by which a particular set of institutional arrangements actually came into being. This book attempts that sort of conscious examination and analysis of institutional design and development.

Understanding the processes by which institutions are designed, established, and modified or eliminated requires a particular approach. Unless one presumes that institutions create themselves or are guided by some "invisible hand" or are "induced" by the characteristics of a situation, one must treat institutional arrangements as human creations. This entails taking some perspective on human action. Here, I view human action in the creation of institutions as intentional problem solving under constraint.

In an effort to understand both the problems that people were trying to solve and their intentions in designing the institutional arrangements that govern groundwater in southern California, I found it necessary to review documents, notes, minutes of meetings, reports, and studies written and compiled during the period of institutional development and to interview individuals who had been involved in these processes. I also talked to several people who work within those governance structures today, who bear the responsibility for maintaining water supplies for a metropolitan region of 15 million people. I collected and analyzed data from numerous sources to try to ascertain whether and to what extent the institutional arrangements they have designed and modified over time have performed as intended in dividing the waters of southern California among all these people.

In research of this type one imposes on a lot of people's time over a period of years and accumulates a great many debts. I am happy to be able to acknowledge them.

In the West and Central basins, where I started, John Joham, general manager of the Central and West Basin Water Replenishment District and of the Central Basin Municipal Water District, was extraordinarily generous. I benefited greatly from my visits with him, from his willingness to find information for me, and especially from his extensive comments on an earlier draft of the chapters on West and Central basins. John Joham also provided me with a copy of Carl Fossette's book, which the Central Basin Municipal Water District published after Mr. Fossette's death in 1985. It is an invaluable account of the development of water resource management in the San Gabriel River watershed by one who was a vital participant. During the period of this research, John Joham retired after many years of service. I wish him well. Richard Atwater, his successor, has been very helpful in the past two years by responding to requests for updated information.

Thomas Stetson of Stetson Engineers was present through each step in the development of governing institutions and water resource management programs in the San Gabriel Valley and has served both as a member of the San Gabriel River Watermaster and as the Consulting Engineer to the Main San Gabriel Basin Watermaster. He also has been involved in the Mojave River case. Mr. Stetson made time freely available for extended interviews, and his recollections proved invaluable in helping me understand both the geohydrology of the area and the process of institutional development. Kevin Smead of Stetson Engineers also helped me acquire the documentation used in this study, including several items prepared by Mr. Stetson and by Stetson Engineers in conjunction with water resource management in the San Gabriel River system.

Geologist John Mann was the expert consultant in the San Gabriel River adjudication. I met Dr. Mann while I was researching the San Fernando Valley case, in which he was intimately involved. He also was involved in the Mojave River case. He could not have been more helpful. He discussed these cases with me during my visits to southern California, corresponded, put me in touch with other people, sent me copies of useful documents, and offered welcome words of encouragement. He volunteered to contact Alfred Jorgensen, formerly of the city of Monrovia and an active participant in the San Gabriel River adjudication, and had Mr. Jorgensen send me a copy of his 1967 master's thesis on that adjudication. It is doubtless the most thoroughly documented description of that process available and yet, because it is unpublished, would otherwise probably have escaped my attention.

I might not have met John Mann if it had not been for Mel Blevins of the Los Angeles Department of Water and Power. Mr. Blevins is the court-appointed watermaster for the Upper Los Angeles River Area—the San Fernando Valley. He helped me understand the development of the basin governance structure and management system there, provided access to files and records, responded to follow-up requests, and also provided much-appreciated encouragement that I was on the right track in understanding a case that has been the subject of several controversies.

Robert Berlien made an entire day available to me at the office of the Upper San Gabriel Valley Municipal Water District and arranged for an interview with Linn Magoffin, the chairman of the Main San Gabriel Basin Watermaster and a longtime participant in water resource issues in the San Gabriel Valley. Mr. Berlien also provided free access to available copies of watermaster reports, the two principal judgments, and early records of the district and responded swiftly to follow-up requests for information.

Robert Beach of the Sonoma County Water Agency first told me about the Mojave River adjudication and recommended that I include it in this study, a recommendation for which I am grateful. In researching this controversial case, I needed the perspectives of several participants. I especially appreciate the time made available by Martin Whelan, Jr., Arthur Littleworth, Carl Coleman, Stan Shaw, Jim Gilliam, and Jon Edson. Mr. Whelan and Mr. Littleworth were attorneys on opposing sides in the Mojave River case: each graciously provided me with thoughtful and thorough recollections of the occurrences there. Mr. Coleman and Mr. Shaw were also on opposing sides in that case—Mr. Coleman was general manager during the first several years of the adjudication that Mr. Shaw opposed, and they each served at different times on the Mojave Water Agency Board of Directors. Their recollections of the political conflicts over water in the Mojave River area were invaluable. Judith Pfeffer and other staff members at the *Victor Valley Daily Press* provided valuable assistance in recovering news accounts concerning the Mojave River case.

Don Peters of the Chino Basin Watermaster was also extremely generous with his time during my visit to the Chino Basin Municipal Water District. He provided copies of documents and maps and access to the district's library and responded to follow-up requests. I had almost no prior information about the Chino Basin when we met, and he patiently guided a political scientist from Indiana through the geology, history, and management of the basin.

At the California Department of Water Resources Southern District office in Los Angeles, Carlos Madrid and Chris Nagler helped orient me to their office's role as watermaster for the West and Central basins and as staff support to the watermaster service for Raymond Basin. They and their staff also met several requests for copies of documents, maps, and records. In Sacramento, Arthur Gooch, Helen Peters, James McDaniel, and Carl Hauge also provided useful insights into the department's perspective on groundwater problems and management in the state.

At the Foothill Municipal Water District in the Raymond Basin, Ron Palmer generously provided me with his time and insights, as well as access to the district's library and a quiet place to make notes. At the Orange County Water District, Lola Handy provided me with a tour of the district's facilities, access to the district's library, and a place to work.

Special thanks go to Susan Trager, who helped me understand the Chino Basin and Orange County cases. In addition, she has been a much-appreciated reviewer of my research, providing lots of assistance and encouragement mixed with words of advice, caution, and thoughtful criticism.

In addition, I am indebted to many colleagues in the academic community. It is impossible, however, to convey what I owe to Elinor and Vincent Ostrom. It *is* possible to say without doubt that I would not have undertaken this project without them. They supported my research in every way imaginable. They have read, commented upon, and helped to improve every version of this manuscript. They have shown and continue to show me what it means to be part of a scholarly community.

Several colleagues at or affiliated with the Workshop in Political Theory and Policy Analysis at Indiana University have also reviewed and commented on this research or portions of this manuscript during its development: Roy Gardner, Roberta Herzberg, Ron Oakerson, Roger Parks, Edella Schlager, Yan Tang, Jimmy Walker. Special thanks also for the support of the staff at the workshop, especially Patty Dalecki, Gayle Higgins, and Linda Smith.

In addition to asking Elinor Ostrom a question that began this entire project ten years ago, Paul Sabatier at the University of California-Davis read this manuscript and provided helpful comments and much-appreciated encouragement. Thanks also to Larry Kiser at Eastern Washington University, Helen Ingram at the University of Arizona, and William Lord for their insights and support.

I also am grateful to my colleagues at the Department of Political Science at Indiana University, Indianapolis. In addition to providing an enjoyable working atmosphere, they have supported this research through released-time arrangements and by "going easy" on a junior colleague.

The maps used in this book were prepared by Kevin Mickey of the Cartographic Services office of the School of Liberal Arts at Indiana University, Indianapolis. The support of the school in providing Kevin's services is gratefully acknowledged.

Funding from the U.S. Geological Survey under grant number USGS 14-8-001-G1476 supported the travel and data collection necessary for this project.

Special thanks go to Bob Hawkins at the Institute for Contemporary Studies for his support of this project over the past four years (which was two years longer than I originally told him it would take). Sam Harper and Elise Paylan's enthusiasm during the development of the International Center for Self-Governance also helped move the project along. The staff at ICS Press have been remarkably efficient, helpful, and friendly, especially Barbara Kendrick, the book's editor.

Susan Trager, Zachary Smith of Northern Arizona University, and Louis Weschler of Arizona State University reviewed the manuscript for ICS Press. Their comments, suggestions, and criticisms improved the book considerably.

Although I am immeasurably indebted to all of these individuals, none of them bears any responsibility for any errors or defects that remain. Finally, I am happy to thank my wife, Kerry, who had the questionable judgment to marry a man in the middle of writing a book and who developed her own love-hate relationship with it.

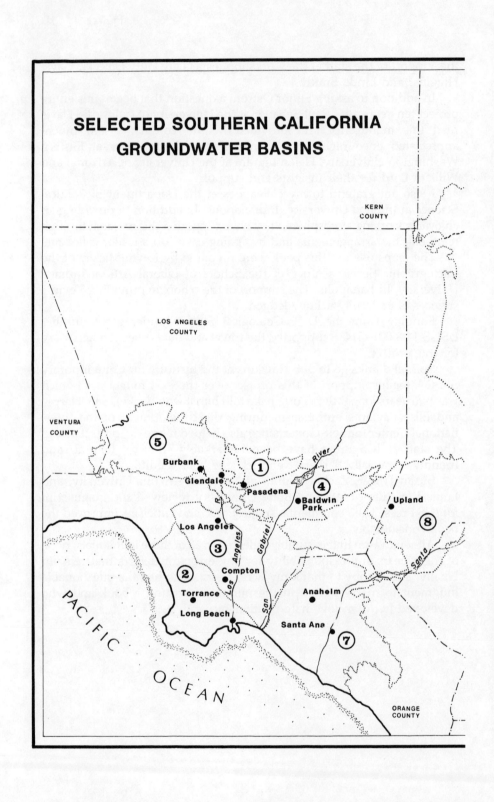

SELECTED SOUTHERN CALIFORNIA
GROUNDWATER BASINS

KERN
COUNTY

LOS ANGELES
COUNTY

VENTURA
COUNTY

⑤

Burbank

Glendale ① River

Pasadena

④

Baldwin
Park

Upland

⑧

Los Angeles

③

Compton

② Torrance

Anaheim

Long Beach

Santa Ana

⑦

PACIFIC

OCEAN

ORANGE
COUNTY

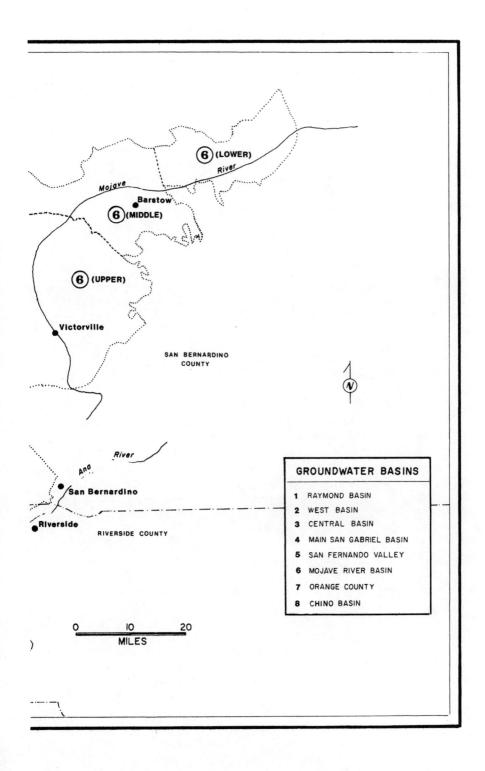

GROUNDWATER BASINS

1	RAYMOND BASIN
2	WEST BASIN
3	CENTRAL BASIN
4	MAIN SAN GABRIEL BASIN
5	SAN FERNANDO VALLEY
6	MOJAVE RIVER BASIN
7	ORANGE COUNTY
8	CHINO BASIN

PART 1

They Prefer Chaos
Groundwater and Governance

The citizens . . . do not want a comprehensive regional master plan, or a water czar, although that is probably what they should have. They prefer chaos.

—*Colorado water broker on "ABC World News Tonight,"*
August 22, 1989

1

Chaos or Order?

On Christmas Eve 1989, the lead editorial in the *Los Angeles Times* was not about gang violence or homelessness on the streets of Los Angeles. It was not about the dismantling of the Berlin Wall, or the demise of the Ceaucescu government in Romania, or the U.S. invasion of Panama, each of which had occurred the preceding week. That night the paper's lead editorial pronounced, "Water: This Time It's Serious."

Southern California's surface water supplies, the editors wrote, were drying up. It was the fourth consecutive year of drought, the driest four-year period in California since 1929–33, and several reservoirs were less than one-third full. As a result of the drought and the growing concern about water quality in the Sacramento–San Joaquin Delta, the water being brought south by the State Water Project was becoming more scarce and less predictable. Pressured by lawsuits over the ecological impact of its water imports from the Mono Basin and Owens Valley, the city of Los Angeles had reduced those imports substantially. At the same time, the Metropolitan Water District of Southern California was on the verge of losing its access to surplus Colorado River water in 1990, since the three Lower Colorado River Basin states—California, Arizona, and Nevada— were expected to consume their combined 7.5 million acre-feet allocation. Meanwhile, southern California was still gaining about 350,000 residents per year.

Water has always been "serious business" in California, especially in southern California. Cycles of precipitation and surges of development ever since 1790 have made "southern California" and "water shortage" practically synonymous and water development the necessary companion

3

of economic development. The water supply stakes are huge. Southern California is now home to about twenty million people and boasts one of the world's most prosperous economies. Yet the region has a near-desert climate and the state's water laws have long encouraged overuse.

As elsewhere in the West, water development in southern California has been accompanied by ambition and conflict. The projects referred to in the *Los Angeles Times*—the Los Angeles–Owens Valley Aqueduct, the Colorado River Aqueduct, and the State Water Project—tapped sources hundreds of miles away and became the subject of legends, books, and even movies.[1] Although some have viewed these feats of engineering as exercises of raw power, they enabled southern California to prosper through most of the dry periods of the twentieth century with little discomfort and dislocation. Indeed, these projects have made it possible for southern California to withstand severe and sustained droughts (Getches, 1991: 6). Little wonder, then, that the *Times* editors were alarmed at the prospect of all these sources being curtailed simultaneously.

What has received far less attention is the fact that the economic development of southern California has also depended greatly on the water supplies underlying much of the state. A well and a pump drawing from an invisible groundwater basin do not hold the same fascination as a 300-mile aqueduct being blasted through mountains and laid across deserts.

California's groundwater supplies and storage capacity are enormous. Groundwater basins underlie all of California's developed valleys and coastal plains, and most of the southern deserts. The estimated "usable storage capacity" of the state's nearly 450 groundwater basins is 143 million acre-feet (California DWR, 1975), which is more than triple the capacity of California's many surface reservoirs.

Groundwater serves two-thirds of the state's thirty million residents (Solley, Merk, and Pierce, 1988) and provides about one-third of all the water used in southern California (Getches, 1991: 43). Some parts of southern California depend on groundwater almost completely. For example, it provides roughly 90 percent of the water supply for the more than one million residents of the San Gabriel Valley in Los Angeles County.

Not long ago, some southern California groundwater basins were being depleted at alarming rates. In 1955, for example, the local water supplies of coastal Los Angeles County (between the San Gabriel Mountains and the Pacific Ocean) were being tapped 30 percent more per year than they were capable of sustaining (California DWR, 1964a: 46). Even with substantial amounts of groundwater in storage, this pace could not have been maintained without disastrous effects in the not-too-distant future.

But the *Times*'s editorial of Christmas Eve 1989 did not even mention groundwater, for by then some parts of the state had groundwater management programs in place, primarily in areas where communities had to compete for water from common aquifers, such as around Los Angeles. Actually, groundwater use had been brought under control in most of the area's major groundwater basins by 1980. How this happened, and the institutions and organizations created to bring about and sustain that control, are the subjects of this study.

Is There Groundwater Management in California?

Some observers may find strange the very idea of studying groundwater management in southern California, for many Californians would argue that there is no groundwater management in the state. Usually it is particle physicists and theologians who are told that the object of their research does not exist (and who generally have the good sense to ignore such remarks). Not only do many deny the existence of groundwater management in California, but these denials have made their way into important publications and should not be disregarded. Indeed, because they reflect deeper theoretical and methodological issues concerning institutional structures, it is important that they be discussed.

Those who argue that there is no groundwater management in California rest their case on the fact that California does not have any comprehensive statute or program for managing and regulating the use of groundwater (see Knapp and Vaux, 1982: 61). Some have even complained that the state's " 'no action' groundwater management system can only lead to disaster" and that a comprehensive management program "would ensure efficiency in the beneficial use of groundwater" (Mallery, 1983: 1286, 1298).

Others argue that the absence of a comprehensive statewide program does *not* mean state officials regard water management as unimportant:

> The legislature has moved cautiously with respect to groundwater problems and legislation has focused on local solutions, with emphasis on the importance of fashioning management solutions to meet local conditions and local needs. *Nevertheless, water resources management in California is treated as an issue of great public interest and given high priority,* in large part because of the scarcity of water resources in the areas with the greatest demand. (Trager, 1988: 53, emphasis added)

Because California has treated groundwater management as primarily a local function, a great variety of local governance structures have been created to design and implement management programs for many of the groundwater basins in the state. Some basins do not have governance systems or management programs. Most state legislative activity concerning groundwater has authorized the creation or modification of local governance systems (Schneider, 1977: 3; Trager, 1988: 53). The principal state agencies involved with water supplies—the Department of Water Resources and the State Water Resources Control Board—have provided investigative and technical support for local efforts.

In many quarters, these efforts are regarded as successful. A report prepared for the Los Angeles District office of the U.S. Army Corps of Engineers, for example, describes the area's groundwater basins as "well managed" (UINTEX, 1985: II-39); an engineer who has spent much of his career on water supply matters considers that "groundwater management under the existing laws of California is working very well where it has been applied" (Stetson, 1982: 3-4); and an extensive RAND Corporation study concluded, "Southern California has a relatively well-developed and diverse system of local groundwater management that has evolved on a piecemeal basis over many years" (Lipson, 1978: 1). The RAND report also concluded, "Since there is already a locally developed management program in place in major Southern California basins, there is no need for the state to impose yet another management scheme" (Lipson, 1978: 21). One author of a history of California water development was more emphatic: "There is no need for an outside agency to replace the initiative and experience which has already accomplished so much in the state" (Harding, 1960: 216).

These various evaluations differ not only in their degree of support for the present methods used to manage groundwater, but also in their focus. Critical appraisals are quick to point out that forty-two groundwater basins (roughly one in ten) are currently in overdraft, with eleven of these in a "critical condition of overdraft."[2] More positive assessments focus on the basins in southern California and around San Francisco Bay that were in overdraft, even in "critical overdraft," but are no longer in that condition.

At a deeper level, the disagreement relates to "state" versus "local" groundwater management. Proponents of state control focus on local areas that do not yet have management programs. They also contend that existing local political jurisdictions do not match the boundaries of groundwater basins and thus are incapable of managing the resource (no reference is made to the fact that no groundwater basin matches the shape of the state, either). Local governments are expected to come into conflict over groundwater resources and "need a neutral statewide program as referee to help resolve the dispute" (Mallery, 1983: 1294). But the basic complaint is that "local management cannot provide for the management of the limited resource at a statewide level" (Mallery, 1983: 1294). That statement is true by definition but has little bearing on the value of state versus local schemes. The real question that needs to be addressed here is: Can the diverse local governance structures in California be regarded as a "system," or do they form nothing more than a chaotic mass?

Unorganized Chaos, or a Diverse Order?

In other words, the conflicting views on groundwater management in California revolve around local governance and the diverse institutional rules for water supply management and the diverse water users' organizations created for this purpose. Not all local institutions or systems will have the same degree of success. Some will work better than others; some may fail to work well at all. At any given moment, some localities will have working programs in place and others will not. In these respects, people in some areas will be better off than people in other areas. These are the undeniable implications of the diversity that is characteristic of local governance. For some observers, those implications are simply unacceptable.

These concerns about local governance are not new. They have been particularly pronounced in critiques of the multiplicity of approaches and organizational forms associated with federalism (notably American federalism). Discussions on this topic abound with terms such as "piecemeal," "patchwork," "fragmented," "duplication," "overlap," "wasteful," "inefficient," "crazy-quilt," and "confusing." As the quotation at the beginning of this part of the book suggests, some people equate the diversity of local governance with "chaos."

But surface appearances of disorder may be deceiving. As Alexis de Tocqueville (1945: I, 89) pointed out in *Democracy in America*, "The appearance of disorder which prevails on the surface leads one to imagine that society is in a state of anarchy; nor does one perceive one's mistake until one has gone deeper into the subject." The aim of this book, then, is to go deeper into the subject and uncover the order of local governance that lies behind the surface appearance of chaos.

The cases presented here represent deliberate attempts by water users to craft and operate self-governing arrangements for the collective control and individual use of groundwater basins. These arrangements were not designed in a haphazard or ad hoc way; neither were they "comprehensive," in the sense of addressing simultaneously all problematic variables with full information about each. Rather, the institutional arrangements for governing and managing groundwater in California emerged during problem-solving processes that required considerable investments just to develop shared understandings of the problems users faced and organized means of communicating about them. Elinor Ostrom has described the processes as "incremental, sequential, and self-transforming institutional change" (1990: 137).

The processes of institutional design and development were marked by innovation, adaptation, learning, and entrepreneurial skill. But the processes were also constrained—by California water law, by the physical characteristics of the groundwater basins and what they could and could not do in the way of providing the desired supplies, by the southern California climate, by the fact that the existing political jurisdictions did not necessarily correspond to the boundaries of natural physical systems, by existing or simultaneously developing arrangements for land use and wastewater collection and discharge, by state and federal projects such as the State Water Project and the Central Valley Project, and by the patterns of past institutional development. Moreover, some problems emerged in the wake of efforts to solve previous problems, and the options available at a given moment were largely the result of choices made in the past. The processes were evolutionary, meaning both adaptive and path-dependent.

Although these processes yielded myriad organizations and interorganizational arrangements and rules to govern the behavior of water users, the governance systems and management programs were deliberately put together and cannot be dismissed merely as chaos. The problem is that we still know too little about polycentric structures—how they develop, how they are organized, and how they perform. Social scientists concerned with the artifactual world of human endeavor need to investigate the order underlying surface appearances of chaos just as much as physical scientists do who explore the natural world. Tocqueville urged humankind to develop a "new science of politics" based on a "science of association" in order to understand the governance of democratic societies.

Unfortunately, polycentric governance structures are not readily captured by the organizational models—markets and hierarchies—that have dominated much of the work in the social sciences. Yet, they claim our attention for important empirical and normative reasons. Empirically, nonmarket, nonhierarchical polycentric systems are ubiquitous; modern societies are not limited to two types of institutions but employ many forms (Ostrom, 1990: 14; Eggertsson, 1990: 37). One could argue that at least as much of social behavior is conducted in polycentric systems such as associations, covenants, contracts, and interorganizational arrangements as in either markets or hierarchies. Normatively, polycentricity offers better prospects for yielding self-governing systems that match the capabilities of human beings (who are neither automatons nor omniscients).

A comparative study of the institutions used to govern groundwater systems in southern California can provide considerable insight into the diverse orders of polycentric systems. As Vincent Ostrom (1962: 450) has pointed out, "Few areas . . . offer a richer variety of organizational patterns and institutional arrangements than the water resource arena.'' A central concern in managing water supplies is how to allocate a scarce resource across rival uses, which is (or was) also a question at the heart of economics. Another concern is how to resolve conflicting claims of competing interests, a question at the heart of political science. Furthermore, water management requires a clear understanding of the diverse ways in which collective efforts can be organized to solve problems and their performance assessed, which is an objective of social theory and public policy. As Ostrom (1971: 1) has also observed:

> Institutional arrangements for water resource development conform neither to the market model traditionally used by economists for conceptualizing efficient organization of economic relationships nor to the bureaucratic model used by administrative analysts for conceptualizing an efficient system of public administration.

Many efforts have been made to understand polycentric systems outside the context of water resources. Scholars studying natural resources in general, especially common-pool resources, have uncovered diverse institutional arrangements for coordinating individual behavior. One review of the work in this area concludes that associations and organizations of resource users account in large part for the presence of considerably more collective action in the management of natural resources than would be predicted using other models of human action (Uphoff, 1986: 37; see also McCay and Acheson, 1987: 9). Others have argued that an ''institutionally rich environment'' improves the prospects of individuals attempting to resolve complex problems surrounding the joint use of resources (Nunn, 1986). Several examples have been presented to demonstrate that people are capable of developing sustainable, successful self-governing regimes for coordinating their behavior and managing a resource they all use (Ostrom, 1990).

Beyond the natural resource context, John R. Commons (1968) emphasized that ''going concerns'' and their ''working rules'' integrate human behavior through a variety of contractual and other rule-ordered relationships. Such relationships can form a particular kind of organizational structure for the provision and production of collective goods at the local level in metropolitan areas, known as ''public economies'' (Ostrom, Tiebout, and Warren, 1961; Bish and Ostrom, 1973). Public economies are neither markets nor hierarchies, but they do exhibit a structure and can be crafted to convert individual preferences into the provision and production of collective goods in ways tending toward efficiency (V. Ostrom, 1991). Subsequent research studies have attempted to model the structure of public economies and have investigated their workings in particular metropolitan areas (U.S. ACIR, 1987, 1988, and 1991).

Assessing Performance across Diversity

Of course, those who seek to understand collective behavior are interested not only in organization but also in performance. It is one matter to conclude that there is order beneath a superficial appearance of chaos; it is quite another to conclude that the underlying order performs well enough that people might actually *prefer* it. To assess performance, we need examples to examine and a set of criteria by which to compare them.

The cases drawn from southern California in this volume illustrate diverse institutional arrangements at work. Both the design and the performance of the governance systems and management programs differ from case to case, yet there are enough similarities to make them useful for our purposes. The cross-cultural and cross-temporal differences that can complicate comparative studies are reduced when the cases pertain to the same kind of resources in the same part of the world over the same period of time. Some of the groundwater basins included here are even connected to one another within the same watersheds. Thus, we can compare the design and performance of the institutional arrangements with less concern that we are comparing apples and oranges.

The criteria needed to assess performance should be ones that can be applied across types of institutional and organizational arrangements (see Sproule-Jones, 1989: 47–48). The criteria used here for this purpose are compliance, effectiveness, efficiency in administration, efficiency in resource use, equity, and adaptability (for a detailed description of each, see Chapter 13).

Evaluating institutional arrangements on the basis of individuals' compliance with them recognizes that institutional arrangements are sets of rules permitting, requiring, or forbidding actions (Commons, 1968; Field, 1979; Runge, 1984; Ostrom, 1986a; Bromley, 1989: 39; Eggertsson, 1990: 70). Institutional arrangements that fail to secure the compliance of the individuals whose actions are supposed to be influenced cannot in any meaningful sense be judged to be effective, efficient, equitable, and so on.

As used here, *effectiveness* refers to whether institutional arrangements have worked as intended to resolve the problems for which they were designed and implemented. It is distinguished from *efficiency*, which for many has come to denote an inherent property of certain institutional arrangements. Controversies over the organization of natural resource management have stemmed largely from the tendency to equate certain organizational models with efficiency in performance. Depending on what literature you most often read, firms in a market, private property rights, centralized administrative structures, or other institutional arrangements simply *are* efficient, period.[3]

We will use efficiency as a criterion but in two somewhat more restricted senses that can be compared across cases. We will consider the costs of basin governance systems and management activities in evaluating *efficiency in administration*. All other things being equal, institutional arrangements that are equally effective and consume fewer resources are preferable to those that consume greater resources. We shall also consider *efficiency in resource use*. Again, all other things being equal, management activities that do a better job of directing resources to uses that are more highly valued would be judged preferable to management systems that do this less well.

Equity refers primarily to the distribution of the costs and benefits associated with the performance of institutional arrangements. The equity of institutional arrangements will be assessed primarily by how closely the distribution of costs in supporting the management system is related to the distribution of benefits from the use of the resource, and whether individuals with assets in the use of the resource have retained something of value.

A word should also be said about *adaptability*, which is not made an explicit criterion of performance as often as it should be. Since human action usually takes place in a changing world that continually alters the utility of current arrangements and throws up new problems and opportunities, adaptability will greatly affect the performance of the institutional arrangements people create to help them solve their problems (Bromley, 1989: 49). This is especially so when people have deliberately taken changing conditions and circumstances into account in devising solutions to problems (as they have in managing water supplies in southern California). The demonstrated ability of those institutional arrangements to respond to change should be included as a measure of their performance (see Ostrom, 1990: 58).

As we shall see, not all of the institutional arrangements described and evaluated in this book were able to eliminate groundwater problems, and none is free from criticism. In one case, local water users have still to develop a working basin governance system, much less a basin management program. In other cases, results have fallen short of expectations or desires, owing to poor institutional design, legal or political constraints, or both.

On the other hand, where self-governing systems such as these have generated successes, it is important to study them (see Ostrom, 1986a: 9). By analyzing successes, as well as shortcomings and failures, we improve our understanding of human behavior and the ability of people to put together solutions to complex problems. Finally, it is important to study relatively successful polycentric, self-governing systems in order to rebut the notion that the only alternative to master plans and water czars is chaos.

NOTES

1. See, for example, Ostrom (1953), Cooper (1968), Kahrl (1982), and Reisner (1986). The widely acclaimed 1974 Roman Polanski film *Chinatown* weaves a tale of intrigue through the story of the Los Angeles Aqueduct and the development of the San Fernando Valley.

2. None of these is in the more heavily populated counties of southern California.

3. See, for example, the extensive literature on common property rights versus privatization in the allocation of resources. Brief reviews can be found in Blomquist (1987a) and Ostrom (1990). The better part of a career could be passed merely in counting the number of times it has been written that a system of private property rights "yields," "generates," "ensures," or "results in" efficiency—apparently regardless of what individuals do with their rights or their property. See Bromley (1989: 12–18) for a strong critique of this practice of equating private property with efficiency.

2

Groundwater Basins
Their Value and Characteristics

Since the cases presented in Part 2 may be difficult to follow without some background about groundwater and groundwater basins, this chapter provides a few details on their general characteristics, their value as resources, and the rationale for some deliberate effort to manage and protect them. It also explains how basins may differ and why a knowledge of their particular features is essential for effective and skillful basin management.

General Characteristics

Underground water supplies are generally obtained from aquifers—which are zones or strata of saturated sediment beneath the surface of the earth. The composition of the sediments in an aquifer affects its ability to receive and transmit water. Aquifers composed of porous materials (such as gravel and coarse sand) will receive and transmit water more readily than those composed of finer material.

A groundwater basin consists of one or more aquifers bounded by nonwater-bearing material (such as bedrock) or an underground displacement of rock (such as a fault or divide). Multiple aquifers may occur in vertical sequence or side by side (with some overlap), in both cases separated by less permeable material such as clay.

Water enters a groundwater basin either by percolating through the soil and overlying sediments or by flowing in from adjacent underground water across a fault or other subterranean divide. The percolating water may originate from precipitation on the surface of the earth, from streams or other bodies of water on the surface, or from water applied to the overlying lands by people.

The rate of percolation depends on the characteristics of the overlying soil and sediments—the more porous these are, the faster that water can infiltrate them. Areas in which water percolates rapidly into an aquifer are known as forebays. As water percolates, it passes through unsaturated sediments (known as the vadose zone) into the saturated zone. The surface of the saturated zone—the plane dividing it from the unsaturated zone—is known as the water table. The water table in a groundwater basin rises and falls with the amount of water stored in the basin.

Human beings have devised ways to replicate and promote the natural processes by which water in a basin is replenished. Artificial replenishment endeavors either to raise the level of the water table or to increase the amount of water in storage. This is usually accomplished by capturing and retaining water with surface impoundments such as dams, dikes, and water spreading grounds, from which the water percolates into the underground supply.

Groundwater will travel from a basin with a higher water table to a basin with a lower water table; and within an aquifer, it will move from areas of higher elevation toward areas of lower elevation. Like the percolation rate, the rate at which water moves through an aquifer (known as the transmissivity rate) depends on the characteristics of the sediments.

The slope at which water moves within an aquifer is called the hydraulic gradient. Generally, this slope tends to be steeper nearer the area where water is entering the aquifer. Because soil and sediments provide some resistance to the movement of water, groundwater takes time to enter and move through the saturated zone. A "mound" of groundwater may even develop beneath a forebay or other area in which water is being introduced more rapidly than it is being distributed.

Water moves not only into a basin but also out—both by natural and by artificial means. In the latter case, groundwater may be extracted by wells and pumps. Such extraction affects the movement of water through an aquifer, since it temporarily lowers the groundwater level in the immediate vicinity and creates a depression in the water table. An isolated depression in the underground water level is called a "cone"; a series of depressions is called a "pumping trough." Water from the surrounding area will move toward the cone or trough and thus diverge from its natural path. Wells are sometimes said to be "pulling water," since pumping appears to pull water within the aquifer toward the well.

Water flowing through an aquifer eventually reaches a confining boundary. There, depending on such factors as the hydraulic gradient and the amount of water in storage, it may be pushed out of the basin. Water may leave a basin in three principal ways. First, the departing water may flow into an overlying stream channel, which is especially likely to occur if a surface stream has carved a channel in the bedrock or fault boundary of the basin and also exits from the overlying land at that point. Water that leaves in this manner is called "rising water."

Second, if, instead, the basin water meets an overlying layer of relatively impermeable material, it will be confined within the aquifer and be unable to escape as rising water. Eventually, the pressure of the water moving into the aquifer may become great enough to force water through a fissure in the overlying material, and it may emerge at the surface as a spring. If a pipe or well is driven through the confining material into the pressure zone, water may flow to the land surface. This is known as "artesian water," and such a well as an "artesian well" or "flowing well." If the pressure is insufficient to bring water all the way to the land surface, the level to which it rises in the well is known as the piezometric level.

Third, groundwater may also flow into an adjacent basin across an underground divide, as already mentioned. Basins often occur in a series beneath streams and rivers, as is the case in each of the watersheds discussed in this book. The groundwater in such a watershed crosses from basin to basin, sometimes emerging on the surface as rising water, otherwise passing across hydrologic divides as subsurface flow. If the water system at the surface empties into an ocean, the last in the underlying series of basins usually will be in hydrologic contact with the ocean and some fresh groundwater may pass into it.

In a typical basin, groundwater is a renewable resource. A certain amount may be "harvested" over regular intervals without impairing the resource, that is, without seriously depleting the amount of water in storage in the basin. This is the safe yield of a basin. The "annual safe yield" of a basin would be roughly equivalent to its long-term average annual natural replenishment.

The supply of groundwater in a basin is regulated by this natural replenishment and natural disposal, which may not be equal at any given moment but can achieve a balance over time. In periods of heavy rainfall and percolation, the basin will receive a temporary surplus of water, the water table will rise, and underground "mounds" may form beneath forebays. But as the excess water moves into and through the basin, eventually it will be disposed of as additional rising water, subsurface outflow, or artesian flow, or it may be removed by increased extractions from wells.

This natural balance can be exploited to stabilize or regulate natural fluctuations in surface water supplies and variations in human demand for water. Over the centuries, people have devised ways to regulate the flows of surface water systems by impounding rivers and streams behind dams to capture and retain water for use in dry periods and releasing controlled amounts in order to regulate instream flows. In more recent times, they have also discovered that groundwater basins may be used in conjunction with surface water supplies to contend with the variability of the latter. Water may be stored underground when surface water is in abundance to create a hedge against periods in which surface water is in short supply. During such periods, the stored water can be pumped from underground and used to meet present demands. Stored underground water may also be used to meet "peak" demands, so that surface water storage and distribution systems can be built to an average-demand capacity rather than a peak-load capacity (Young, 1987: 206). Over the long term, the balance between replenishment and disposal can be maintained, while greater benefits are being reaped from the groundwater resource. Such a "conjunctive use" of groundwater and surface or imported supplies improves the general efficiency and value of a water system (Bredehoeft and Young, 1983: 1120).

Depending on their physical characteristics, groundwater basins may also serve as underground water distribution systems. Wells sunk into a groundwater basin can provide water near the point of use for a community of water users extending over hundreds (sometimes thousands) of square miles in much the same way that facilities built and maintained to convey surface water from a natural supply source (such as a lake or stream) or an impoundment structure (such as a dam and reservoir) serve points of use miles away.

Common Threats: Overdraft and Contamination

The fact that water levels in underground aquifers rise or fall depending on the balance between replenishment and disposal gives rise to two important potential problems: overdraft and contamination. Overdraft occurs when the amount of water being removed from a basin exceeds the amount of water being restored—in other words, when the "safe yield" is persistently exceeded. Overdraft means, among other things, that the groundwater in storage is being used, in addition to the renewable yield of the resource.

Overdrafting in modest amounts and for limited periods is unlikely to cause serious adverse consequences in most groundwater basins. Persistent overdraft, however, can create a number of problems, particularly for water users. If water is being lifted to the surface by pumps, the increased pumping lifts impose greater costs on water users. After levels fall below a certain point, wells must be deepened. Groundwater pumpers who cannot meet these increased expenses may find themselves excluded from the water supply. Pumpers near the edges of the aquifer may find that they can no longer obtain water at all, regardless of their "willingness to pay."

If the water removed from the spaces within the water-bearing material is not replaced, the sediments can become compacted and storage space in the aquifer may dwindle or even disappear. With extensive compaction, land may subside and structures built on it may weaken or collapse.

When underground water levels drop drastically, contamination also may occur. As sediments lose their porosity and become compacted, the minerals they contain may emerge and mingle with the remaining underground water, causing water quality to decline. In a coastal basin, such a fall may allow seawater to intrude into the freshwater in the aquifer, which would also affect water quality.

Managing Groundwater Basins: Why Bother?

Groundwater and groundwater basins are valuable resources because of the quantity of supply and the possibility for storage and distribution, but their use must be regulated to preserve or enhance their value. Groundwater basin management represents a deliberate effort to derive greater benefits from the use of this resource while avoiding its depletion and the associated human welfare costs.

The importance placed on managing groundwater basins stems from the concern for welfare losses resulting from depletion of the resource, including the costs imposed on water users and the benefits forgone. Most communities faced with dwindling groundwater supplies would be forced to turn to surface water to meet their needs, perhaps importing it from a distant source. To get an idea of the costs of importing a water supply to an area that has lost its local supply one need only look at southern California. To replace local groundwater supplies in coastal Los Angeles County with enough imported water from the Metropolitan Water District of Southern California to maintain current levels of use would cost water users at least $28 million more per year (Ostrom, 1990: 168).

As figures presented in Chapter 13 indicate, however, such replacement would be the least expensive loss that the destruction of groundwater resources would impose on southern California water users. The value of groundwater basins for water storage and distribution as part of a conjunctive use program may even exceed their value as sources of water supply. This value may be approximated by looking at the cost of constructing artificial surface storage and distribution facilities sufficient to contain and convey surface or imported water supplies.

Underground storage is also preferable in several respects to storage in surface water reservoirs. Water stored underground does not evaporate, as it does in surface impoundments and aqueducts (Burges and Marnoon, 1975: 33; California DWR, 1975: 129). If the water needs to be stored for long periods, evaporation losses can be a serious concern, especially in arid regions where evaporation rates are high. Groundwater basins also do not require continual maintenance and repair, as do surface water impoundments, which are more vulnerable to damage and erosion. Furthermore, above-ground water storage, especially in large facilities such as dams, supplants existing and potential land uses and has a greater impact on the surrounding habitats and ecosystem than underground water storage. If an area experiences droughts only occasionally, above-ground water storage translates into a large investment in physical facilities that are unneeded most of the time (Howe and Easter, 1971: 3). Underground storage can reduce the need for such costly facilities.

These advantages of underground storage were clearly perceived many years ago by California's Division of Engineering and Irrigation:

> By combining surface and underground storage in a coordinated plan, the maximum service will be attained from these waters, even a greater service than could be obtained from storage in surface reservoirs, for with complete development by surface storage, about one-third of all the water would be lost by evaporation. Without some surface storage, however, to partially equalize the flow, large volumes of flood water would rush off into the ocean too quickly for absorption by the gravels in the stream beds or diversion to artificial spreading grounds. (California DPW, Division of Engineering and Irrigation, 1923: 50)

When a groundwater basin is destroyed, water users not only lose the comparative advantages of underground water storage and distribution, but they also suffer enormous financial costs. Surface storage and distribution systems are expensive to construct, especially in metropolitan regions where land for such facilities is scarce and its purchase price is high. Any such replacement of groundwater storage and distribution capacity, even if feasible, "would be an economic disaster of major proportions" (Ostrom, 1990: 169).

Some natural resource economists have argued, however, that groundwater basins could still be maintained and beneficially used without deliberate efforts to manage them. Their view is that uncontrolled pumping would result in falling water levels and rising pumping costs, which "would eliminate the less valuable users progressively until the water table stabilized, with the average rate of replenishment equal to the rate of extraction by the remaining users" (Bain, Caves, and Margolis, 1966: 454).

This "competitive equilibrium" argument has a number of problems. For one thing, it fails to address the potentially significant welfare losses associated with this equilibrium, or to assess those losses against the benefits and costs of the "special policy measures" taken to manage the resource. At the competitive equilibrium, fewer water users enjoy the same or smaller water yield at higher pumping costs. The costs of basin management may be more than offset by the welfare differential between the competitive equilibrium and managed use of the resource that would sustain the yield of the resource for a greater number of users over a longer period of time at lower pumping costs. (See Chapter 13 for further discussion of this empirical question.)

Moreover, it is assumed that the costs of lowered water levels fall equally across all pumpers, so that the uses of the basin that are curtailed are the less valuable or less efficient uses. This might be true in the case of a flat-bottomed aquifer of even thickness in which water is evenly distributed. If it is bowl-shaped or tilted (or both), however, as most aquifers are, a drop in the water table will drive out water users at the edges or at the higher end of the basin regardless of how dearly they value the use of the basin or how efficiently they operate. Those pumpers' wells simply will fail to reach water. We therefore cannot rest easy in the assumption that the competitive equilibrium will ensure that higher-valued uses are preserved and lower-valued ones are eliminated.

The competitive equilibrium argument also fails to recognize the negative consequences of overdrafting to the basin itself: namely, the destructive potential of sediment compaction, land subsidence, or degradation of water quality resulting from sustained lower underground water levels. Pumpers' actions are assumed to impose no negative externalities on one another apart from the increased pumping costs, which are internalized by each identically situated pumper in making benefit and cost calculations about whether to continue pumping. Some proponents of this argument suggest that these negative consequences (together with their known likelihood of occurrence) are taken into account by pumpers, who then overdraft the basin and lower water levels to a point that will balance the increased costs of pumping with the benefits therefrom while forestalling compaction, subsidence, degradation, or any other negative consequences. Pumpers, in other words, are either blessed or brilliant.

The competitive equilibrium argument further assumes that there are no interbasin consequences of overdrafting and the lowering of water levels. Each groundwater basin is assumed to exist in complete isolation from any surface water system or other basins. Otherwise, the actions of pumpers in lowering water levels in the basin would tend to reduce or eliminate subsurface or rising water outflow to other basins and other water users and would increase subsurface inflow and percolation from other water supplies.

In sum, the competitive equilibrium argument presumes a flat, isolated aquifer of even thickness throughout, which can be overdrafted and maintained at lowered water levels for indefinite periods without adverse consequences other than increased pumping costs for the remaining pumpers. As soon as such an aquifer can be found, the analysis can be applied; as soon as *two* such aquifers can be found, the competitive equilibrium approach can be compared with the basin management approach. Of course, *no* such aquifer can be found.

The basic flaw in this argument is not just that no real-world groundwater basin has *all* of these characteristics but that precious few have *any* such characteristics. The argument ignores virtually all of the potential problems that cause people to consider basin management in the first place. Why people bother with groundwater basin management, then, is not just that they want to take care of some extremely valuable resources. They also see a host of problems other than increased pumping costs, and the extent and severity of these problems depend upon the basin's particular characteristics.

Particular Characteristics

Groundwater hydrology, the general knowledge of groundwater basins, obviously is important to understanding the properties and processes at work in a specific location. Nevertheless, it is a mistake to believe that one can move from general knowledge of groundwater basins to a general model of a groundwater basin to a plan for the use of a particular basin and to the implementation of that plan. Just as the competitive equilibrium argument has little connection with the situations actually faced by groundwater users, so will any model or plan based on an idealized basin. Groundwater basin management cannot proceed without both general and specific knowledge, the latter of which is decidedly more important.

The Basin

Among the particular circumstances that must be taken into account, one of the first is whether and in what ways the given basin is connected with other water supplies. If it is connected to an adjacent basin, for instance, even a small lowering of the water level in one may choke off subsurface inflow to the other, depending on the kind of the juncture between them. Where a groundwater basin supplies the base flow of a surface stream with rising water, excessive lowering of the groundwater levels will reduce the streamflow and thus the supply for surface water users.

The shape of the individual basin must also be taken into account. In a relatively flat basin, the pumping action of water users will have an effect on their immediate neighbors, since the pumping cones or troughs created by such action will form localized gradients within the basin, as mentioned earlier. In a basin with a distinct slope, users pumping water in the higher parts of the basin will affect downgradient water users, even though they may be miles away. Changes in water levels will not affect groundwater users equally: those using water from the upper part of the slope may feel the effects of dropping water levels, whereas downgradient users may be affected by rising water levels if the water table comes too near the land surface.

The shape of a particular aquifer also affects the differential benefits and costs of water level changes. The Ogallala, or High Plains, aquifer provides an interesting example. This aquifer is shaped not like a bathtub but an egg carton, with its deeper parts separated by shallower ones. Thus, even though users are drawing from a common supply and will all experience increased pumping lifts when water levels drop, those drawing water from deeper parts of the aquifer are in less danger of losing their water supply than those drawing from shallower parts. This means that falling water levels may cause more problems for some users than for others (Nunn, 1986: 181–85).

The structure and component materials of an aquifer also matter. Karst aquifers, created by the collapse of limestone formations or dolomite or gypsum beds, tend to be enclosed depressions and underground caves filled with water. These structures are relatively fragile compared with alluvial-filled valley basins, and groundwater depletion through overdrafting, even for a short period, can result in sudden land subsidence. In contrast, many alluvial basins can be overdrafted for long periods with less likelihood of adverse effects other than increased pumping lifts. Although sediments can still become compacted, land can subside, and the water quality can deteriorate, the effects are more gradual. Volcanic and other "hard-rock" basins tend to be relatively small and porous and are dewatered much more rapidly than alluvial basins. These differences clearly affect the options for basin use. Practices that would be suitable in alluvial basins (such as raising and lowering water levels as part of a conjunctive use program) would be considerably more risky in aquifers that were created by different processes and composed of different materials.

Furthermore, whether an aquifer is confined and under pressure makes a considerable difference to the possibilities for artificial replenishment. Completely confined aquifers can only be replenished by subsurface inflow, by very slow leakage of water through the confining material, or by the injection of water. Confined aquifers that are not entirely covered may receive replenishment from the land surface over a portion of the aquifer. Unconfined aquifers are not shielded from the ground surface and can receive water directly by percolation from the overlying area. Although unconfined aquifers are more easily replenished and have greater water storage potential, they present other concerns. Because there is no substantial barrier between the land surface and the water table, nothing impedes the upward movement of the water table toward the land surface, or the downward movement of contaminants toward the water supply.

The presence of multiple aquifers in a groundwater basin is yet another factor affecting basin use. In a basin with layered and separated aquifers, if the water supply from one aquifer becomes degraded or depleted, water users may be able to reach another aquifer and still pull adequate quantities of high-quality water. If a basin has only one producing aquifer, or if it has more than one but they are not completely separated from one another, then depletion and reduced water quality will have even more serious ramifications for the water supply available to water users.

Coastal groundwater basins give rise to additional concerns, particularly if they are adjacent to bodies of saltwater. As mentioned earlier, when the water level in an aquifer falls, the freshwater it holds can be invaded by saltwater—which has a greater density than freshwater and will tend to replace the freshwater from below whenever the two come in contact (Banks, 1962: A-11). If water levels in a coastal aquifer are drawn down far enough, seawater will displace the freshwater and render the underground supply useless. If water levels in the aquifer are maintained higher inland, the ocean water that comes into contact with the freshwater in the aquifer will remain static and will not contaminate the freshwater supply. If the gradient toward the sea is too great, however, freshwater will flow out of the basin into the ocean and be wasted. Ideally, a static confrontation needs to be maintained between the freshwater in the aquifer and the saltwater in the ocean, but this is extremely difficult.

An essential point to consider here is that groundwater basins are hidden from view. It is one thing to recognize the importance of the particular basin characteristics described above. It is another thing altogether to imagine that groundwater users automatically know and incorporate these matters into basin use decisions. For example, Banks (1962: A-12) identifies five causes of increased salinity in a groundwater basin *other than saltwater intrusion*, but there are usually no means for peering into a basin to see which is causing the salinity problem. Whether the basin is in contact with other water supplies, whether there are several aquifers beneath the land surface, what shape they have, whether any or all of them are completely confined (and if partially confined, where the confining material begins and ends), whether any or all of the aquifers in a coastal basin are in hydrologic contact with the ocean, even the boundaries of the basin itself—all are matters of vital importance and yet are highly unlikely to be known before the fact by water users. As a result, it is entirely possible for water users to be wrong in their estimation of the properties of the particular basin on which they rely, and those errors themselves have consequences for basin use.

The Overlying Area

Other important factors for water users to consider have to do with the area overlying the groundwater basin. These areas differ in many respects, beginning with the use to which the land is put, notably agricultural versus urban use.

Agricultural land use tends to require the application of greater quantities of water per acre than urban use. An acre of irrigated cropland generally consumes more water than an acre of residential or commercial land. The development of a particular area for irrigated agriculture is likely to place as much or more strain on local water supplies as would urban development, even though urban development places many times more people on the same overlying land. This suggests that total water demands on a groundwater basin would decline if land is converted from agricultural to urban uses. Frequently, this is the case.

Return flows, however, must also be taken into account. Clearly, water that does not evaporate or is not consumed by the crops sinks back into the ground. Urbanized areas, on the other hand, usually construct sewage and wastewater systems to collect used water from homes and businesses and transport it to a surface water supply such as a river or ocean. As land converts from agricultural to urban uses, per-acre water requirements decline, but so do per-acre return flows, and the net balance between these two reductions has important ramifications for the underground water supply.

Urbanized areas also create different replenishment problems. Other things (such as soil composition) being equal, water falling on or flowing over agricultural or undeveloped lands will be more likely to percolate directly underground than water falling on an urbanized area. As urbanization proceeds and more areas are built up and paved over, less land is available for direct percolation—put simply, rainfall does not percolate through parking lots. Storm flows are more likely to be gathered by stormwater drains and ushered out to a river or ocean. It may become necessary to identify particularly good recharge zones in urbanizing areas and protect them and thereby ensure that water continues to be supplied to the underlying groundwater basin (Dutcher and Peterson, 1975). Although urbanization is not an unmixed blessing from a water supply standpoint, neither is it a curse, which means that water users need to pay close attention to land uses as they attempt to define their problems and prospects.

The Significance of Time-and-Place-Specific Information

The point of this discussion is not to demonstrate that groundwater basins are like snowflakes or fingerprints—no two are exactly the same—and that no generalizations can be made about them. The fact that no two individuals have identical sets of fingerprints does not keep us from usefully thinking and talking and writing about "people," and the uniqueness of each snowflake does not prevent us from considering the properties of "snow." Similarly, we can recognize the particular characteristics of a groundwater basin and still be able to think and talk and write about "groundwater basins."

What is important to recognize is that the difficulties encountered by groundwater users in any given location will depend in large measure on the properties of the basin on which they rely. If users hope to cope with and overcome those difficulties, they will have to know not only the general principles of "how a groundwater basin works" but also learn about the particular characteristics of the basin they are using. The solutions they devise (if they do) will relate to the particular characteristics of that basin and may not resemble the solutions arrived at in another place (even an adjacent basin), despite the fact that users in both places are drawing their supplies from groundwater basins and applying some general knowledge of groundwater in the process.

In other words, it is important to distinguish between "general" or "scientific knowledge," which is "the knowledge of general rules," and that "body of very important but unorganized knowledge" that is "the knowledge of the particular circumstances of time and place" (Hayek, 1945: 521–22). In the modern world, we are enamored of general or scientific knowledge and seem convinced that if we can only accumulate and refine sufficient quantities of this knowledge of general rules, we will eventually be able to resolve problems. Yet, "the economic problem of society," which is to allocate resources in a way that produces desired benefits under conditions that require "rapid adaptations to changes in the particular circumstances of time and place" (Hayek, 1945: 524), makes the knowledge of the latter more valuable (see also Lindblom, 1990). As has also been pointed out, "Unfortunately, failure or success often reflects the willingness to depart from rules when conditions have changed; what counts, then, is not only imitative behavior but the willingness to abandon it at the 'right' time and circumstances" (Alchian, 1950: 218).

With respect to the coordinate use of a groundwater basin, the importance of time-and-place-specific information has been recognized by those who have been closely involved with the processes. James Krieger and Harvey Banks, both of whom spent most of their adult lives working on water resource issues in California (Krieger as one of the state's premier water rights attorneys, Banks as an engineer and administrator who became the director of the California Department of Water Resources), wrote: "Effective basin management encompasses much more than the hydrology, engineering, and legal rights, powers, and responsibilities. Also involved are complicated problems of economics, financing, and organization" (Krieger and Banks, 1962: 58). As Thomas Stetson, another engineer who has been occupied primarily with water resource issues, has noted: "To set the stage for a planned ground water basin management operation requires considerable time and study, including in most instances legal, engineering, economic and environmental disciplines, as well as others" (Stetson, 1982: 2). Anne Schneider, an attorney who served on the staff of the Governor's Commission to Review California Water Rights Law, observed: "The geology, hydrology, and water quality of groundwater basins are generally complex. Basin characteristics vary a great deal from basin to basin throughout California" (Schneider, 1977: 1). Gary Weatherford, another attorney and frequent contributor to the literature on water resource problems in the West, has added:

> Efficient, equitable and environmentally sensitive water management requires continuous respect for the contours of hydrologic basins. In the last analysis, the secret to greater constancy of basin perspective in water management does not lie in grandiose regional designs for resource management, but in a broad based public awareness that the unavoidable task of adjusting and integrating multiple purposes within the hydro-commons often is more readily achieved with an understanding of and mutual respect for natural hydrologic features than not. (Weatherford, 1990: 20)

These observations show an interesting pattern. The attorneys recognize and write about how much the physical characteristics of groundwater basins differ, and how much those specific differences matter, while engineers observe how much the legal, economic, and political circumstances of groundwater basins differ, and how much these specific differences matter. For all those involved, it has become clear that much of what needs to be known and taken into account in managing groundwater systems lies beyond the ken of their discipline or profession, and that the fundamental problem is how to make use of "knowledge not given to anyone in its totality" (Hayek, 1945: 521). The information requirements are enormous, and go beyond the need for "more data."

Means must be found to bring together both the general knowledge and the time-and-place-specific information needed to develop an accurate understanding of the physical characteristics of a particular basin. And this must be accomplished in ways that increase rather than reduce the possibilities for adapting to changing conditions and correcting erroneous calculations or conclusions.

In addition to devising physical solutions based on detailed knowledge of particular basin characteristics, different human perspectives and interests must be brought together in complementary ways, as well. In *Water and Politics*, Vincent Ostrom quoted a 1928 publication of the California Division of Engineering and Irrigation:

> Ahead of the engineering accomplishment is the engineering of men. The decision of the community must be made. For accomplishment, its public body, its semipublic water organizations, and its individuals must unite in team work to pool, rearrange and compromise existing interests, to legislate and to create a competent organization to carry out the engineering solution. (California DPW, Division of Engineering and Irrigation, 1928: 32)

The next chapter turns to the lay of the land and the particular characteristics of the southern California groundwater basins considered in the remainder of the book. It is followed by a description of the historical and legal backgrounds of developments in the eight cases we will investigate.

3

The Lay of the Land
Four Southern California Watersheds

As Chapter 2 indicated, groundwater systems are often related to surface water systems. That is true of the eight systems discussed in this volume. These eight are situated in four neighboring southern California watersheds—the San Gabriel River watershed, the Los Angeles River watershed, the Santa Ana River watershed, and the Mojave River watershed (see the map at the beginning of the book). Three of them—the San Gabriel, Los Angeles, and Santa Ana rivers—run south or southwest from the coastal side of the mountains toward the Pacific Ocean. The Mojave River rises on the other side of the mountains and runs northeast into the Mojave Desert.

The four watersheds are made up of these four rivers plus their tributary streams and associated underground water systems, which are subdivided into multiple groundwater basins. The eight chosen for this study are the Raymond, Main San Gabriel, Central, and West Coast basins of the San Gabriel River watershed; the San Fernando Valley area in the Los Angeles River watershed; the Chino and Orange County basins in the Santa Ana River watershed; and the Mojave River basins in the Mojave River watershed. Each of these is described briefly in this chapter (for additional details on the physical characteristics, see Blomquist, 1987b, 1988a, 1988b, 1988c, 1988d, 1989, 1990a, 1990b).[1]

The San Gabriel River Watershed

The San Gabriel River rises in the San Gabriel Mountains in the area directly north of the present-day cities of Pomona and Claremont. It descends from the mountains through Glendora Canyon, reaching the floor of the San Gabriel Valley in the vicinity of Azusa and Glendora. At the southern end of the valley, the river passes through a constriction known as the Whittier Narrows, below which it enters the broad Coastal Plain. The Whittier Narrows divides the San Gabriel River watershed into an Upper Area, which is the site of the Raymond and Main San Gabriel basins, and a Lower Area (the Coastal Plain), which is the site of the Central and West Coast basins.

In the Upper Area, the San Gabriel River crosses the San Gabriel Valley, where it is fed from both sides by tributary creeks and washes that also drain the slopes of the San Gabriel Mountains. Additional creeks and washes enter the San Gabriel Valley from the northwest, after first crossing a part of the watershed known as Raymond Basin.

Raymond Basin

A triangle-shaped area of approximately 40 square miles toward the center of Los Angeles County, the Raymond Basin constitutes the northwest corner of the San Gabriel River watershed. All or parts of the cities of Pasadena, Altadena, La Canada-Flintridge, Monrovia, San Marino, Sierra Madre, and South Pasadena lie over this basin, and the cities of Alhambra and Arcadia border on it.

The Raymond Basin is somewhat smaller than the other basins included here. Its long-term average annual yield is about 30,000 acre-feet. As a source of water supply and as an underground water storage facility, however, Raymond Basin is of considerable importance to its overlying and adjacent communities. This area is now completely urbanized and has more than 300,000 inhabitants, but its average annual rainfall is only about 21½ inches, and surface water is in short supply.

The basin's northern boundary, which trends from northwest to southeast, is at the foothills of the San Gabriel Mountains. Its western border, which runs more nearly from north to south, is formed by the San Rafael Hills. The southeastern border of the basin, separating it from the remainder of the San Gabriel Valley floor, is formed by the Raymond Fault, a 7-mile-long underground fracture that blocks most groundwater movement from the northwest side of the fault to the southeast, or valley, side.

The floor of the basin consists of alluvium deposited over thousands of years by streams and runoff washing down the sides of the San Gabriel Mountains and San Rafael Hills. This alluvium is contained by the basin's bedrock sides and bottom like sand in a great bowl, and it absorbs and retains the water that flows down the hillsides and across the basin floor in creeks and washes.

The basin slopes from north to south, with elevations ranging from 1,500 feet above sea level at the foot of the San Gabriel Mountains to about 500 feet above sea level at the Raymond Fault. Groundwater in the basin therefore moves from north and west to south and east, toward the Raymond Fault, which impedes its further movement into the San Gabriel Valley. Underground water elevations on the Raymond Basin side of the fault are 200 to 300 feet higher than those in the Main San Gabriel Basin on the southeast side of the fault. Some groundwater moves into the Main San Gabriel Basin across the eastern reaches of the Raymond Fault, although the amount is generally limited to 5,000 acre-feet per year or less, depending on the relative underground water elevations on both sides of the fault.

The Raymond Basin itself has two more underground ridges that divide it into three subareas. Monk Hill, north of Pasadena and southwest of Altadena, is the main point of a ridge that crosses the northwest corner of Raymond Basin, which is known as the Monk Hill subarea. The eastern corner of the Raymond Basin triangle, known as the Santa Anita subarea, is separated from the large central part of the basin (the Pasadena subarea) by a less pervious underground barrier.

These three subareas are traversed by surface stream channels originating in the San Gabriel Mountains. The largest of these streams, the Arroyo Seco, flows through the Monk Hill subarea and along the western edge of the Pasadena subarea and contributes about one-third of the natural inflow to the basin. It flows out of the basin to the southwest, through the San Rafael Hills and into the Los Angeles River. Eaton Creek, also called Eaton Wash, passes through the Pasadena subarea and exits to the south, across the San Gabriel Valley to the Rio Hondo. In the Santa Anita subarea, Big Santa Anita Creek and Little Santa Anita Creek (also known as Sierra Madre Creek) join to form the Santa Anita Creek, which also flows southward, across the valley to the Rio Hondo.

Main San Gabriel Basin

The Main San Gabriel Basin underlies most of the San Gabriel Valley and is the principal source of the local water supply for the valley's one million residents. With a surface area of approximately 195 square miles, the Main San Gabriel Basin is about five times the size of Raymond Basin.

The land surface of the Main San Gabriel Basin slopes southward from an elevation of about 1,100 feet above sea level in the vicinity of Glendora Canyon to about 300 feet above sea level at Whittier Narrows. The basin's northern boundary is formed by the Raymond Fault and the base of the San Gabriel Mountains. A semicircle of low rolling hills forms the western and southern boundaries. From west to east, these are the Repetto, Merced, Puente, and San Jose hills, with the Whittier Narrows appearing as a low-lying floodplain between the Merced and Puente hills. The eastern boundary of the basin is a subsurface bedrock ridge from the San Jose Hills to the San Gabriel Mountains.

Within these boundaries, the Main San Gabriel Basin is an alluvium-filled, unconfined valley basin. Its basement drops from about 800 feet above sea level in its northeastern portion, near San Dimas, to about 1,600 feet below sea level in its central portion, near Baldwin Park. Water-bearing materials range in thickness from 250 to 300 feet in the northeast corner to nearly 2,000 feet around Baldwin Park (Stetson, 1976: II-1, II-2). The basin's total storage capacity has been estimated to be 9.5 million acre-feet (California DWR, 1966b: 96). The upper 100 feet of the saturated zone, which is where the underground water level varies the most, holds approximately 800,000 acre-feet.

The natural water supply to the basin is derived from precipitation and runoff, and from surface and subsurface water inflow. Precipitation occurs primarily in the winter months and averages about 40 inches per year in the mountains and about 18.5 inches on the valley floor. Surface water inflow is contributed mainly by the San Gabriel River and its tributaries. Subsurface inflow of groundwater to the Main San Gabriel Basin comes from Raymond Basin to the west and from the Chino and Puente basins to the east. The percolation and transmissibility rates are greatest in the center of the valley along the stream channels.

The San Gabriel River bisects the valley surface overlying the Main San Gabriel Basin. In the middle of the San Gabriel Valley, the river's natural channel splits, forming another channel known as the Rio Hondo, which runs west of, and parallel to, the San Gabriel River. The channel of the Rio Hondo passes through Whittier Narrows alongside that of the San Gabriel River, but then diverges in a more southwesterly direction across the Coastal Plain, eventually joining the Los Angeles River.

The paths of the San Gabriel River, the Rio Hondo, and the tributary surface streams are mirrored in the direction of groundwater movement in the Main San Gabriel Basin. Groundwater moves predominantly from north to south, with some movement from the east and west toward the center of the basin. Thus, the groundwater flows southward from the perimeter of the basin toward Whittier Narrows.

The groundwater passes through the Narrows as both a surface and subsurface outflow. Because of an underground ridge at Whittier Narrows, the water-bearing materials in this area are only about 800 feet thick. As subsurface water moves toward Whittier Narrows, some of it is forced to the surface and appears as rising water in the natural channels of the Rio Hondo and the San Gabriel River. As a result, those channels are wetted throughout the year in the vicinity of Whittier Narrows. Whittier Narrows is the exit for water from the Upper Area of the San Gabriel River watershed and the entrance for water to the Lower Area, or Coastal Plain.

Central Basin

The Coastal Plain of Los Angeles County covers an area of more than 420 square miles, extending from the city of Los Angeles south to the Pacific Ocean. The Coastal Plain slopes gently to the south and east, toward the ocean and into Orange County.

This gradual slope is disrupted by a line of low hills extending from the northwest to the southeast, which include the Baldwin, Rosecrans, Dominguez, and Signal hills. This line of hills is the surface manifestation of the Newport-Inglewood Fault zone, which extends from the northwest border of the Coastal Plain into Orange County toward Newport Beach. Also called the Newport-Inglewood Uplift, the fault divides the Coastal Plain into two underground basins. The area northeast of the uplift is the Central Basin; that to the southwest is the West Coast Basin.

Central Basin is the largest of the groundwater basins in the San Gabriel River watershed, underlying an area of 277 square miles. Like the rest of the San Gabriel River watershed, Central Basin is now completely urbanized, covered from border to border with cities, including a substantial part of the city of Los Angeles at its northern end and much of the city of Long Beach at its southern end. Its boundaries also encompass all or parts of the cities of Bell, Bellflower, Compton, Downey, Huntington Park, Inglewood, Lakewood, Montebello, Norwalk, Paramount, Signal Hill, South Gate, Vernon, and Whittier.

On its northwest side, Central Basin is bounded by Hollywood Basin; the boundary between them runs through the city of Los Angeles. The remainder of the northern boundary of Central Basin extends along the Merced Hills, across Whittier Narrows, then along the Puente Hills; it terminates at the Orange County line, which forms the eastern boundary of Central Basin. This boundary is not well defined hydrologically, and aquifers in this area reach into the Orange County Coastal Plain. The south-southwest boundary of the Central Basin is the Newport-Inglewood Uplift, which separates Central and West basins from Long Beach up to the Baldwin Hills, just north of the city of Inglewood.

Central Basin is crossed by three surface streams. The San Gabriel River enters through Whittier Narrows and runs south to the Pacific Ocean near Long Beach. The Rio Hondo enters the basin at Whittier Narrows parallel to the San Gabriel River, proceeds southwest and joins the Los Angeles River midway across Central Basin. The Los Angeles River enters Central Basin from the northwest through the Los Angeles Narrows and proceeds south across Central Basin, exiting through Dominguez Gap into West Basin.

Central Basin contains a number of shallow aquifers and three large, deeper ones. These three aquifers—Silverado, Sunnyside, and Lynwood—are the source of most of the groundwater produced from Central Basin. The basin's total underground water storage capacity is estimated to be in excess of 13 million acre-feet.

The Central Basin aquifers receive water primarily from the percolation of surface and subsurface inflow at the Montebello Forebay, just below Whittier Narrows. In the forebay, the underground aquifers merge and are unconfined and thus are capable of receiving large quantities of water from percolation. The channels of the San Gabriel River and the Rio Hondo are unlined in the vicinity of the Montebello Forebay, so percolation can occur directly from the stream channels. Also, the construction of Whittier Narrows Dam helps to contain flood flows so they also may percolate in the forebay area. By contrast, the Los Angeles Forebay area, in the northwest part of the basin below the Los Angeles Narrows, was largely eliminated as a source of freshwater replenishment to Central Basin by the lining of the Los Angeles River channel and the paving over of the Forebay Area.

The Central Basin is divided into a nonpressure zone and a pressure zone. The nonpressure zone is in the northern half of the basin and is composed of the forebay areas, where the aquifers can receive water directly. The pressure zone, which is in the southern half of Central Basin, is covered by an impermeable layer of clay that extends to the Pacific Ocean and therefore also covers all of West Basin. Rainfall and surface flows in the pressure zone do not recharge the underground supply. The pressure zone receives water only by underground flows from the nonpressure zone.

The San Gabriel River drains into the Pacific Ocean at Alamitos Gap, at the southernmost tip of the pressure zone, but the clay covering of the pressure zone has been eroded in this gap, and the aquifers are exposed to seawater intrusion here. If underground water levels in the Alamitos Gap fall below sea level, seawater can move up the gap and into the Central Basin aquifers.

West Basin

The West Coast Basin, known more commonly as West Basin, lies under the southernmost part of Los Angeles County. West Basin is about 25 miles long from northwest to southeast and averages about 7 miles wide. Its land surface extends approximately 170 square miles.

The northern boundary of West Basin follows the crest of the Ballona Escarpment, just south of and parallel to Ballona Creek and not far from

Los Angeles International Airport. The Newport-Inglewood Uplift forms West Basin's northeastern boundary, from the Baldwin Hills to the Los Angeles–Orange County line near Long Beach. The coastlines of the Pacific Ocean and San Pedro Bay form the western and southern boundaries of the basin, respectively, with one exception. In the southwest corner of the basin, the drainage divide of the Palos Verdes Hills is treated as the boundary rather than the coast, because those hills are composed of materials that are not water-bearing, and waters on the seaward side of the divide do not influence West Basin water conditions.

As the Coastal Plain basins were formed, coarser materials were sandwiched between finer, relatively impermeable materials, creating a "stack" of aquifers in which fresh groundwater is confined. The largest of these is the Silverado aquifer, which underlies more than 80 percent of West Basin and merges with other aquifers in the remainder of the basin. The other, smaller aquifers are the Gardena, Gaspur, San Pedro, "200-foot sand," and "400-foot gravel" aquifers. The total groundwater in storage in this set of aquifers underlying West Basin is estimated at 6.5 million acre-feet.

Because clay soils cover West Basin, its aquifers receive little replenishment from local rainfall, which averages 15 inches a year. Moreover, rainfall hitting the land surface in West Basin drains primarily into storm channels that flow out to the ocean. Consequently, surface conditions have little effect on underground water levels in the basin. At the same time, West Basin contains virtually no suitable locations for artificial recharge by surface water spreading.

West Basin is the last in the series of interconnected groundwater basins of the San Gabriel River watershed. Its ultimate source of freshwater is miles away, in the rainfall and runoff of the San Gabriel mountain range. Its entire supply of freshwater comes from subsurface flows across the Newport-Inglewood Uplift from Central Basin. The uplift "resembles a ground water cascade" (Jennings, Engstrand, and Henrikson, 1963: 19), and the rate of flow across it depends on the difference in water levels between Central Basin and West Basin. The greater the difference between the higher water levels on one side of the uplift and the lower water levels on the other side, the greater the volume flowing from one side to the other.

Here and there, groundwater movement across the uplift is facilitated by erosion of the fault, caused by ancient surface stream flows. These "gaps" are filled with somewhat more porous materials, and water passes through them more easily. Ballona Creek crosses the uplift at Ballona Gap and then flows to the Pacific Ocean along the northern boundary of West Basin. The Los Angeles River crosses the uplift through Dominguez Gap and empties into San Pedro Bay. The San Gabriel River crosses the uplift close to the ocean at Alamitos Gap, situated between Bixby Hill in Los Angeles County and Landing Hill in Orange County. Water travels fairly readily through these underground channels.

Central Basin is West Basin's source of freshwater supply but is not its only possible source of water. West Basin can also receive water along its western and southern boundaries, from the Pacific Ocean. The relentless movement of the Pacific has eroded West Basin's clay covering along the coast, so the coastal aquifers are in contact with the ocean floor, separated only by permeable material marked by the gaps described earlier. The relative elevation of the underground water in West Basin and the ocean determines the exchange of water with the Pacific. If the underground water drops below sea level, saltwater from the ocean invades the freshwater supply. Altogether, then, West Basin is a highly valuable, but also highly exposed, source of water.

The Los Angeles River Watershed

The lower reaches of the Los Angeles River cross the Central and West Basins of the Los Angeles County Coastal Plain. Those basins are considered part of the San Gabriel River watershed, however, since that is the natural source of their freshwater recharge. The Los Angeles River does not contribute to the freshwater supply of those basins and would not despite its present-day concrete-lined channel, because the river crosses the Coastal Plain pressure zone, where the basins are confined by an overlying layer of clay.

For our purposes, the San Fernando Valley, northwest of the Coastal Plain, can be considered the Los Angeles River watershed. The San Fernando Valley and its surrounding mountains constitute the Upper Los Angeles River area (ULARA), the drainage area of the Los Angeles River.

The ULARA consists of 174 square miles of mountains, 153 square miles of foothills, and about 175 square miles of valley lands (Los Angeles Board of Public Service Commissioners, 1916: 32). Elevations range from 7,078 feet above sea level at Mount Pacifico in the San Gabriel Mountains to about 300 feet above sea level at the Los Angeles Narrows.

The ULARA lies almost entirely within Los Angeles County; the Los Angeles–Ventura County line runs through its far western hills. The ULARA is bounded on the north by the San Gabriel Mountains and the Santa Susana Mountains. The Simi Hills form the western boundary and the Santa Monica Mountains the southern boundary. These mountains and hills enclose some foothills and a broad valley floor, dividing the ULARA into four distinct subareas.

The alluvium-filled, unconfined San Fernando Valley Basin is by far the largest of these subareas, occupying virtually all (91 percent) of the valley floor in the ULARA. The basin's porous soils are up to 1,000 feet thick and readily receive water from the surrounding highlands and overlying creeks and washes. The San Fernando Valley Basin is naturally replenished by precipitation on the valley floor (which averages about 16.5 inches per year), by recharge from the overlying river and streams, and by a small amount of subsurface inflow from the Sylmar and Verdugo subareas. The basin's total storage capacity is approximately 3.2 million acre-feet.

The Sylmar Basin, which lies to the north of the San Fernando Valley Basin, is the northernmost subarea of the ULARA. It is bordered on the west by the Mission Hills and the eastern slopes of the Santa Susana Mountains, on the north by the San Gabriel Mountains, on the east by the Upper Lopez Canyon along the Pacoima Wash, and on the south by an extension of the Little Tujunga syncline. The average annual rainfall in the higher elevations of the basin is 22 inches. A small amount of subsurface outflow from Sylmar (estimated at about 550 acre-feet per year) moves across its southern boundary into the San Fernando Valley Basin through two small notches eroded in the underground divide.

The surface area of the Sylmar Basin is only about one-twentieth of that of the San Fernando Valley Basin. Sylmar's total storage capacity is estimated to be 310,000 acre-feet, but much of it is in confined aquifers that are not directly recharged, and the annual groundwater yield is quite small. Although unconfined and confined aquifers are both present in the Sylmar subarea, it is primarily the confined aquifers of the Saugus Formation that supply the wells in Sylmar Basin.

Verdugo Basin in the eastern part of the ULARA is the water-bearing area of the Verdugo Canyon, which is located between the Verdugo and San Gabriel mountains. The canyon floor is comparatively flat and narrow—less than a mile wide at its widest point. This subarea contains an aquifer with a storage capacity of approximately 160,000 acre-feet. Groundwater in the Verdugo Basin tends to move southeasterly through the canyon toward Glendale in the eastern part of the San Fernando Valley Basin. The subsurface flow from Verdugo Basin to the San Fernando Valley Basin is negligible, however, because there is a submerged dam across the groundwater divide (constructed in 1895 and reconstructed by the city of Glendale in 1935) and groundwater is extracted on the Verdugo side of that dam.

Along the eastern edge of the Verdugo Basin, there is some hydrologic contact between the ULARA and the Raymond Basin of the San Gabriel River watershed. Pickens Canyon (between the San Gabriel Mountains and the San Rafael Hills) connects the Verdugo Basin of the ULARA with

Raymond Basin. When the groundwater is low, some water escapes from the Verdugo subarea into the Monk Hill subarea of Raymond Basin. When it is high, water can move westerly from the Monk Hill subarea into Verdugo (UINTEX, 1985: WA-5).

The smallest ULARA subarea is Eagle Rock, located in the southeastern corner of the watershed. The Eagle Rock Basin is a separate artesian groundwater basin at the base of the San Rafael Hills just north of the Repetto Hills at the western end of the Raymond Fault. Its surface area is only 807 acres and its estimated storage capacity just 6,000 acre-feet, with an extremely small annual groundwater yield.

Southwest of the Eagle Rock Basin, at the eastern end of the San Fernando Valley Basin, lie the Los Angeles Narrows. This is where the Los Angeles River rises from water flowing north-south and east-west through the basin. The river rarely appears as a surface stream within the San Fernando Valley, but emerges at the Narrows after gathering in the ULARA. The original location of Los Angeles, as an agricultural pueblo, was next to the river and immediately below the Narrows, where a stable flow of water was available.

The Santa Ana River Watershed

The Santa Ana River watershed lies to the east of the San Gabriel River watershed and is drained by the Santa Ana River and its several tributaries. It covers an area of about 2,500 square miles, most of which is in San Bernardino, Riverside, and Orange counties, but a small part falls within the eastern boundary of Los Angeles County.

Like the San Gabriel River watershed, the Santa Ana River watershed narrows in the middle and is divided into an Upper Area and a Lower Area. Santa Ana Canyon, between the Puente Hills and the Santa Ana Mountains, constricts the Santa Ana River to a fairly narrow passage as it flows from the much larger Upper Area (in San Bernardino and Riverside counties) to the smaller Lower Area (entirely within Orange County). Prado Dam, built in the Santa Ana Canyon by the U.S. Army Corps of Engineers in 1941, drives the river water to the surface and channels it through floodgates.

The Santa Ana River's headwaters are in the San Bernardino Mountains, about 80 miles inland from the Pacific Ocean. The river originates in the confluence of a number of creeks that drain the mountains. From this confluence, the river extends southwesterly through the San Bernardino Valley, fed by additional creeks that rise in the southern slopes of the eastern San Gabriel Mountains and cross the Chino Basin. Below Santa Ana Canyon, the river opens out into the Orange County Coastal Plain, turns more directly southward, and empties into the Pacific Ocean between Huntington Beach and Newport Beach.

Except at Santa Ana Canyon and at Riverside Narrows in the Upper Area, the Santa Ana River normally disappears at various points along its course, sinking underground and then surfacing again further downstream. Likewise, most of the streams that feed the river sink into the alluvial fans of the San Bernardino Valley or the Chino Basin and move toward the river as underground streams. Only during periods of abundant rainfall does surface runoff from the tributaries reach the river channel.

Along its course, the Santa Ana River supplies, and is supplied by, nine groundwater basins, all but one of which are in the Upper Area. The last in the series of Upper Area groundwater basins is the Chino Basin. The groundwater basin in the Lower Area is known as the Orange County Basin.

Chino Basin

Chino Basin, at the southwest end of the Upper Area, stretches from the foot of the San Gabriel Mountains to Santa Ana Canyon. It is a broad and gently southward-sloping plain, narrowing toward the canyon at its southern tip. Elevations range from 2,000 to 2,500 feet at the foot of the mountains to about 500 feet near the Santa Ana River. The basin has a land surface of about 230 square miles, 5 percent of which is in Los Angeles County, 15 percent in Riverside County, and the remaining 80 percent in the West End of San Bernardino County.

The Chino Basin is bounded by the San Jose Fault and the Pomona Valley to the northwest, the Cucamonga Fault and Cucamonga Basin to the north, the Rialto-Colton Fault and the Rialto-Colton Basins to the northeast, the Bloomington Divide and the Jurupa Mountains to the east, the Santa Ana River and Canyon to the south, and the Chino and Puente Hills to the west. Within these boundaries, the Chino Basin receives its natural water supply from precipitation (which ranges from about 25 inches per year near the mountains to about 12 inches near the canyon), and from surface and subsurface inflow from overlying streams and adjacent basins.

The San Jose Fault, between the San Jose Hills and the San Gabriel Mountains, operates as an imperfect groundwater divide separating Chino Basin on the east and the Pomona Valley and Main San Gabriel Basin on the west. Some subsurface flow occurs across this divide between Chino Basin in the Santa Ana River watershed and Main San Gabriel Basin in the San Gabriel River watershed.

Several surface water streams draining the southern face of the San Gabriel Mountains enter and cross the Chino Basin in a southerly direction, contributing to the water supply. San Antonio Creek, which becomes Chino Creek, traverses the western part of the basin. Cucamonga Creek travels from north to south across the central part of the basin. Day, Deer, and East Etiwanda creeks cross the eastern part. These streams deposit their waters on the broad alluvial plain of the Chino Basin, and typically disappear below the surface except in very wet periods. Like the surface water, the groundwater in the basin generally moves from north to south, with a steeper gradient nearer the mountains in the northern part of the basin than in the southern part.

Chino Basin is underlain by water-bearing sediments that absorb, retain, and transmit the waters collected over time from the percolation of precipitation and surface inflow. The basin's total storage capacity has been estimated at 11.0 to 14.0 million acre-feet, and its capacity within 100 feet of the water table (that is, its "usable" storage capacity) is in excess of 1.2 million acre-feet (California DWR, 1959a: 34). Depth to water in Chino Basin generally ranges from less than 50 feet (fairly close to the land surface) in the southern part of the basin to 500 feet or more in the northern part.

Chino Basin discharges water to adjacent basins by surface and sub-surface outflow. Water exits the basin at three points: at the northwestern edge of the basin in the Pomona-Claremont area, at the eastern boundary across the San Jacinto Fault in the Lytle Creek area, and through the Santa Ana River Channel (the predominant exit point) into the lower area of the watershed.

Orange County Basin

The Orange County Basin is bounded by the Santa Ana Mountains to the east, the Chino and Puente Hills to the north, and the Pacific Ocean to the southwest. To the west, the Orange–Los Angeles County line provides an imperfect boundary between the Orange County Basin and the Central and West basins of the San Gabriel River watershed.

The Orange County Basin underlies an area of about 300 square miles. It contains three major aquifers, arrayed in layers. The upper aquifer extends from close to the ground surface to a maximum depth of approximately 1,500 feet. The middle aquifer is 1,300 to 2,600 feet deep. And the lower aquifer is 2,600 to 4,000 feet deep. It contains poor-quality confined water with a high level of dissolved solids. The maximum depth of freshwater in the basin is approximately 4,000 feet around Santa Ana and Garden Grove. The basin's total storage capacity is about 15 million acre-feet, with 10 percent or 1.5 million acre-feet in active, or usable storage capacity.

The water in the upper aquifer of the coastal basin is of high quality and can be extracted easily. Because the Coastal Plain is at a low elevation, the groundwater in the upper aquifer comes close enough to the land to be supplied by shallow artesian wells. In fact, areas near the ocean in Orange County were once swampy because the underground flow was so near the land surface. In the absence of human intervention in the form of groundwater extractions, groundwater elevations in the Coastal Plain remain above sea level, so that as the overland terrain gradually declines to sea level, the groundwater may reach the land surface.

Subsurface displacements along the Orange County coast separate the fresh groundwater of the Orange County Basin from the Pacific Ocean. The Newport–Inglewood Uplift runs parallel to the coast from the southeastern part of the basin in Orange County on into Los Angeles County, forming a sort of underground "wall" between the ocean and the basin. This wall has been breached at points along the coast, however, permitting hydrologic contact between the basin and the sea. Channels carved across the fault zone by the ancient courses of the Santa Ana and San Gabriel rivers subsequently filled with sand and gravel, creating four "gaps"—the Alamitos, the Bolsa-Chica, the Bolsa-Sunset, and the Talbert. The Bolsa-Chica and Bolsa-Sunset gaps appear to have been sealed from the ocean by later underground shifts, but the Alamitos and Talbert gaps continue to permit water exchanges between the Pacific Ocean and the aquifers of the Orange County Basin.

As a coastal basin at the downstream end of a watershed, the Orange County Basin in the Santa Ana River watershed stands in a similar exposed position as the West Basin in the San Gabriel River watershed. The basin depends entirely on upstream sources for its freshwater supply and is exposed to saltwater intrusion from the ocean.

The Mojave River Watershed

On the other side of the San Bernardino Mountains from the Santa Ana River watershed, the Mojave River watershed extends eastward into the Mojave Desert. Three closely interconnected groundwater areas along the river—the Upper, Middle, and Lower Mojave River basins—are treated here as a single case.

Pushed upward by seismic activity of the San Andreas Fault Zone, the San Bernardino Mountains have become a barrier to the rainfall that used to reach the terrain on their inland side, which was once the site of a body of water, as attested by the numerous fossils of marine animals found there. Today, storms moving in from the Pacific Ocean deposit most of their rain and snow on the seaward side of the San Bernardino and San Gabriel Mountains.

Rainfall at Bear Valley Dam in the San Bernardino Mountains (altitude 6,500 feet) averages about 35 inches per year, which is comparable to that in many parts of the eastern United States. On the inland, or desert, side of the mountains, the average annual rainfall drops sharply, to approximately 8 inches at Hesperia, 4 inches at Barstow. The area from Barstow east to the Colorado River is one of the driest in the United States.

At about 4,000 to 6,000 feet above sea level on the northeast side of the San Bernardino Mountains, the washes that drain the mountainsides form creeks. The largest two are Deep Creek, which forms in the area between Lake Arrowhead and Big Bear Lake and flows northwesterly, and West Fork, which rises west of Lake Arrowhead and north of Lake Gregory and flows to the northeast. They meet at The Forks, at the base of the San Bernardino Mountains, approximately 3,300 feet above sea level. From there, the desert floor slopes away to the east. At Hesperia, the elevation is 3,200 feet above sea level; at Victorville, 2,700 feet; at Barstow, 2,200 feet.

The Mojave River is the principal source of water supply for an area of more than 1,000 square miles. Unlike other southern California rivers—such as the Los Angeles, the San Gabriel, and the Santa Ana—the Mojave does not drain into the sea, or any other body of water. Over most of its reach, it travels underground, through the absorbent soils of the desert. Rising water conditions result in the appearance of the river above the land surface at five locations along its channel—at The Forks, at the Upper Narrows and the Lower Narrows at Victorville, near the old Camp Cady site, and at Afton Canyon near the river's end. As the river passes through the porous soils, much of its water is absorbed and lost. Some water percolates into groundwater basins along its course. The water that remains nearer the surface is absorbed by native vegetation. Between the absorption of the soils and the consumption of the native vegetation, the Mojave River is a losing stream from its source to its terminus. By one calculation, only 28 percent of the streamflow that entered the Mojave River channel at The Forks between 1931 and 1972 reached as far as Barstow, which is only about halfway down the river (Durbin and Hardt, 1974: 4).

Unreplenished by rainfall or other streams, it dies in the desert, evaporated by the sun and swallowed up by the sand. The full course of the Mojave River from The Forks to its terminus is 90 to 110 miles, depending on how the river's end is defined.

The desert region through which the Mojave meanders is filled with mountains and valleys. Small mountain ranges such as the Little San Bernardino, Ord, Sidewinder, Granite, and Calico mountains, and isolated mountains such as Fry, Bell, Silver, and Pinto are scattered throughout the Mojave River area. Many of these interior mountains correspond to and are aligned by faults in the deeper crust and bedrock. The faults advance inland as parallel lines in the same northwest-southeast alignment as the dominant San Andreas Fault and the San Bernardino Mountains. Among these lesser faults in the San Andreas system are the Helendale, Lockhart, Waterman, and Calico-Newberry. Some of the faults, such as the 50-mile-long Helendale Fault, remain active.

The extensive faulting in the region has produced not only the visible mountains but the invisible groundwater basins. The desert valleys are filled with material eroded from the mountains. Deep alluvial basins fill the valleys, and broader but shallower alluvial fans form on the mesas. The accumulated debris is now hundreds of feet thick in places throughout the desert. These deposits store water readily and yield it freely to wells.

There are nine groundwater basins in all, arrayed along and adjacent to the Mojave River—the Upper, Middle, and Lower Mojave River basins, Harper Basin, Coyote Basin, Caves Basin, the Cronise Valley basins, and the Soda and Silver Lake basins. The groundwater basins of the Mojave River watershed contain huge amounts—millions of acre-feet—of groundwater stored over thousands of years. As a result of the area's present climate, however, those basins receive little replenishment from year to year. In most of the desert basins of the region, the groundwater in storage is many times as great as the annual recharge (French, 1978: 1; Cooper, 1968: 132).

The Upper Mojave River Basin is an alluvial plain of approximately 600 square miles, underlain by porous material reaching hundreds of feet deep. Its southern boundary is the San Gabriel and San Bernardino mountains. An alluvial high built up by Sheep Creek and running from the San Gabriel to the Shadow mountains creates the western border. The northern border is the Helendale Fault. The Granite, Sidewinder, Stoddard, and Silver mountains form an arc around the basin to the east and northeast.

The Upper Mojave River Basin is bisected by the Mojave River channel, which runs from south to north. Surface and subsurface inflow from the Mojave River, plus subsurface inflow from adjacent areas (Sheep Creek and Buckthorn Wash to the west, Lucerne Valley to the east, and the foothills to the south) supply water to the Upper Basin. The basin's water storage capacity is estimated to be upwards of 26.5 million acre-feet, of which 8 million acre-feet are readily usable (California DWR, 1975: 78).

The Middle Mojave River Basin adjoins the Upper Basin along that part of the Helendale Fault running from the Shadow Mountains to Silver Mountain. The Middle Basin is bounded along the south by the Stoddard and Ord mountains. The eastern boundary is an alluvial divide that passes Barstow, extending from the Ord Mountains to the Waterman Hills. The northern boundary is another alluvial divide from the Kramer Hills past Iron Mountain to Waterman Hills. The area encompassed by these borders measures about 430 square miles.

The Middle Basin is narrower than the Upper Basin, and most of the mountains and hills scattered throughout the area are composed of non–water-bearing materials. The Middle Basin is smaller and shallower than the Upper Basin, with an estimated storage capacity of 8 million acre-feet, with just over 3 million acre-feet deemed usable (California DWR, 1975: 78–79). In some locations in the Middle Basin, groundwater quality is not good enough for domestic and irrigation use.

Water is supplied to the Middle Basin by the surface and subsurface flows escaping the Upper Basin. Water leaves the Middle Basin in two directions. Some subsurface flow escapes northward through Hinkley Valley into the Harper Basin. However, most of it exits as surface and subsurface flow to the Lower Mojave River Basin.

The Lower Mojave River Basin underlies a land surface area of approximately 300 square miles. It is bordered on the west by the alluvial divide that passes through Barstow, on the north by the Waterman Hills and Calico Mountains, on the east by another underground divide stretching from Harvard to the old Camp Cady site, and on the south by the Newberry Mountains. Within the Lower Basin, the Calico-Newberry Fault impedes the underground flow of the Mojave River, with water levels in wells on the upstream side of the fault up to 100 feet higher than those on the downstream side.

The storage capacity of the Lower Mojave River Basin is estimated to be 8.7 million acre-feet, its usable capacity slightly more than 3 million acre-feet (California DWR, 1967: 34). The Lower Basin receives water from the Middle Basin, but only when inflow to the Upper and Middle basins is large. In many years, there is no recharge to the Lower Basin. From 1958 to 1981, there were only six years in which measurable recharge flowed to the downstream Newberry subbasin, and 95 percent of the total recharge for that period occurred in three flood years, during which more than 160,000 acre-feet flowed through and exited the basin. The Lower Basin is recharged only by those Mojave River flows that reach the basin without being lost at the downstream end, and such amounts are erratic and relatively small (C M Engineering, 1982: IV-7).

This, then, is the lay of the land for the cases that follow. The groundwater basins of the San Gabriel, Los Angeles, Santa Ana, and Mojave River watersheds provided the local water supplies essential to the organized settlement and subsequent development of southern California. That development in turn stimulated new demands for water projects, water organizations, and water rights.

NOTES

1. This series of eight volumes provides a detailed description of the geology and hydrology of the basins, a history of the development of the overlying area and the associated water problems, the development of institutional arrangements for addressing those problems, and the operation and performance of those arrangements (see the Bibliography for volume titles). Each volume contains tables and figures, which in many instances include well hydrographs and groundwater contour maps that show the deterioration and recovery of basin water conditions. These monographs are available from the Workshop in Political Theory and Policy Analysis, 513 N. Park, Bloomington, Indiana 47405.

4

Water Development and Water Law in Southern California

Each of the eight cases discussed in Part 2 has a unique history—especially with respect to its water supply problems and the responses to them. Nevertheless, southern California's climate and historical development and California's unusual law of water rights affected them all, and their water problems.

The Beginnings of Organized Water Use

The native population of southern California may have been as large as 130,000 at the time the first Spanish overland expeditions arrived in 1769, but there is no evidence that these people developed any organized or sustained agriculture in the area (Scott, 1977: 8; Bruman and Meighan, 1981: 4). From 1769 to 1776, three Spanish expeditions that were to make lasting contributions to the area's development crossed southern California—the Portola, Serra, and Garces expeditions.

In June 1769, Gaspar de Portola, the Spanish governor of California, began an overland expedition, accompanied by Fra Junipero Serra. After establishing a mission at San Diego, the Portola group journeyed north, reaching the Santa Ana Valley in what is now Orange County on St. Anne's Day, July 28, 1769. They named the river and the valley in honor of St. Anne.[1] On August 2, 1769, the Portola expedition camped farther north, by a flowing stream surrounded by trees. Portola gave the name Rio do Porciuncula to what is now the Los Angeles River and noted in his journal that it would be a desirable place for a settlement (Mann, 1976: 267). On August 5, after crossing the Santa Monica Mountains through

Sepulveda Canyon, the Portola expedition camped in a broad valley northwest of the Porciuncula site. They named the valley Santa Catalina de Bononia de los Encinos, but it is known today as the San Fernando Valley (Robinson, 1961: 3–4).

Father Serra led another expedition to the area in 1771, at which time he established Mission San Gabriel in the valley to the east of the Pociuncula site. The valley, and the river flowing through it, later took their name from the mission.

In 1776, Fra Francisco Garces began an expedition westward across the southern California desert from the Colorado River toward the coast. With some Mohave Indians as guides, Garces reached the Mojave River on March 11, 1776. After crossing the San Bernardino Mountains through Sawpit Canyon and traveling northwest along the foothills of the San Gabriel Mountains toward Mission San Gabriel, the Garces expedition camped at Cucamonga Creek in what is now Chino Basin. The creek's name was adapted from the native Cocamungo, meaning, appropriately, "sandy place."

The earliest recorded use of local water supplies in southern California was at the Mission San Gabriel in 1771. The mission was located in the Main San Gabriel Basin on the southeast side of the Raymond Fault, and its water came from groundwater springs and cienegas related to the fault and the high water table on the Raymond Basin side. The mission fathers and their converts diverted these waters to cultivate food for the settlement. Eventually, the local water supplies irrigated as many as 6,000 acres of mission lands (California DWR, 1966b: 13).

Spanish colonization of California consisted of the establishment of religious missions such as Mission San Gabriel, military towns or presidios, and agricultural settlements, or pueblos (Hutchins, 1956: 256). The Portola party's campsite on the Porciuncula was chosen to be an agricultural pueblo because of its water supply. On September 4, 1781, at the direction of Governor Felipe de Neve and by order of King Charles III of Spain, a group of forty-six persons in eleven households established El Pueblo de Nuestra Senora la Reina de Los Angeles de Porciuncula.

In the early 1800s, the Spanish began to encourage private development in southern California outside of the missions and the pueblos by issuing land grants. The first Spanish land grant in the area was received in 1810 by Jose Antonio Yorba. Yorba established his Rancho Santiago de Santa Ana around the confluence of Santiago Creek and the Santa Ana River, where the Orange County city of Santa Ana is located today. The land grant also permitted the use of the flows of the Santa Ana River adjacent to the land and the groundwater beneath the land, and the first irrigation diversion from the Santa Ana River was made by Jose Antonio Yorba and Juan Pablo Peralta in 1810 or 1811.

Irrigation in southern California remained scattered and localized until the establishment of additional ranchos during the period of Mexican possession of California, from 1822 to 1848. By the 1840s, much of the land in the Santa Ana and San Gabriel River watersheds was covered by large cattle-raising ranchos. Also during Mexican possession, some mission lands were secularized and either returned to the public domain or reissued as private ranchos.

Following the Mexican-American war and the acquisition of California by the United States in 1848, ranchos began to be broken up and sold to the Americans migrating westward toward the Pacific coast. This period is associated with the beginning of widespread irrigation and increased water use, at least in the Santa Ana and San Gabriel River watersheds (Scott, 1977: 1).

California became a state in 1850, and westward migration increased rapidly on the promise of possible riches and available new lands. The population exploded from 15,000 in 1849 to 92,597 in 1850, and 250,000 in 1852 (Crouch et al., 1956: 15). Although most of this boom occurred in northern California, the little agricultural pueblo on the Porciuncula grew, too. Los Angeles was incorporated as a city in 1850, with a population of 1,610. By 1860, the population had more than doubled to 3,700.

Growth slowed in the 1860s. Westward migration declined as a result of the Civil War and renewed Indian attacks, and surveys of possible railroad routes to California were suspended. The population of San Bernardino County dropped from 5,551 in 1860 to 3,988 in 1870. On the coastal side of the mountains, severe flooding inundated the Coastal Plain in 1861. Only a few years later, many of the large ranchero holdings were devastated by the Great Drought of 1863–64. The initial phase of agricultural development in southern California had come to an end.

Floods and Droughts: The Southern California Climate

The unexpected flooding in 1861, followed by the Great Drought of 1863–64, introduced the new settlers to southern California's climate. The beauty of the region's natural landscape and the usual mildness of its climate tempted and delighted new arrivals then as now. Southern California is, after all, one of only five places in the world that can properly be described as having a "Mediterranean climate," with dry summers, rainy winters, and generally favorable temperatures. But, as the winter storms of March 1991 and February 1992 demonstrated once again, the southern California climate can also bring drought and wildfires one year and flooding and mudslides the next.

In a normal year, southern California receives little or no precipitation during the summer. Eighty percent of the average annual precipitation occurs from November through March. During these months, in a normal year, Pacific storms sweep in, depositing rain on the coast and inland valleys, and greater amounts of rain and snow on the mountains. Runoff from the mountains feeds surface streams and rivers and replenishes groundwater supplies, with melting snowpack sustaining the runoff into the summer. In a normal year, precipitation on the Coastal Plain is about 12–16 inches, in the inland valleys about 18–24 inches, in the mountains about 35–40 inches, and in the deserts on the inland side of the mountains about 5–8 inches.

However, southern California is not given to normal years.[2] Cycles of years of above-normal or below-normal precipitation are more typical. Occasionally, there have been consecutive years of severe drought, where rainfall seems almost to disappear. The Great Drought of 1863–64 was such a period, as were 1960–1962, 1976–77, and 1987–1991. There also have been decade-long droughts of consistently below-normal precipitation. The years from 1895 to 1904 constituted such a period, as did 1920 to 1937 and 1945 to 1965. These are separated by long periods of years of above-normal precipitation, such as 1905–1919, 1938–1944, and 1966–1975. These droughts and wet periods are associated with important changes in water supply development, use, and management.

The Coastal Plain, the inland valleys, and the Mojave Desert are also susceptible to destructive flooding. When heavy storms assault the coast and mountains, the rainfall exceeds the absorptive capacity of the soils. Water crashes down mountainsides and canyons, gathering huge amounts of debris along the way and disgorging it on the valley floors or desert floors below. Floodwaters spread across the alluvial fans and Coastal Plain, inundating agricultural land and destroying homes and businesses. One day's flood flows in a "twenty-five-year flood" in California could supply an urban population of seventy million for a year (California DPW, 1923: 31).

Destructive floods struck southern California not only in 1861, but again in 1884 (when supposedly it was possible to row a boat from Santa Ana to Los Angeles), 1914, 1916, 1927, 1938 (the most destructive flood ever in southern California), and 1969. According to one writer, "Strangely enough, in this land of little rain [the Mojave River watershed] the monetary losses due to excessive rainfall probably exceed those due to all other climatic conditions" (Thompson, 1929: 97). Flooding produced greater losses than drought in most of southern California through the mid-twentieth century. In many communities, flooding provided the impetus for organizing water districts and public works.

Water has been crucial to southern California's development since the late 1800s. At times there has been too much, at many others not enough. Water users have altered their behavior in response to the vicissitudes of local water supplies and have sought means of overcoming the area's climatological extremes.

Growth and Groundwater

Westward migration, active trading in land, and agricultural development all resumed toward the end of the 1860s, and general prosperity returned to southern California in the 1870s. By 1868, an "embryonic real-estate boom" was under way, as the remnants of the Mexican ranchos continued to be divided and sold (Cleland, 1951: 163). Willing buyers were easily found, thanks to renewed speculation that southern California would soon be linked to the north and east by rail.

Land sales and the anticipation of rail transportation spurred the formation of new communities. In the Coastal Plain of the San Gabriel River watershed, Compton was established in 1867, Norwalk was founded in 1868, Inglewood in 1873, and Santa Monica in 1875. In the San Gabriel Valley, the Indiana Colony was founded in 1874, and renamed Pasadena in 1875. The famous speculator E. J. "Lucky" Baldwin arrived in the valley in 1874 and acquired the 6,000-acre Rancho Santa Anita as the first of his holdings. At the eastern end of the valley, Pomona was laid out in 1875.

In 1868 on the Coastal Plain of the Santa Ana River watershed, A. B. Chapman and Andrew Glassell received as payment for attorneys' fees 40 acres of land in what is now Orange County. They started a development named Richland. The next year, William Spurgeon founded the community of Santa Ana on land that had been part of the original Rancho Santiago de Santa Ana. To the east of Santa Ana, James Irvine began accumulating parcels of land that would form the vast Irvine Ranch, which eventually covered approximately one-third of what is now Orange County. Farther north, San Bernardino (founded by Mormons in 1852) was incorporated in 1869, and the community of Riverside was founded as Jurupa in 1870.

The demise of the San Fernando Farm Homestead Association in 1869 left the San Fernando Valley divided among four powerful Californians. The southern half of the valley passed to Isaac Lankershim and Isaac Van Nuys, the northern half to state senators George K. Porter and Charles Maclay. Porter and his associates were interested in ranching and wheat production and formed the Los Angeles Farming and Milling Company. Maclay, on the other hand, was interested in subdividing and selling his lands. He prepared a subdivision, showing streets and lots and labeled "Map of the City of San Fernando," which he took to the Los Angeles County Recorder's office in September 1874 (Robinson, 1961: 24–25).

San Fernando was the site of a Southern Pacific Railroad tunnel through the Santa Susana Mountains. The tunnel was completed in 1876, and the main Southern Pacific line through the interior of California was connected with Los Angeles, Anaheim, and Santa Ana by 1878 (Bancroft, 1890: 594–617; O'Flaherty, 1972: 148).

The coming of the railroads also raised interest in the southern California desert. Renewed frequency of travel across the Mojave Desert and the prospect of rail transit led to the first efforts to develop the agricultural potential of the desert's fine alluvial soils and long growing season. In 1870, the Thirty-Fifth Parallel Association was formed and purchased 30,000 acres of land along the upper reaches of the Mojave River from the United States Land Office. The first officially recorded appropriation of water from the Mojave River was made in 1872. The association was unable to develop its land acquisition sufficiently to remain in business, however, and sold its lands in 1886 to the Hesperia Land and Water Company (Thompson, 1929: 382; Stickel et al., 1980: 162).

Elsewhere in the desert, the 1870s ushered in a mining boom that lasted to the end of the century. The principal deposits worked in the area were borax and silver. Subsequently, more productive borax deposits were found in Death Valley, and the Calico silver mines went bust. Nevertheless, railroad and mining fever and the early attempts at organized agricultural development during the 1870s had restored active growth and interest in the desert.

On the coastal side of the mountains, except in the wheat fields of the San Fernando Valley, agricultural development took a new and highly prosperous turn in the 1870s. Crop production in the Coastal Plain and in the upper areas of the San Gabriel and Santa Ana River watersheds shifted to citrus. The local environment favored citrus trees, and citrus production quickly became the mainstay of the local economy.

The key to this transition was the orange. Local orange trees were cultivated in the San Gabriel Valley for the first time in 1867 (Walters, Calvert, and Bengel, 1961: 2) and in the vicinity of Anaheim around 1870 (Scott, 1977: 2). The navel orange was introduced near Riverside in 1873 and proved to be especially well-suited to the area. Orange production spread throughout the Coastal Plain and the inland valleys. By 1875, southern California was home to nearly 100,000 navel orange trees, and approximately five million oranges were being shipped annually to San Francisco (Cleland, 1951: 198). In 1875, Chapman and Glassell's community of Richland renamed itself Orange. Pasadena was aggressively promoted by the San Gabriel Orange Grove Association and by the end of 1875 had a population of 6,500 and formed the urban center of San Gabriel Valley development. In 1889, Orange County was established out of the southeastern corner of Los Angeles County.

The development of lands throughout the Los Angeles, San Gabriel, and Santa Ana watersheds in the 1870s affected the availability and use of water supplies. Early water use in southern California had relied on the area's surface water supplies, but the 1870s marked the beginning of groundwater use for irrigation and for municipal supplies. Four elements—need, convenience, constraint, and technology—contributed to the development of groundwater at this time.

After the Great Drought of 1863–64, farmers, ranchers, and the leaders of the new communities in the area recognized the need for water supplies that were less vulnerable to climatic variations. In many areas of southern California in the late 1800s, artesian flows could be produced simply by driving a pipe into the ground. Water rose to the surface by natural pressure and flowed year-round, relatively independent of seasonal rainfall. Irrigators could take advantage of the lengthy growing season and ample sunshine despite below-normal annual rainfall and runoff in most years from 1850 to 1880.

As landholdings were subdivided and smaller parcels developed, groundwater use became more convenient. Wells could be placed on smaller properties nearer the point of use, with less reliance on extensive surface-water diversion systems. Furthermore, a California Supreme Court ruling in 1866 upheld the riparian system as the basic California law of surface water rights, reducing surface water availability for land not immediately adjacent to a surface water source. A smaller landowner might not be riparian to a surface stream, but did possess a right to the water beneath the land.

Well-drilling rigs and the first deep-well mechanical pumps were introduced to the area in the 1870s. These technologies facilitated development in nonartesian areas of the more reliable and convenient groundwater supplies.

Around 1870, some of the new communities of the Coastal Plain in the San Gabriel River watershed began to tap artesian wells and springs along the Newport-Inglewood Uplift (California DWR, 1968: 3). On the Coastal Plain in the Santa Ana River watershed, William Spurgeon had a 340-foot well and a 2,500-gallon storage tank constructed in 1873 to serve as the first groundwater-based municipal "water works" for his community of Santa Ana. To the east, the growing Irvine Ranch was developing an irrigation system that drew on both surface and groundwater supplies.

Increased water use also brought the first conflicts and court fights, and the creation of public jurisdictions to acquire and protect water supplies. In the upper reaches of the San Gabriel Valley, the "Dalton Ditch dispute," complete with confrontations between armed claimants, was a harbinger of this aspect of southern California's future. Rancher Henry Dalton and settlers on lands claimed by Dalton repeatedly squared off over the conveyance of water across Dalton's claimed lands. During those disputes, the settlers persuaded the Los Angeles County Board of Supervisors on three separate occasions to create new public jurisdictions—a San Jose Water District in San Jose Township in 1871, a separate Azusa Township with a Board of Water Commissioners in 1873, and a separate

Duarte Township with a Board of Water Commissioners in 1878—in order to gain eminent domain powers with which to construct diversion facilities and to claim rights to San Gabriel River water. Dalton successfully challenged the creation and powers of the first two of these jurisdictions in the California Supreme Court in 1873 and 1875 (Clark, 1970: 156–57). Settlers on the east and west sides of the San Gabriel River continued to feud over water rights until well into the 1880s (Walters et al., 1961: 2).

The 1880s: Prosperity Explodes

The agricultural prosperity of the 1870s, the formation of new communities, the establishment of direct rail transportation, and the relentless promotion of the region set the stage for a wild expansion in the 1880s. The great southern California real estate boom of the 1880s was triggered by the arrival of additional railroad lines—particularly the Atchison, Topeka, and Santa Fe in 1885—and the onset of competition in rail fares.

The arrival of the Santa Fe had several important effects. In the desert, new communities grew up as railway crossing points (such as Barstow, originally named Waterman Junction but renamed after William Barstow Strong, president of the Santa Fe) or as railway watering stations (such as Victorville). On the coastal side of the mountains, the Santa Fe brought travelers from the east through the broad inland valleys past thousands of acres of orange groves, depositing passengers eagerly willing to enter the great southern California sweepstakes.

Passenger fares from Chicago to Los Angeles through 1885 were $118 for a first-class ticket and $85 for second-class. By the end of 1886, rate wars had brought fares down to a dollar for trains leaving from Kansas City, and $15 was the highest fare between southern California and Missouri (O'Flaherty, 1978: 16). Cheap fares made it possible for tens of thousands of easterners and new immigrants to venture out to "the magic land of climate and opportunity" (O'Flaherty, 1978: 15). In 1887, at the peak of the rate wars, the Southern Pacific brought 120,000 passengers to its Los Angeles station, and the Santa Fe had three or four trains per day arriving at its station. New arrivals and existing residents were swept up

> in the wildest, most spectacular real-estate boom the state has ever known. . . . Towns were laid out on cattle ranges, sheep ranches, deserts, mountains, and sand hills. Lots were sold in town sites no human eye had ever seen; and investors stood in line to buy business frontages in cities . . . still as tenuous and insubstantial as the air. (Cleland, 1951: 196)

One major subdivision in Santa Ana sold $80,000 of lots (upward of $1 million in 1990 dollars) in two hours, and another in Fullerton sold

$90,000 in half a day. The Azusa site promoted by the Slauson-Bicknell syndicate sold $280,000 of lots in one day (O'Flaherty, 1978: 31–35).

There was a related boom in the incorporation of communities. Riverside incorporated in 1883. Pasadena, Santa Ana, and Santa Monica incorporated in 1886. South Pasadena, Compton, Pomona, Orange, and Redlands all incorporated in 1888.

Although most of the new cities still had fairly small populations at the close of the 1880s, the population of the region and of the already established cities grew phenomenally during the decade. Los Angeles County's population tripled during the decade, to more than 100,000 residents, despite the creation of Orange County out of Los Angeles County's southeastern corner in 1889 (see Table 4.1). The population of the city of Los Angeles quintupled, from 11,183 in 1880 to 50,395 in 1890. The population of San Bernardino County tripled to 25,497. By 1890, there were more than 150,000 residents in Los Angeles, Orange, and San Bernardino counties, where there had been just over 40,000 a decade before.

The boom of the 1880s brought more disputes over rights to surface water supplies. Conflict over access to waters of the San Gabriel River

TABLE 4.1
Population of Southern California Counties, 1860–1990

Year	Los Angeles	Orange	Riverside	San Bernardino
1860	11,333			5,551
1870	15,309			3,988
1880	33,381			7,786
1890	101,454	13,589[a]		25,497
1900	170,298	19,696	17,897[b]	27,929
1910	504,131	34,436	34,696	56,706
1920	936,455	61,375	50,279	73,401
1930	2,208,492	118,674	81,024	133,900
1940	2,785,643	130,760	105,524	161,108
1950	4,151,687	216,244	170,046	281,642
1960	6,038,771	703,925	306,191	503,591
1970	7,041,980	1,421,233	456,916	584,072
1980	7,477,503	1,932,709	663,166	895,016
1990	8,863,164	2,410,556	1,170,413	1,418,380

a. Earliest U.S. Census figure available for Orange County.
b. Earliest U.S. Census figure available for Riverside County.
SOURCE: Population Abstract of the United States (1983); 1990 figures from U.S. Bureau of the Census.

in the upper part of the San Gabriel Valley continued through the 1880s, until several prominent valley men negotiated an agreement known as the Compromise of 1889. The compromise divided the San Gabriel River water among its claimants and established the San Gabriel River Water Committee (the Committee of Nine). The committee was composed of representatives of the disputing claimants and administered the provisions of the Compromise of 1889, maintaining a self-governing system along the river for several decades.

Conflict spread to other watersheds. A dispute arose between settlers on opposite banks of the Santa Ana River on the Coastal Plain. Water users in the Anaheim area (on the northern side of the river) disagreed with water users in the Santa Ana area (the southern side) over rights to divert water from the river. The northern, or Anaheim, interests attempted a preemptive move in the 1880s by filing an action in state court to establish a paramount right to the river water. They prevailed at the trial level, but the judgment was reversed by the California Supreme Court, which recognized Santa Ana as having inherited the riparian water right of the Rancho Santiago de Santa Ana, dating back to 1810 (OCWD Annual Report, 1983).

In the Upper Area of the Los Angeles River watershed, Los Angeles acted to protect its right to the river against upstream diversions by San Fernando Valley irrigators. By the late 1870s, nearly the entire surface flow of the river was being diverted for domestic purposes of the city. Any diminution of the river's flow by upstream uses imposed losses on the city and its growing populace. In 1879, the city destroyed a number of upstream irrigation ditches and was sued by the owners of those ditches. The California Supreme Court held in favor of the city in 1881, on the ground that the city was the successor in interest to the original Spanish pueblo's right to the waters of the old Rio de Porciuncula.[3]

Signs of Trouble

The disputes in the Los Angeles, San Gabriel, and Santa Ana River watersheds indicated that the scarce surface water supplies of southern California already were being pressed to their limits by the expansion of population and irrigated agriculture. The disputes encouraged further reliance on groundwater supplies throughout the Coastal Plain and inland valleys. In the 1890s, new developments brought signs of trouble in southern California, above ground and below.

The real estate boom exhausted itself in the late 1880s and collapsed. Occasional signs of resurgence in the 1890s were squelched by the financial instability of the nation as a whole. Southern California continued to add new residents, but the pace of growth cooled substantially. The city of Los Angeles doubled its population, from 50,395 in 1890 to 102,479 in 1900, but the population of the remainder of Los Angeles County hardly increased. Orange County added 6,000 new residents during the decade, and San Bernardino only 2,400 (nearly all in the city of San Bernardino). The pace of new municipal incorporations also slowed: Ontario incorporated in 1891 (but added only 39 new residents from 1890 to 1900), Redondo Beach incorporated in 1892, Corona in 1896, Long Beach in 1897, and Whittier in 1898.

The depressed economy affected plans for the expansion of irrigated agriculture. After the passage of the Wright Act in 1889 authorizing the creation of irrigation districts, several were formed in southern California, especially in the Santa Ana River watershed (Moreland, 1972: 11). These irrigation districts were created to finance and undertake water-development projects. Falling land values and crop prices, combined with the instability of the financial markets, brought many of the Wright Act districts to financial ruin within a few years. In 1897, the Wright Act was repealed, more stringent provisions for irrigation district formation were enacted, and the organization of new districts ceased for about ten years (Crouch et al., 1956: 278).

Conflicts over surface water supplies and the failure of new water-development projects for irrigation were compounded by the beginning of a decade-long drought. Rainfall at Los Angeles dropped to 7.5 inches in 1894, reached a low of 4.8 inches in 1898, and did not return to the normal 15 inches per year until 1905.

As surface streams dried up, additional extractions of groundwater became vital to the survival of many farmers and communities. But the increased groundwater use and a decline in natural replenishment from surface supplies caused the water level and artesian water pressure on the Coastal Plain to drop. The situation was growing serious in the Upper Area of the Santa Ana River watershed and in the San Bernardino Valley, but the worst news came from the Coastal Plain. In 1904, the tenth year of the drought, J. B. Lippincott's study for the U.S. Geological Survey reported that there were more than 100 producing wells in West Basin alone, underground water levels were falling throughout the Coastal Plain, and the area of artesian flow had been reduced by one-third (Los Angeles Board of Public Service Commissioners, 1916: 35; California DPW, 1952: 29).

At the Los Angeles pumping plant on Slauson Avenue, the underground water level fell 9 feet in the first four years of the drought. By 1904, the flow of the Los Angeles River, fed by the movement of groundwater from the San Fernando Valley, had become "alarmingly low" (Mann, 1976: 267). In 1898, an official with the new Federal Reclamation Service warned: "You are taking water out faster than it is flowing in. Some day you will strike bottom" (O'Flaherty, 1978: 221).

Water users responded to the drought in various ways. Los Angeles municipalized its water supply system, taking it back from the Los Angeles Water Company in 1902, and continued legal actions against upstream pumpers and diverters. In the San Gabriel and Santa Ana River watersheds, residents increased groundwater use and began experimenting with storing water underground, recharging groundwater basins by impounding surface water flows when they were available. In the San Gabriel Valley, Pasadena began spreading water at the mouth of Arroyo Seco canyon. In the Santa Ana River watershed, water users in the northwest part of Chino Basin began to spread San Antonio Creek waters in 1895 and organized the Pomona Valley Protective Association to oversee the activity. On the Coastal Plain, the Irvine Ranch Company began spreading water from Santiago Creek for storage in 1896 (California DPW, 1930a: 49). The Gage Canal Company, and the East Lugonia Mutual, San Antonio, Etiwanda, Cucamonga, and Fontana Union water companies began similar operations in 1903 (Scott, 1977: 222).

In 1907, shortly after the drought ended, Orange, Riverside, and San Bernardino counties formed the Tri-Counties Reforestation Committee, which successfully sought the withdrawal from entry of 960 acres of federal land to be used for water spreading downstream from Santa Ana Canyon. In June 1909, the Tri-Counties Water Conservation Association was formed to attempt water conservation on a basin-wide scale. The association authorized the construction of a dam at the mouth of Santa Ana Canyon, with a diversion ditch to the water-spreading area. Spreading operations began in 1911 (Scott, 1977: 221; Skrove, 1989b: 6).

Big Projects and Urbanization: Making Southern California Happen

Southern California has been described a "hydraulic have-not" that "made itself happen through will and water" (Starr, 1990). In 1905, after a decade-long drought, voters in Los Angeles, a city of about 200,000 people, approved by a 14-to-1 margin a bond issue of $1.5 million to purchase land and acquire water rights for an aqueduct of almost 240 miles to the Owens Valley. The city purchased 135,116 acres—an area approximately double that of the city itself. When the Board of Water Commissioners went back to the voters in 1907 for approval of an additional $23 million in bonds for the construction of the aqueduct, the measure passed by a 10-to-1 margin. The aqueduct (longest in the world at the time) was completed in 1913. On November 5, its first delivery of water poured into a reservoir at the aqueduct's terminus in the San Fernando Valley, before a celebrating crowd of about 30,000. At the same time, because city policy did not allow surplus water to be made available to lands outside the city's limits, the San Fernando Valley (except the already incorporated cities of Burbank, Glendale, and San Fernando) was annexed to Los Angeles.

Other southern California efforts during this period focused on the recurring problem of too much water. The drought broke in 1905 and a wet period followed. Rainfall at Los Angeles was above normal in nine of the twelve years from 1905 through 1916, and flooding occurred in 1907, 1914, and 1916. The year 1916 became a high-water benchmark throughout the region, against which surface water flows and underground water levels were measured for decades thereafter.

In 1908, the U.S. Army Corps of Engineers rechanneled the Santa Ana River on the Orange County Coastal Plain in an attempt to reduce future flood damage. After a destructive flood in 1914, the Los Angeles County Board of Supervisors sought approval from the state to create a flood control district. The Los Angeles County Flood Control District was created in 1915 and soon undertook several projects to rechannel and control the flows of the Los Angeles and San Gabriel rivers, as well as the Rio Hondo and some of the tributary streams in the county.

In the 1910s and 1920s, as southern California grew and prospered and its population and property valuation increased, the prospects of flood damage became a serious local government concern. Orange County created the Orange County Flood Control District in 1927. In 1930, Los Angeles County Flood Control District Chief Engineer E. C. Eaton wrote that a flood of equal or greater proportions than the one experienced in 1914 "would cause, in the present extensively developed state of the county, damages to property easily running into many millions" (California DPW, 1930b: 13).

Oil, Autos, and a New Boom

Eaton based his flood damage projections and his comment about "the present extensively developed state of the county" on the fact that from 1914 to 1929 the county valuation rose from $700 million to $3 billion (California DPW, 1930b: 15). Tremendous growth occurred throughout southern California in the 1910s and 1920s. Oil discoveries on the Coastal Plain and improved access to the region via the automobile touched off a new southern California boom equaling that of the 1880s in its intensity and madness. At times during the peak years 1923–1927, the city of Los Angeles gained 100,000 new residents per year.

As the boom gained momentum, it swept everything before it. Grazing lands, grain fields, orchards, truck gardens, and chaparral-covered hillsides were subdivided and thrown on the market as fast as the necessary maps could be recorded. Vacant crossroads suddenly developed into important business centers; quiet villages woke to find their skylines broken by towering office buildings and spacious apartment houses; and almost overnight compact little communities changed into sprawling, hectic metropolitan centers. Glendale, whose population in 1910 was only 2,700, became "the fastest growing city in the world" and by 1930 boasted 62,000 inhabitants. Between the census of 1920 and that of 1930 the population of Long Beach rose from 55,000 to 142,000. (Cleland, 1951: 296)

By the end of the 1920s, the Coastal Plain and inland valleys of Los Angeles, Orange, Riverside, and San Bernardino counties had become home to more than 2.5 million residents.

During this second boom, southern California began to urbanize in earnest. Total developed acreage in coastal Los Angeles County more than tripled between land-use surveys in 1904 and 1926 (see Table 4.2), and acreage devoted to urban and suburban uses increased more than tenfold. By 1932, nearly as much land in coastal Los Angeles County was devoted to urban and suburban uses as to irrigated agriculture. From 1900 to 1920, many communities throughout the region incorporated as cities, including Arcadia (1903), Fullerton (1904), Glendale, Wilmington, San Pedro, and Newport Beach (1906), Claremont (1907), Inglewood (1908), Huntington Beach (1909), Hollywood (1910), Burbank and San Fernando (1911), El Monte (1912), San Gabriel and San Marino (1913), Beverly Hills (1914), Anaheim (1915), and Culver City (1917). By 1920, Los Angeles, Orange, Riverside, and San Bernardino counties had a combined population of 1.1 million, and the incorporated cities of the four counties contained a combined population of 875,549, or 78 percent of the total.

The most spectacular population growth continued to be in Los Angeles County, where the population tripled from 1900 to 1910, nearly doubled between 1910 and 1920, then more than doubled from 1920 to 1930 to 2.2 million. Most county residents continued to be in the city of Los Angeles, which by 1930 had a population of 1.2 million, but a million county residents lived outside the city of Los Angeles. Despite annexations that more than doubled its territory between 1900 and 1930, Los Angeles found that its share of the county population had declined.

There were fifty-seven incorporated cities in the South Coastal region as of 1930, some of them growing quite large. Long Beach had a population of nearly 150,000, and Pasadena and Glendale both had populations of more than 60,000. Riverside and San Bernardino both had populations of 30,000 or more. Orange County and San Bernardino County had populations in excess of 100,000, and Riverside County was fast approaching that mark. Population growth and urbanization had begun to spread across the land. Among other things, those changes meant that several

TABLE 4.2

Developed Land Use, Coastal Los Angeles County, 1880–1960 (in acres)

Year	Irrigated agriculture	Urban/suburban	Total
1880	36,100	0	36,100
1888	41,800	0	41,800
1904	94,100	13,800	107,900
1926	219,500	149,800	369,300
1932	185,500	153,000	338,500
1942	178,500	172,100	350,600
1950	132,300	380,800	513,100
1955	87,400	456,500	543,900
1960	45,530	564,990	610,520

SOURCE: California State Water Resources Board (1956) and California Department of Water Resources (1964a).

municipalities besides Los Angeles would be looking for reliable water supplies to accommodate their present needs and future growth.

Another Dry Period, 1922–1937

The most active municipal water seeker was Pasadena. By 1920, Pasadena was clearly the urban center of the San Gabriel Valley. The city had a population of 45,000, and was even then being surrounded by suburban satellites such as South Pasadena, Alhambra, San Gabriel, and San Marino. Pasadena's civic leaders had in mind, if not to be another Los Angeles, at least to be the other major city in southern California. To fulfill this destiny, they needed more water.

Pasadena had been spreading water at the mouth of Arroyo Seco canyon since the drought years of 1895–1904. Nearly all of its municipal water supply came from Raymond Basin groundwater. Observing the Los Angeles experience, Pasadena's leaders were convinced that an outside water source was a desirable means to ensure future growth. If Los Angeles could bring water from the Owens Valley to the San Fernando Valley, Pasadena would bring water to the San Gabriel Valley from some similarly underdeveloped source on the other side of the mountains. In 1920, the city of Pasadena proposed to divert water from the headwaters of the Mojave River and transport that water over the San Gabriel Mountains for municipal use in the Raymond Basin. Pasadena filed an application with the California Division of Water Rights, but the application was denied after land and water companies, irrigation districts, and farming associations in the Mojave River area organized and opposed the move.

In 1923, Pasadena attempted to secure additional water somewhat closer to home. The city applied for permits to appropriate all of the unappropriated flood waters of the San Gabriel River. The city planned to impound San Gabriel River flood flows when they occurred, store them, and divert them westward to Pasadena. The city and the Los Angeles County Flood Control District, which was also interested in the impoundment and conservation of flood waters along the San Gabriel, jointly financed (at a cost of more than $87,000) an investigation of the waters of the San Gabriel River watershed by the California Division of Water Rights.

Pasadena's forays in search of additional water supplies were motivated by necessity as well as invention. By the mid-1920s, another dry cycle was under way in southern California, which lasted through 1937. The dry period was not as severe from year to year as the 1895–1904 drought, but it presented serious water supply problems nevertheless, since three times as much acreage was developed and in need of regular water service as had been under use in 1904.

The new dry cycle brought more water studies and more water conservation efforts.[4] Again, the news was bad. Particularly disturbing was the finding that water supply conditions had not improved during the wet years of 1905–1917. Except in the San Fernando Valley (where aqueduct water was being used for irrigation) and the less-developed Mojave River area, water levels had at best remained steady, and at worst had continued to decline despite the years of above-normal precipitation and runoff.

In response to the increasing demand for water service in the early decades of this century, the deep-well turbine pump represented an important technological advance. The new pumps could extract larger quantities of water more rapidly and from greater depths than the mechanical pumps of the late 1800s. They made it possible to develop more acreage, but increased the overall draft on groundwater supplies. Increased withdrawals at least kept pace with increased water supplies over most of the Coastal Plain during the 1905–1917 wet period, and in some locations outpaced them.

Although it was not widely understood at the time, the increase in groundwater extractions accounted for a peculiar occurrence of the period. In 1912, the Southern California Edison Company had to abandon a well at Redondo Beach because it was pulling salty water. By the late 1920s, it was apparent that the Redondo Beach occurrence had been a warning, not a fluke. In 1930, the California Division of Water Resources reported these sobering observations:

> In 1929 some of the wells of the Standard Oil Company at El Segundo were rendered unfit for use. Since then other wells have become similarly affected, until now in 45 square miles of west coast territory wells are

becoming saline. In an additional 117 square miles water is being drawn from below sea level and the water plane over the South Coastal Basin is receding. Salt water is being found in a small area along the Santa Ana River over a mile from the coast. . . . Once wells are thus ruined it is not certain that they can be brought back to productivity. (California DPW, 1930b: 73)

A 1934 report by the division mapped the area of saltwater intrusion, which had been found all along the coast.

Saltwater intrusion, declining water levels, and vacant groundwater storage capacity were noted in report after report through the 1920s and 1930s. In 1925, the California Division of Engineering and Irrigation observed that measurements taken in 1922 and 1924 of the depth to groundwater in a large number of wells showed a decline "over practically the entire region with great variation in the different parts. In one section, the water plane dropped 100 feet during the two years. The recession over considerable areas was as much as 20 to 40 feet" (California DPW, 1925: 14). The investigation of San Gabriel Valley water conditions financed by Pasadena and the Los Angeles County Flood Control District and performed by the California Division of Water Rights found underground water levels in the valley had dropped 30 feet or more during the 1923–24 and 1924–25 water years.

The division's Bulletin 32, published in 1930, contained the broadest assessment to that date of the region's water conditions. In the San Gabriel and Santa Ana River watersheds, aggregate shortages were between 200,000 and 250,000 acre-feet. And, in all of the groundwater basins of the south coastal area combined, more than 2.2 million acre-feet of storage capacity had been emptied since the high-water mark of 1916 (California DPW, 1930b: 10–16). (An estimate reported a year earlier had put the emptied capacity as high as 2.6 million acre-feet; California DPW, 1929: 1.)

Local water organizations, including water users' associations and flood control districts, initiated or increased water conservation efforts. Works were constructed along the San Gabriel and Santa Ana rivers and all tributary creeks and washes with the intention of keeping every drop that fell from the sky or trickled down the side of a hill or mountain from reaching the ocean without first having been caught, diverted, spread, sunk underground, pumped out for use on the land, and preferably returned underground for reuse downstream. Additional water users' organizations, such as the San Gabriel Water Spreading Corporation, the San Gabriel Valley Protective Association, and the Chino Basin Protective Association, formed during this period. These groups added their efforts to those of the Tri-Counties Water Conservation Association in the Santa Ana River watershed, the Los Angeles County Flood Control District in the San Gabriel River watershed, and the city of Los Angeles in the Los Angeles River watershed (California DPW, 1930b: 70).

In addition to documenting the deteriorating water supply conditions and water conservation efforts in southern California during the 1920s and 1930s, several reports during the period looked ahead to the effects of water supply problems on the region's future. Some focused on the impact of future water shortages on existing local communities. A 1929 Division of Water Resources report noted that the total annual water shortage for the Los Angeles, San Gabriel, and Santa Ana River watersheds had reached 190,600 acre-feet, and was expected to jump to 447,000 acre-feet by 1940, 641,000 acre-feet by 1945, and 846,000 by 1950. The Division of Engineering and Irrigation foresaw not only shortages but a race to the bottom: "Unless large amounts of water can be [imported], the southern communities must suffer from the destructive competition of pumping from underground sources that have a receding water-plane" (California DPW, Division of Engineering and Irrigation, 1927: 43).

Other reports focused on the tremendous opportunities that would be forgone. Southern California was running out of water faster than it was running out of irrigable land for crops and habitable land for people. Despite the growth in the late 1800s and early 1900s, only about half of the habitable acreage of coastal Los Angeles County had been developed for agriculture or urban use by 1930, and this was the most heavily developed part of southern California. If development stalled at current levels, great opportunities would be missed:

> Utilizing four-fifths of the available local water, less than half of the favorable area is occupied by cities or towns and irrigated lands. In order that growth and expansion may continue to the full limit of the natural resources other than water, the Pacific slope of southern California will require three times the volume of water that can be obtained from nature's allotment to this territory. Unless this additional water can be secured, the future must face a curtailed growth incommensurate with the opportunities offered by the other natural endowments of this remarkable territory. (California DPW, 1927: 43)

Water studies and water conservation would not be enough. What was needed was more water, period. With additional water, southern California could really happen: "about a million acres of new lands [could] be furnished domestic, irrigation or industrial supplies by coordinating local development with the importation of water. Three thousand cubic feet per second would eventually have to be obtained" (California DPW, 1925: 14). How could an additional supply of 3,000 cubic feet per second be obtained? "There being no nearby source of additional supply, great works to bring in water from a distant source will be necessary. Preliminary reconnaissance indicates that such a supply may be had from the Colorado River."

MWD and the Colorado River Aqueduct

Pasadena was not the only southern California city eyeing possible supplemental water sources in the early 1920s. In 1923, at the suggestion of William Mulholland, the local hero of the Los Angeles Aqueduct, the Los Angeles Department of Water and Power conducted preliminary studies of the possibility of constructing an aqueduct across the desert to the Colorado River. In 1924, Los Angeles filed for and was granted rights to 1,500 cubic feet per second of Colorado River water.

This time, however—for a variety of reasons that included the enormous expense of the undertaking, the amount of supplemental water potentially available, and the fact that the water supply situation of other southern California cities was even more precarious than that of Los Angeles—the city decided not to go it alone. Pasadena was, of course, one of several other cities interested in the scheme.

Such a project could only be financed and operated by a new public organization, a unit of local government that would itself be composed of local governments. State legislative authorization was secured for the creation of a "metropolitan water district." This new jurisdictional creature would be governed by a board composed of representatives of the participating local government units within its territory, where "participating" meant paying the costs of the district's operations—which would initially be financed through bond sales, secured against the valuation of real property in the participating localities.

Once authorized to do so, interested cities set about organizing a metropolitan water district. On February 15, 1928, the Pasadena city commissioners adopted an ordinance "declaring that 'public necessity and convenience require the organization and incorporation of a metropolitan water district'" (Cleland, 1966: 340). Originally, the cities of Anaheim, Beverly Hills, Burbank, Colton, Glendale, Los Angeles, San Bernardino, San Marino, Santa Ana, and Santa Monica joined the district along with Pasadena. San Bernardino and Colton subsequently withdrew from the organization, but Compton, Fullerton, Long Beach, and Torrance took their places (Cleland, 1966: 340–41). In all, thirteen cities became "charter members" of the Metropolitan Water District of Southern California, the MWD.

The MWD commissioned some additional studies of the local water supply situation, but focused primarily on acquiring supplemental supplies from the Colorado River. By November 1930, the district's general manager, Frank E. Weymouth, recommended to the MWD Board of Directors a site on the Colorado River, near the town of Parker and about 150 miles below Hoover Dam, for the construction of a diversion dam across the Colorado River. Completion of the project could bring as much as a million acre-feet of water per year to southern California.

In September 1931, the MWD board agreed to submit to voters in the thirteen cities a bond issue for the whopping Depression-era sum of $220 million. The bond issue passed in November 1931 by a combined margin of 5 to 1. Construction of MWD's Colorado River Aqueduct began in December 1932 and was completed in June 1941, for a total cost approximately 20 percent less than estimated (MWD, 1962: 14). The aqueduct lifts Colorado River water about 600 feet up to the floor of the desert, and then carries it over 340 miles to and through the south coastal area, with another 1,000 feet of pumping lift at three pumping stations along the way. The water is conveyed across 242 miles of desert, through 55 miles of covered conduits, 62 miles of concrete-lined canals, 29 miles of siphons, and 29 tunnels that vary in length from 338 feet to 18.3 miles, and then throughout southern California in a network of feeders (Cleland, 1966: 341).

Southern California Transformed: The Postwar Urbanization

The first water deliveries from the Colorado River reached Pasadena on June 17, 1941, and other member cities soon thereafter, just in time to handle another population explosion that transformed most of the area from agriculture to metropolis. The population of coastal Los Angeles County increased 47 percent from 1945 to 1955. In 1955, the *Los Angeles Times* offered this perspective: "If the entire population of Pittsburgh and Baltimore—1,755,000—were transported westward and settled within the Los Angeles metropolitan area you would have a fair estimate of our population increase between January 1, 1945 and January 1, 1955" (quoted in Cleland, 1966: 413).

The population of Los Angeles County reached 6 million in 1960. Thereafter, the focus of population growth shifted to other parts of southern California. Orange County's population more than tripled from 216,244 in 1950 to 703,925 in 1960, and then doubled to 1,421,233 in 1970. By 1970, the cities of Riverside and San Bernardino each had more than 100,000 residents, and Riverside and San Bernardino counties each contained a half million people.

In addition to sparking the development of additional land, the postwar population boom urbanized formerly agricultural lands. Los Angeles County still led all counties in the United States in total value of farm products as late as 1952. By 1962, the amount of acreage devoted to irrigated agriculture in coastal Los Angeles County was as small as it had been in the 1880s. In 1954 alone, 4,100 acres of citrus orchards in coastal Los Angeles County were converted to residential subdivisions (California SWRB, 1956: 16).

Southern California urbanized in waves. The San Gabriel and San Fernando valleys were transformed during the late 1940s and through the 1950s. Orange County urbanized during the 1950s and 1960s. The most recent wave of urbanization is still occurring, in the upper Santa Ana River watershed and across the mountains in the Mojave Desert.

Because most postwar urban and suburban development replaced irrigated agriculture, annual water requirements have grown, but not at the same breakneck rate as the population. An acre of southern California land devoted to irrigation requires about the same amount of water (slightly more or less depending on crop selection) as an acre devoted to residential or commercial use. In some basins, the replacement of irrigated agriculture with residential and commercial land usage actually lowered total water consumption. Urbanization also meant, however, the installation of sewer systems that collected wastewater and sent it to the ocean through concrete channels and pipelines. Therefore, water used on the overlying urbanized landscape did not return underground in the same amounts as it did when water was being applied to agricultural lands.[5]

The net result was some increase in total water requirements in southern California. If, however, the water requirements of southern California had more than quintupled since 1930 as the population has done, the region's water supply problems would have been even more difficult to resolve. As it was, allocating water supplies entailed a long, complex, and demanding series of tasks.

The "Uncommon Law" of Water Rights in California

Once extensive use—and in several places overuse—of local groundwater supplies was under way in southern California, water users had engaged all the complexities of California's law of water rights. That law defined not only separate systems of rights to the use of surface waters and groundwater, but different types of rights within each of those systems and two other types of water rights outside those systems. California law, and its development and modification by the California courts through the 1920s, identified surface water riparian rights, surface water appropriative rights, groundwater overlying rights, groundwater appropriative rights, and groundwater correlative rights, as well as pueblo water rights and prescriptive water rights.

Article XIV of the California Constitution of 1879 declared as a matter of policy that the state's water resources should be put to their fullest possible use. That constitutional provision also denied the ownership of bodies of water to individuals, stating instead that the waters in the state were the property of the people. What individuals (including private and public corporate entities) could possess was a usufructuary right—a right to the *use* of water.

Riparian and Overlying Rights

The traditional common law means of acquiring a usufructuary water right is by owning land that is adjacent to a body of surface water or that lies over a body of groundwater. With respect to surface streams, this is known as a riparian right; with respect to groundwater, it is an overlying right. Riparian and overlying rights to the use of water extended only to its use on the adjacent or overlying land.

Riparian and overlying rights were not limited to any specific amount of water use. This was not a problem in places with abundant water, such as England and the eastern United States, but unquantified and unlimited water rights that inhere in land ownership have more serious implications in arid regions such as California.

Appropriative Rights

In California, the surface riparian right and the overlying groundwater right existed alongside a system of appropriative rights. Appropriative rights allow water users to divert or extract water for use on nonriparian or nonoverlying lands. Much land in California is not riparian to a surface stream or does not lie over a groundwater body, yet can be made productive only by the availability of a water supply.

According to historians, appropriative rights arose by custom during the early development of the West, particularly in relation to water diversions in mining camps. Other practical considerations played a role. As private water development companies, public districts, and municipal governments were organized to undertake the capital costs of providing a water supply to numerous water consumers, those entities necessarily delivered water to lands they did not own. Appropriation gave these suppliers rights to the use of water beyond what they could use on their own lands.

The appropriative rights system followed three principal rules: (1) rights were limited to the amount of water actually put to use and did not accrue to diversion capacity or to water diverted but wasted; (2) rights were contingent on continuous use, with cessation of use tantamount to abandonment of the right; and (3) among appropriators, a "first-in-time, first-in-right" practice assigned priority in rights by seniority in use. A shortage would be handled by reducing or eliminating use by the most junior appropriator, then the second junior appropriator, and so on. The most senior appropriator was thus protected against invasion of his right by junior appropriators.

The appropriative rights system was made part of the statutory law of California with the adoption of the Civil Code in 1872. From that point, by law as well as custom, California had a dual system of water rights, one based on land ownership and conferring an unquantified right to water use, the other based on actual use conferring a "first-come, first-served" right to a specific quantity. Furthermore, each of these systems of water rights existed separately for surface and groundwater supplies; the law differentiated riparian and appropriative surface water rights from overlying and appropriative groundwater rights, even where surface and groundwater systems were physically connected.

There were two sources of conflicts over rights under this dual system. The first problem involved defining the rights of riparian or overlying owners in relation to those of appropriators when both types of rights were being exercised in a common water supply. The second problem involved defining the rights of riparian or overlying owners in relation to one another, since the riparian/overlying rights system did not come with a built-in allocation such as the seniority allocation of rights among appropriators. Both of these issues came before the California courts at the beginning of the twentieth century.

"Reasonable Use" and Correlative Rights

By the turn of the century, it had become clear that in a water shortage, riparian or overlying owners' claims could be enforced to the point of eliminating appropriative uses from the same source. This possibility presented problems in light of the state's declared policy that water resources were to be used to the fullest beneficial extent. If overlying owners could enforce claims to water they were not using against appropriators who were (by definition) using the water, then the state's water resources would not be used to the fullest possible beneficial extent (Krieger, 1955: 1).

In *Katz v. Walkinshaw*, 141 Cal. 116 (1903), the California Supreme Court concluded from the state's policy that no one should be allowed to "sleep on his rights." A person's water right should be determined by the amount of water he pumps and puts to beneficial use (141 Cal. 116 at 134). The California Supreme Court limited the absolute water rights of overlying landowners to the amount of water that was put to "reasonable use" for some beneficial purpose (141 Cal. 116 at 135). This "reasonable use" language was subsequently formulated as an amendment to the California Constitution, ratified in 1928.

The reasonable-use doctrine had two profound implications. First, by placing some restraint on the overlying water right, it implied the possible existence of "surplus" water in a groundwater basin. Surplus water was any water beyond that to which the landowner's superior right extended, that is, the amount reasonably necessary for use on his land. Appropriators were entitled to take and acquire rights to the surplus.

Without this modification, the appropriative rights system eventually would have become mere print in the statute books inasmuch as overlying and riparian rights were enforced against appropriative claims in one case after another. Second, the restriction of an overlying owner's right to the amount of water needed for reasonable use on his own land and the availability of the surplus for appropriation encouraged overlying owners to use more water in order to expand and protect their rights.

Also in *Katz v. Walkinshaw* (1903), the California Supreme Court addressed the question of the status of riparian or overlying water rights relative to one another. Even with the reasonable-use limitation, multiple water users supplying themselves from a common source still could find themselves imposing damage on one another and the common water supply if their collective extractions or diversions exceeded the available yield. The opinion of the California Supreme Court described the problem of joint use of a groundwater supply as follows: "If the water on his lands is his property, then the water in the soil of his neighbors is their property. But when he drains out and sells the water on his lands, he draws to his land, and also sells, water which is the property of his neighbors. . . . In short, the members of the community have a common interest in the water" (141 Cal. 116 at 140).

The California Supreme Court modified the overlying rights into correlative, or proportional, ownership. When shortage resulted in a dispute among overlying owners, a court would treat the disputing parties as coequal owners of correlative rights and determine for each a reasonable proportion of the water supply. The *Katz v. Walkinshaw* doctrine of proportional ownership was reiterated in 1921 in the California Supreme Court decision in *San Bernardino v. Riverside*, 186 Cal. 7 (1921).

As of the 1920s, the California law of water rights allocated usufructuary rights as follows: (1) overlying and riparian owners had rights to the reasonable use of waters upon their lands; (2) with respect to each other, overlying owners had correlative rights and would share proportionately in water supply reductions in the event of shortages; (3) appropriators had a seniority system of rights with respect to one another, with reductions in water use imposed in reverse order of seniority; and (4) between overlying owners and appropriators, overlying owners had a superior right to the amount of water for their reasonable use, and appropriators had a right to the surplus remaining, if any. This system was complicated enough, but there were two more elements to contend with—the Spanish law tradition of pueblo water rights, and the common law tradition of acquiring possession by adverse use, or prescriptive water rights.

Pueblo Water Rights and the City of Los Angeles

Under California law, the city of Los Angeles was the successor in interest to the pueblo of Los Angeles, created by royal decree in 1781. One of the pueblo's interests to which the city succeeded was the interest in the waters of the Los Angeles River. As noted above, Los Angeles began to assert and defend its rights to the waters of the Los Angeles River as early as 1879.

The plaintiffs in the cases of *Feliz v. City of Los Angeles* and *Elms v. City of Los Angeles* claimed the right to the use of the waters of the river under appropriations dating back to 1844. The city claimed that it was successor in interest to all of the river waters it needed, and that its right dated back to the pueblo's founding in 1781. The trial court held for the plaintiffs, and the city appealed. In 1881, the California Supreme Court reversed the trial court's judgments, and held for Los Angeles. In so holding, the Supreme Court declared:

> From the very foundation of the pueblo, in 1781, the right to all the waters of the river was claimed by the pueblo, and that right was recognized by all the owners of land on the stream, from its source. . . . The city, under various acts of the Legislature, has succeeded to all the rights of the former Pueblo. [Therefore,] we hold that, to the extent of the needs of its inhabitants, it has the paramount right to the use of the waters of the river, and the further right . . . to manage and control the said waters for those purposes. (58 Cal. 73 at 79)

The *Feliz* case was the first decision of the California Supreme Court regarding the so-called pueblo water right of Los Angeles. The pueblo water right is a special class of water right in California. When the United States acquired possession of California from Mexico, it acknowledged an obligation to recognize property rights established under Mexican law. Established ranchos, missions, presidios, and pueblos retained legal titles to their lands, while the United States became possessor of all ungranted lands in the public domain (Ostrom, 1971: 174). Some California cities succeeded to pueblo or presidio grants of title to lands and water. Los Angeles was one such city. The pueblo water right superseded riparian, overlying, or appropriative rights to the use of surface or groundwaters. This special class of water rights thus vested its possessor with a superior right with respect to any and all other competing claimants upon a common water supply.

The favorable ruling obtained by the city in the *Feliz* case formed the basis for the city's position in several later legal actions. The city was involved in a number of litigations in the next two decades, through which it extended its pueblo water right to waters needed for areas added to the city by annexation, and ultimately, to the groundwater of the San Fernando Valley that fed the base flow and rising waters of the Los Angeles River.[6]

In *City of Los Angeles v. A. E. Pomeroy et al.*, 57 P. 585 (1899) and in *Los Angeles v. Hunter et al.* and *Los Angeles v. Buffington et al.*, 156 Cal. 603 (1909), the California Supreme Court recognized that the San Fernando Valley was the source of the Los Angeles River, and that the city's pueblo right to the waters of the river extended to the waters of the San Fernando Valley that constitute the source of the river. In *Pomeroy*, the court stated that "all the waters of the San Fernando Valley, except what is lost by evaporation or consumed in plant life, flow out through the narrow pass . . . either on or beneath the surface" (57 P. 585 at 591). These decisions extended the city's pueblo water right to San Fernando Valley groundwater.

Prescriptive Rights

In the context of real property, possession by adverse use is commonly referred to as "squatters' rights." In our context, it is called "prescriptive rights." Through the "open and notorious" taking or holding of property belonging to another, continuously for a prescribed period, a person can acquire a common law ownership of the taken property. In California, by open, notorious, and continuous adverse use of water for a five-year period, a person could perfect a prescriptive right to the use of that water. The owner of the original water right could not dislodge that person from that prescriptive right.

If surplus water were available from a groundwater supply, one could not acquire a prescriptive right, because the taking of water would create no adverse use. Water taken for reasonable use on overlying lands would be considered an ordinary exercise of one's overlying water right, and water taken "openly, notoriously, and continuously" for use on non-overlying lands would create an appropriative right. (Even the pueblo water right allowed others to take surplus water.) Only a taking that harmed the original owner—that is, a taking of nonsurplus water—could ripen into a superior prescriptive right.[7]

By all appearances, then, the availability of water rights through possession by adverse use would seem a rather innocuous additional element in the water rights scheme. Although the possibility of perfecting a prescriptive right appears to be quite limited, in fact it was much greater, because of the similarity in the process by which one would acquire a prescriptive right and the process by which one would acquire an appropriative right or exercise an overlying right. The only difference between the acquisitions of right was whether the water diverted and used was "surplus," and this was a factual question not readily determined by an individual water user.

No clear guidance existed concerning when water would be ruled to be surplus. For instance, in *San Bernardino v. Riverside*, 186 Cal. 7 (1921), despite clear evidence of a falling water table, the California Supreme Court ruled that the water being appropriated by the city of Riverside was surplus water. Therefore, even falling water levels would not necessarily cue a water right owner to act to protect his right. Further, the court declared that courts would not undertake an ongoing responsibility for determining when the surplus was gone and adverse use began. "In this environment of legal uncertainty, attorneys often advised water producers to pump as much as they needed and to defend later. The pumping race was on" (Ostrom, 1965: 191).

By the end of the 1920s, the California Supreme Court had heard and decided important cases on overlying water rights, appropriative water rights, correlative rights, and pueblo water rights. It had not yet had occasion to consider a major case involving claims of prescriptive rights in a groundwater basin. That was about to change.

NOTES

1. There was, however, another name given to the river that may be appreciated more by modern Californians. One of the friars in the Portola expedition called it the River of the Sweet Name of Jesus of the Earthquakes (Cleland, 1966: 287).

2. In a 1923 report to the California legislature based on data through 1921, the state's Division of Engineering and Irrigation documented the extremity of the floods and droughts that plague southern California's natural water conditions:

Watershed	Average annual runoff (acre-feet)	Runoff in maximum year (acre-feet)	Runoff in minimum year (acre-feet)
Santa Ana	253,400	720,500	66,200
San Gabriel	150,200	553,400	9,700
Mojave	98,200	407,700	14,600
Los Angeles	71,000	307,000	0

3. *Feliz v. City of Los Angeles* and *Elms v. City of Los Angeles*, 58 Cal. 73 (1881).

4. Some impression of the extent of investigative activity during this period may be gained from the following nonexhaustive list: the Division of Engineering and Irrigation issued reports on water supply conditions to the state legislature

in 1923, 1925, and 1927, and published its Bulletin 19, *Santa Ana Investigation,* in 1928. The Division of Water Resources published its Bulletin 31, *Santa Ana River Basin,* in 1930; Bulletin 32, *South Coastal Basin,* in 1930; Bulletin 33, *Rainfall Penetration and Consumptive Use of Water in Santa Ana River Valley and Coastal Plain,* in 1930; Bulletin 39, *South Coastal Basin Investigation: Records of Ground Levels at Wells,* in 1932; and Bulletin 45, *South Coastal Basin Investigation,* in 1934.

5. I am indebted to Tom Stetson for pointing out to me the connection between urbanization and overdraft, and for encouraging me to look at the relationship between sewage export and overdraft in the San Gabriel Valley. The lack of connection between population growth and consumptive water use when agricultural lands are converted to urban uses is also worth mentioning because it helps to dispel illusions that western water problems have been caused primarily by the influx of population to these areas.

Of course, urbanization that takes place on previously undeveloped lands creates increased demands for water. But urbanization that converts agricultural land to residential and commercial uses (as has been the case with most of the urbanization in southern California) generally substitutes one form of consumptive water use for another, with little net effect. California's urban population of approximately thirty million people is concentrated on a relatively small proportion of lands originally developed for agriculture. The urban population consumes between 10 and 15 percent of the water used in the state.

6. *Vernon Irrigation Company v. City of Los Angeles,* 106 Cal. 237 (1895); *City of Los Angeles v. A. E. Pomeroy et al.,* 57 P. 585 (1899); *City of Los Angeles v. Los Angeles Farming and Milling Company,* 93 P. 869 (1908); *City of Los Angeles v. Jesse D. Hunter et al.* and *City of Los Angeles v. Thomas D. Buffington et al.,* 156 Cal. 603 (1909).

7. This last statement does not apply to the claim of a prescriptive water right against a pueblo water right, however. If at any point the previously unused surplus water were to become needed by the pueblo or its successor, it could assert its pueblo right against any existing appropriator of that water, and that appropriator would have to end the use. Thus, if the water *were* being used by the pueblo, it could not be acquired by any other user, and if the water *were not* being used by the pueblo, it could not be acquired by adverse use. The logic of the pueblo water right made the assertion of a prescriptive right against the pueblo or its successor an impossibility. There are several recognized authorities on this point. In addition to the cases already cited, see Hutchins (1956: 259–61), V. Ostrom (1971: 174–75, 247), and Craig (1971: lxxi).

PART 2

Institutional Design and Development
Eight Cases

5

Raymond Basin
Constituting Self-Governance in a Groundwater Basin

Between 1870 and 1930, California water rights law placed few restraints on water use and even encouraged some users to increase water production. During this period, the land overlying Raymond Basin, a relatively small groundwater basin in Los Angeles County, was developed rapidly for irrigated agriculture and expanding municipalities. Against this background of legal rules and Raymond Basin's physical setting and pattern of development, water users began overdrafting the basin. Over time, they responded to the overdraft by building a governance structure for the basin and implementing a management plan that divided the basin's safe yield among them. In so doing, they added a new doctrine to California water rights law.

Groundwater Problems in Raymond Basin

The first wells in Raymond Basin were drilled in 1881, and groundwater production grew through the early 1900s. By 1914, the level of local water supplies had become a subject of some concern (Blackburn, 1961: 2). That year, the city of Pasadena initiated a program to replenish the basin by conserving and spreading storm runoff on gravel beds at the foot of the San Gabriel Mountains. Pasadena continued the spreading program until 1924, by which time it had replenished the basin by more than 20,000 acre-feet, using water that otherwise would have made its way to the Los Angeles River and perhaps been wasted to the ocean.

Basin conditions deteriorated more rapidly after another dry cycle began in 1922. Pasadena terminated its spreading operation in 1924 partly

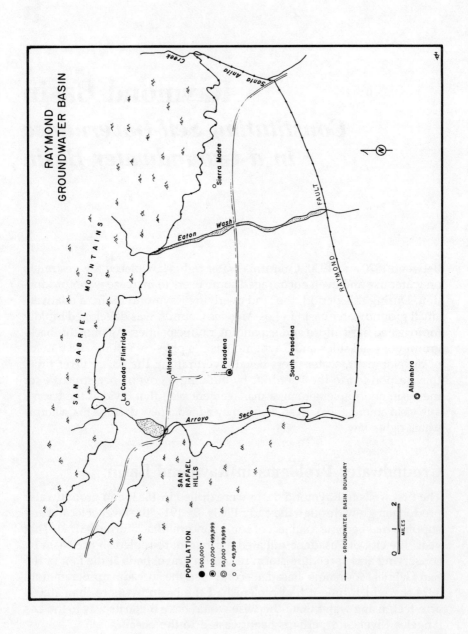

RAYMOND
GROUNDWATER BASIN

San Gabriel Creek

Santa Anita

Sierra Madre

Eaton Wash

FAULT

RAYMOND

SAN GABRIEL MOUNTAINS

La Canada-Flintridge

Altadena

Pasadena

South Pasadena

Alhambra

Arroyo Seco

SAN RAFAEL HILLS

POPULATION
● 500,000+
◉ 100,000-499,999
◎ 50,000-99,999
○ 0-49,999

GROUNDWATER BASIN BOUNDARY

0   1   2
MILES

N

because of the sharp decline in available runoff. Through the remainder of the 1920s, underground water levels dropped, some wells failed, and longer pumping lifts raised operating costs in the others. The drop in water levels was not just seasonal; they no longer recovered in the spring, even in the occasional years of above-average participation.

Analysts often impute to actors rather precise calculations about optimal resource use in the face of scarcity, but this presumes a degree of information and knowledge unavailable to Raymond Basin users at the time. They continued to pump groundwater without fully understanding the effects of their actions on each other and on the basin. Pasadena and the Los Angeles County Flood Control District invested more than $80,000 in an investigation by the California Division of Water Resources of water supplies in the upper San Gabriel River watershed, but even the preliminary results of that investigation were not published until 1930. A full description of the basin's geology and underground water storage characteristics did not appear until the division's Bulletin 45 was published in 1934. And it was not until the early 1940s that users learned the basin had been in overdraft every year since 1913, and that the annual overdraft had averaged 7,000 acre-feet, or roughly 33 percent of the average annual safe yield.

In the meantime, Pasadena focused on acquiring a supplemental water supply. Along with Los Angeles, Pasadena led the effort to form the Metropolitan Water District of Southern California (MWD) to build and operate a Colorado River aqueduct. Even after the MWD was established in 1928, it was evident that Colorado River water would not be available for at least a decade. Also in 1928, the state Division of Water Resources granted Pasadena permits to store and divert flood flows of the San Gabriel River, including a permit to build a dam in San Gabriel Canyon and divert up to 40,000 acre-feet of water per year. In June 1929, Pasadena voters approved a $10 million bond issue to finance the construction of the dam and a conduit to the city. In 1932, with the construction equipment on site, the San Gabriel Valley Protective Association sued to prevent Pasadena from building the dam and diverting the water.

Settlement negotiations between the city and the association were joined by the MWD, which helped resolve the dispute by agreeing to purchase the dam from Pasadena once Colorado River water became available. The association agreed to allow the dam to be completed and to let Pasadena store and divert surplus San Gabriel River water until imported water arrived from MWD.

Pasadena v. Alhambra:
The Raymond Basin Goes to Court

At considerable expense to its taxpayers, Pasadena had taken a number of actions for its own benefit and to the benefit of basin water conditions, including the water-spreading operations and the acquisition of supplemental water supplies from the San Gabriel River and then the Colorado River. Nevertheless, water levels at the city's wells continued to fall through the 1930s, dropping more than 100 feet between 1922 and 1937.

Pasadena officials called together representatives of other known Raymond Basin producers, reviewed the published reports of the Division of Water Resources, as well as Pasadena's own information about the basin, and attempted to negotiate a pumping reduction on a cooperative rather than an adversarial basis. These efforts failed, and city officials contemplated legal action (Sopp, 1943: 431; Blackburn, 1961: 3).

Pasadena officials had reached the limits of their willingness to act alone. The city reduced pumping somewhat when it began to receive additional supplies from the San Gabriel River in 1935. But to redress the overdraft on its own, Pasadena would have had to cut its production by one-half and import substantially more expensive Colorado River water from MWD when available, while other basin users continued to meet all their needs with less expensive groundwater. This Pasadena was unwilling to do.

Pasadena chose instead to defend its right as a senior Raymond Basin appropriator. On September 23, 1937, Pasadena initiated proceedings in Superior Court against the city of Alhambra and other major Raymond Basin water users. The action sought to adjudicate and quiet title to Pasadena's rights in the basin, and to enjoin the annual overdraft. Upon motion of the named defendants, the trial court required the city to amend its complaint to name as defendants all entities in the basin pumping more than 100 acre-feet annually. There were thirty defendants in all. The judge, Frank Collier, also ruled that the suit was not a simple action to quiet title but was a general adjudication of water rights in the basin, with each defendant's answers to the complaint to be treated as cross-complaints against the other defendants, as well.

Users found it advantageous to address their water problems through the California courts for a number of reasons. Court action could encompass all relevant participants, but only the relevant participants, in sorting out the dispute and resolving it authoritatively. In other words, the courts could help water users define the basin "community," the boundaries of which did not match any existing jurisdiction. Within that institutionally defined community, agreements could be negotiated and actions taken for the basin as a whole.

In the California court system at the time, any civil court could function as a court of equity as well as a court of law. Equity jurisprudence had broader discretionary rules for procedure and remedy and could be invoked for the protection of a right or for the redress or prevention of a wrong in circumstances where ordinary legal remedies (such as money damages) did not afford adequate relief. Equity jurisprudence was especially well suited to water rights conflicts because: (1) an ongoing relationship among the parties was implied, so compensation of damages could be seen as an inadequate remedy; and (2) it permitted the parties and the court to search beyond prevailing rules of law for a solution that would effect justice among the parties, even if that meant devising a new set of rules.

City of Pasadena v. City of Alhambra et al., was the first basinwide adjudication of groundwater rights in California, and the first to use the Court Reference Procedure under the California Water Code. That procedure authorized the referral of cases involving the determination of water rights to the Division of Water Resources of the state Department of Public Works for investigation of the physical facts.

On January 31, 1939, twenty parties invoked the court reference procedure and petitioned the trial court to refer the factual issues to the Division of Water Resources for investigation. Judge Collier entered the order of reference on February 8, 1939, directing the referee to review all physical facts pertaining to Raymond Basin, determine the "safe yield" of the basin, and ascertain whether there was a surplus or an overdraft.

The investigation was expensive and time-consuming. The division's expenditures for the reference were $53,274.73, paid by the parties. Nevertheless, the referee's investigation avoided multiple concurrent investigations by the several parties and provided the parties and the court with a coherent, single view of Raymond Basin and its problems (Wright, 1952: 667).

The referee's findings were compiled into a draft report, which was circulated among the parties in October 1941, but not formally submitted to the court until March 15, 1943. The draft report described the basic geology of Raymond Basin and specified the location of the Monk Hill, Pasadena, and Santa Anita subareas. The Santa Anita subarea was identified as the Eastern Unit of the basin, and the Monk Hill and Pasadena subareas as the Western Unit.

The draft report stated that the safe yield for Raymond Basin as a whole was 21,900 acre-feet per year, but that actual withdrawals and claimed rights totaled 29,400 acre-feet, for a total overdraft of about 8,500 acre-feet per year. Withdrawals in the Western Unit averaged 24,000 acre-feet per year, 6,000 acre-feet more than the unit's safe yield. To remedy the situation, the draft report recommended limiting withdrawals to the 21,900 acre-foot safe yield and using imported water to meet demands beyond the safe yield.

As the referee's draft report circulated among the parties, most of them agreed to try to work out a settlement. Negotiation proved more fruitful "in the shadow of the court." Litigation had changed the default condition of the negotiations. Before litigation, failure to negotiate a settlement simply continued the status quo—the pumping race. With litigation under way, if the parties failed to achieve a negotiated settlement, the case would go to trial and the court would decide the parties' water rights. Since Raymond Basin was the first groundwater basin to be adjudicated and California water rights law was very complex, the possible outcomes of a trial were highly uncertain. The court might rule that once reasonable water use on overlying lands had been accorded to overlying owners, the remainder of the basin safe yield should be allocated as surplus to appropriators in order of seniority. Alternatively, the court could rule that the existence of the overdraft meant that there was no surplus. If the court took that approach, it would have to consider whether prescriptive rights had been established, and if so, by whom and in what amounts. For several of the parties, the range of possible outcomes extended from a complete loss of rights to a complete protection of rights. Waiting for the judge's decision was risky.

Furthermore, the parties already had spent four years and considerable sums of money on this dispute. A trial of the issues and a determination of the parties' rights in an adversarial proceeding would involve additional time and cost, to say the least. A negotiated settlement offered the possibility of minimizing additional expense (California DWR, Raymond Basin Watermaster Report, 1958: 5). Negotiation was facilitated by the presence of shared counsel; one attorney, Kenneth Wright of Los Angeles, was either counsel or special counsel for sixteen of the parties. This unusual communication link among a majority of the parties, and their common information base as a result of the referee's report, made it easier to reach a cooperative agreement.

Most parties agreed to appoint a committee of seven attorneys and engineers to work out a stipulated agreement that could be presented to the court. It was completed early in 1943. After studying it, Pasadena and all but two other parties agreed to the stipulation, which they presented to the court in November 1943. It provided (1) an admission by each of the parties that its taking of water from the basin had been continuous, uninterrupted, open, notorious, and under claim of right, and adverse to the claims of all others, and thus satisfied the requirements of a superior prescriptive right for each party as against all others; (2) an allocation of the basin's safe yield among the parties; (3) the declaration and protection of each party's right to its specific proportion of the basin safe yield; and (4) an arrangement for the exchange of pumping rights among the parties.

On November 24, 1943, Judge Collier signed an order requiring the parties to the stipulation to abide by its terms during the pendency of the litigation. On April 5, 1944, the judge designated the Division of Water Resources to serve as monitor, or watermaster, for the stipulation. On

April 28, 1944, one of the remaining parties, La Canada Irrigation District, joined the stipulation, leaving only one holdout.

The California-Michigan Land and Water Company did not agree to the stipulation and pursued a different strategy in the meantime. On March 24, 1943, nine days after the formal submission of the referee's draft report and while the proposed stipulation was being considered by the other parties, the California-Michigan Land and Water Company filed a motion to dismiss the action for failure on Pasadena's part to prosecute it diligently. On the ground that proceeding to trial earlier would have been impracticable, Judge Collier denied the motion to dismiss. California-Michigan petitioned the California Supreme Court for a writ of mandate commanding the trial judge to dismiss the action, but its petition was denied.

On July 12, 1943, the final referee's report was filed with the court, and on August 11, California-Michigan filed objections to the report. After a hearing on those objections, the judge issued an order determining the expense of the reference and apportioning the cost thereof. On November 26, Pasadena moved to set the case for trial, and California-Michigan again moved for dismissal. Pasadena's motion was granted; California-Michigan's was denied. California-Michigan petitioned the California Supreme Court for a writ of prohibition forbidding trial of the case. That petition was denied on March 13, 1944, ending the attempts to avert a trial on the merits. The brief trial began on May 18, 1944.

As the case went to trial, Judge Collier faced difficult choices, each containing legal and practical risks. If he went along with the stipulation's reasoning and entered a judgment declaring that each party had acquired prescriptive rights that could be proportionately reduced to the basin safe yield, he would be forging a remarkable innovation—indeed, a new doctrine—in California water law. The pretrial actions of California-Michigan made it apparent that such a decision would be appealed, so the judge risked reversal. The stipulation circumvented long-standing distinctions among different types and priorities of rights by making all rights both prescriptive and correlative. For the judge, adopting this view risked not merely reversal but ridicule, while still leaving him retrying the case on remand.

Clinging to established water rights law posed other problems. There were arguable claims to overlying, appropriative, and prescriptive rights in the basin, which clearly was overdrawn. To rule that there was a surplus would allow the rights of overlying owners and appropriators to be determined in accordance with settled principles of law, but would stretch "surplus" beyond any reasonable meaning and would probably shut the junior appropriators out of the basin. Yet to rule that there was no surplus would restrict the adjudication to the correlative rights of those with overlying claims and imply that there were no appropriative rights. This would essentially wipe out most of the water rights of the cities and local industry (Goodcell, 1961: 7). Moreover, ruling that there was no surplus still left open the question of prescriptive rights.

On December 23, 1944, Judge Collier signed the judgment in the Raymond Basin case, revealing his decision. He adopted the stipulation worked out by the parties and accepted the risk of reversal. His decision is known as "mutual prescription." It states that (1) in an overdrawn basin there is no surplus water; (2) the rights of users are invaded by the lowering of water levels once an overdraft occurs; (3) water withdrawn from an overdrawn basin for nonoverlying use continuously, openly, notoriously, and under claim of right for five years, is no longer water claimed under an appropriative right but water claimed by adverse use; (4) as to overlying users, their use of an overdrawn basin constitutes an invasion of each other's right to reasonable use; (5) therefore, all users who have been taking water under claim of right for a consecutive five-year period from an overdrawn basin are mutually prescripting against each other; (6) a continuation of the situation would result in waste of the resource and irreparable harm, and protecting the resource requires limiting the amount taken to the basin safe yield; and (7) the coequal status of the users provides for this limiting through a proportional reduction in their rights to withdraw water.

The judgment accepted the referee's determination of a "present unadjusted right" for each party, which was defined as the highest amount of water continuously produced during a five-year period prior to the filing of the lawsuit, provided use had been continuous for at least five years thereafter. Each party owned this right by prescription, and the rights were of equal priority. Judge Collier then defined a "decreed right" for each party, which was that party's present unadjusted right adjusted downward by about one-third so that the sum of all parties' decreed rights matched the estimated safe yield. The judgment also stated:

1. All parties would be enjoined after July 1, 1944, from taking more water than their decreed rights, except California-Michigan, which had not stipulated to the decreed rights, and against which the injunction would take effect July 1, 1945.

2. Each party would be enjoined from taking more than 120 percent of its decreed right in any year, unless the watermaster indicated that an emergency justified it, and in no event could the amount taken by a party over a period of five years exceed five times its decreed right.

3. The Division of Water Resources, as watermaster, would oversee administration of the judgment, the Water Exchange Agreement, and the instructions and orders of the court, assisted by an advisory board representing the parties, designated by the parties, and paid by the parties.

4. Each party would measure and keep records of its surface water diversions, its imports of water, the depth to groundwater in its wells, and its groundwater production, subject to watermaster approval of measuring equipment and methods of recording.

5. Diversions of surface water from sources tributary to the groundwater supply were to be limited to the capacity of the existing works for such diversions at the time the lawsuit was initiated.

6. Whenever the water elevation at the city of Arcadia's Orange Grove wells fell below 500 feet above sea level, the annual extraction from the Eastern Unit would be reduced for the following season from 5,290 acre-feet to 3,261 acre-feet.

7. The administrative costs of enforcing and monitoring the judgment would be chargeable to the parties in proportion to their decreed rights.

8. The Water Exchange Agreement of 1943 was incorporated and made part of the judgment.

9. Decreed rights could be leased or sold, apart from the operation of the Water Exchange Agreement, with the watermaster recording the transfers.

The stipulation and judgment in *Pasadena v. Alhambra* completed the first phase of institution building in Raymond Basin. Although it certainly would *not* appear in the Census Bureau's Census of Governments, water users had constituted a governance structure for the basin through the adjudication process. They had established their rights and duties in the basin, a monitor to observe and report upon their compliance with those duties, means of checking each other's behavior through the publication and circulation of the watermaster's annual reports, means of sanctioning each other's behavior for violations of the court's injunctions, a representative body of water users, a mechanism for financing the governance system, and, through the court's continuing jurisdiction, an institutionalized procedure for altering the governance system in response to changed conditions, new ideas, or dissatisfaction with its performance.

The stipulation and judgment also established a management program for the basin, within and subject to this basin governance system. The management program was fairly simple, a fixed safe-yield operation. Nevertheless, the provisions of the stipulation and judgment had designated the set of authorized users of the basin and provided for their entry and exit; assigned them rights to specific quantities of pumped water each year and provided for the exchange, lease, or sale of those rights; and limited them in the aggregate to the basin's estimated safe yield. This management program was implemented in the 1944–45 water year, approximately seven years after the adjudication began.

Pasadena v. Alhambra II:
The Raymond Basin Judgment on Appeal

The basin governance structure and management program were quickly called into question. As Judge Collier anticipated, his decision based on the stipulation's idea of mutual prescription was appealed by the California-Michigan Land and Water Company. The method of calculating the present unadjusted right had left California-Michigan with a present unadjusted right of 521 acre-feet per year, and a decreed right of 359 acre-feet. At the time the adjudication began, in 1937, California-Michigan was withdrawing more than 800 acre-feet per year from the Western Unit. California-Michigan appealed the determination of its right and claimed instead a right to its 1937 amount of use.

California-Michigan also raised several procedural and factual challenges. These were rejected by the District Court of Appeal; however, the court sided with California-Michigan's challenges to the determination of its right and the mutual-prescription reasoning underlying the stipulation and judgment. Establishment of a prescriptive right required the existence of adverse use and the running of the prescriptive period. The Court of Appeal did not question the running of the prescriptive period but rejected the conclusion of actual hostility in use.

To the other parties and to Judge Collier, the existence of the overdraft established adverse use. The appellate court replied that prescription implies a forfeiture of right, and a forfeiture cannot be made by one who is unaware of invasion of his right. Overdraft alone is insufficient notice of an adverse taking if the owner of the right is unaware of the overdraft or if his own supply appears to him undiminished or not invaded. California-Michigan had an appropriative (or possibly prescriptive) right to a specific amount of water. Invasion of that right required an actual loss of the specific amount of water covered by the right. The Court of Appeal observed that California-Michigan "has never suffered any involuntary diminution in its ground water production and has always had more water available than its use required. Consequently . . . the taking of ground water of the Area by the other parties has not been adverse to appellant's appropriative rights in the water supply" (180 P.2d 699 at 722).

It might be acceptable for the stipulating parties to agree that they had prescripted against each other and to treat their water rights as equal, but with respect to California-Michigan as a nonstipulating party, they had to establish their acquisition of a prescriptive right equal to California-Michigan's. This could not be done merely by showing that an overdraft existed. The District Court of Appeal remanded the action to the trial court for a determination of the priority of California-Michigan's rights in the basin, in order to determine to what extent its water production should be restricted in order to eliminate the overdraft. The Court of Appeal upheld the allocation of water rights between and among the stipulating parties, noting only that the sum of the rights would be adjusted to off-set whatever adjustment was made to California-Michigan's right.

The District Court of Appeal's decision was appealed to the California Supreme Court. On June 3, 1949, the Supreme Court announced its decision overturning the Court of Appeal and affirming Judge Collier's original judgment. The Supreme Court rejected the Court of Appeal's view that California-Michigan's appropriative right remained intact because it was still able to extract all it needed from the basin. Such a view would delay action to preserve the basin until after it had been destroyed, which would serve neither the ends of justice nor the policy of the state. The court majority stated:

> The proper time to act in preserving the supply is when the overdraft commences, and the aid of the courts would come too late and be entirely inadequate if . . . those who possess water rights could not commence legal proceedings until the supply was so greatly depleted that it actually became difficult or impossible to obtain water. (206 P.2d 17 at 30)

The Supreme Court turned next to the issue of remedy. "The main problems presented," wrote the court, "are which of the parties should bear the burden of curtailing the total production of the unit to the safe yield and what proportion, if any, of the pumping by each particular party should be restricted" (206 P.2d 17 at 28). Judge Collier had proposed allocation by proportionate reduction. The Court of Appeal had proposed allocation by priority of right. The Supreme Court, relying on equity principles rather than strict interpretation of the law, ruled that allocation by priority of right "does not appear to be justified where all of the parties have been producing water from the underground basin for many years, and none of them have acted to protect the supply or prevent invasion of their rights until this proceeding" (206 P.2d 17 at 32). None of the parties had come to court with entirely "clean hands." Each had to some extent "slept on his rights." The court was not obliged to favor any of them.

The Supreme Court also considered the interests of the various publics served by Raymond Basin water producers. Proportionate reduction by each producer, according to the Supreme Court, would be less disruptive of the local water economy than the complete elimination of rights for some. Without explicitly endorsing Judge Collier's mutual-prescription reasoning, the Supreme Court sustained his result. This had the effect, intended or not, of adding a new doctrine to California water law.[1]

Although a new doctrine had been added, the California law of water rights had not been overturned or revolutionized. *Pasadena v. Alhambra* had been decided and affirmed without overruling any previous water rights decisions. The *Katz v. Walkinshaw* scheme of allocating water rights to overlying owners, appropriators, and prescriptors in accordance with their priority of right remained. Mutual prescription was not substituted for the old scheme, but allowed to develop alongside it. *Pasadena v. Alhambra* provided an alternative capacity in which groundwater users could resolve overdraft problems. With the Supreme Court's approval of *Pasadena v. Alhambra*, a community of water users who had worked out their own settlement of an overdraft could approach a court with some assurance that the judge would recognize that settlement and place public authority behind it. *Pasadena v. Alhambra* allowed users of an overdrafted basin to constitute their own basin governance systems and management programs.

The mutual-prescription approach had its detractors. Some criticized the expensive and time-consuming court reference procedure (see, for example, Krieger, 1955: 910; Goodcell, 1961: 3). Others criticized the decision's effect on the water right owner and his ability to know the status of, and to protect, his right. The doctrine of mutual prescription, it was argued, meant "there are no longer 'water rights' in the conventional sense. . . . The paper right—the water right created by deed—means nothing" (Krieger, 1955: 909). A producer might find that even pumping continuously and putting the water to beneficial use does not protect a right to that amount, since the proportionate-reduction remedy would leave him with a right only to part of it.

Furthermore, the determination of a producer's right was said to hinge on a matter he could not be aware of or control: "No one knows the exact moment a basin becomes overdrawn. He may find out years later. Notwithstanding this his very rights depend on the later determination of that mythical moment when the basin becomes overdrawn" (Krieger, 1955: 909). The advent of mutual prescription meant that pumpers in every nonadjudicated basin in the state faced this uncertain situation. Therefore, the decision in *Pasadena v. Alhambra* had the unintended effect of encouraging pumpers in other basins to increase pumping in order to enlarge and protect their right after a potential adjudication.

Pasadena v. Alhambra left a considerable hole in the law of water rights concerning the status of public entities and prescriptive rights. A long-standing rule of common law, incorporated into the California Civil Code in 1935 as Section 1007, held that no adverse use of property (including water) owned by a public agency could ripen into a prescriptive right against that agency. Because the Raymond Basin cities and other public enterprises had stipulated to their mutual prescription, the trial court and Supreme Court rulings made no reference to Section 1007. Mutual prescription thus stood on shaky ground. Its application to other cases would depend on the forbearance of public water producers involved in those cases. If they chose to assert their protection under the Civil Code, mutual prescription would not provide a means of determining their water rights.

The Years since *Pasadena v. Alhambra*: Changing Basin Governance and Management

In the forty-five years since the judgment in *Pasadena v. Alhambra* became effective, the parties, the court, and the watermaster have governed Raymond Basin within its terms. On certain occasions, Raymond Basin users have modified the judgment to alter the management program or to reconstitute the basin governance system.

The first modification, based on observed changes in basin conditions, was to the determination of safe yield. Raymond Basin water levels began to improve during the litigation. Rainfall was above normal in six of the nine years from 1937 through 1945, and some parties restrained extractions during the negotiation of the stipulation. The entry of the judgment in *Pasadena v. Alhambra* in 1945 coincided, however, with the beginning of the greatest dry cycle of recorded southern California history. Rainfall at the Los Angeles station was below normal for sixteen of the next twenty years, and less than half of normal in four of those.

Underground water levels throughout Raymond Basin rose through 1950 and held steady through 1955, despite ten years of drought and increased total water use. Late in 1950, Pasadena returned to court and filed a motion for a review of the original judgment's safe-yield determination. The court granted the motion and appointed the Division of Water Resources to make the review. The division's report, filed in October 1954, revised the safe-yield estimate to nearly 31,000 acre-feet, and recommended (after a small allowance for nonparties) that the decreed rights of the parties be increased to 30,622 acre-feet. The court issued a Modification of Judgment on April 29, 1955, increasing the decreed rights of the parties proportionately to a total of 30,622 acre-feet.

As production increased to the new safe-yield level and the drought continued, water levels in Raymond Basin gradually fell and stabilized below their 1950–1955 peak. Since 1960, the pattern of water levels throughout Raymond Basin has remained consistent. At the foothills, water elevations exceed 1,000 feet above sea level; along the Raymond Fault, water elevations stay between 400 and 500 feet above sea level.

Compliance with the pumping limitations has been extraordinarily high, despite the greater water supply costs it has imposed on the parties. Even though total water use in the basin has more than doubled, groundwater extractions have stayed extremely close to the determined safe yield (Table 5.1). MWD imports have grown to make up the difference between

TABLE 5.1

Raymond Basin Parties' Decreed Rights, Extractions, and Total Water Use, 1945–1990 (acre-feet)

Year	Number of owners of rights	Decreed rights	Groundwater pumped	Water imported	Water exported	Total water use in basin
1945	25	21,451	20,109	n.a.	n.a.	n.a.
1946	25	21,451	23,788	n.a.	n.a.	n.a.
1947	25	21,451	19,954	n.a.	n.a.	n.a.
1948	25	21,451	23,916	n.a.	n.a.	n.a.
1949	25	21,451	22,308	n.a.	n.a.	n.a.
1950	25	21,451	19,253	n.a.	n.a.	n.a.
1951	25	21,451	23,377	n.a.	n.a.	n.a.
1952	25	21,451	19,143	12,952	n.a.	n.a.
1953	24	21,451	23,314	20,163	n.a.	n.a.
1954	24	21,451	21,426	22,546	n.a.	n.a.
1955	24	30,622	23,731	21,187	n.a.	n.a.
1956	24	30,622	24,986	22,237	n.a.	n.a.
1957	24	30,622	30,015	20,655	n.a.	n.a.
1958	24	30,622	23,487	17,416	4,667	47,019
1959	24	30,622	33,205	23,885	8,420	54,241
1960	24	30,622	29,278	27,448	6,955	51,833
1961	23	30,622	29,279	29,941	8,392	52,306
1962	23	30,622	28,657	25,887	9,315	49,213
1963	22	30,622	30,434	26,362	9,598	50,654
1964	22	30,622	30,184	26,391	10,594	48,345
1965	21	30,622	28,731	26,341	8,850	49,031
1966	21	30,622	29,368	20,353	11,597	47,597
1967	21	30,622	25,705	18,103	9,444	47,626
1968	21	30,622	34,074	21,472	12,279	49,934
1969	21	30,622	28,398	20,461	10,594	46,565
1970	21	30,622	32,577	21,888	10,166	52,401
1971	21	30,622	30,990	26,843	11,273	51,701
1972	21	30,622	30,561	30,913	9,528	54,420
1973	21	30,622	32,434	23,027	10,504	49,655
1974	21	30,622	31,817	22,801	7,337	51,622
1975	18	30,622	31,810	24,130	10,290	48,931
1976	18	30,622	36,176	26,615	10,450	54,914
1977	18	30,622	32,861	22,282	6,155	51,145
1978	18	30,622	27,186	23,603	9,388	45,089
1979	18	30,622	31,661	23,042	7,868	51,851
1980	18	30,622	39,556[a]	15,391	8,291	51,104
1981	18	30,622	34,970[a]	25,558	12,674	52,419

TABLE 5.1 (continued)

Year	Number of owners of rights	Decreed rights	Groundwater pumped	Water imported	Water exported	Total water use in basin
1982	17	30,622	32,376 [a]	22,489	6,474	52,089
1983	17	30,622	32,899 [a]	20,062	9,082	48,840
1984	17	30,622	37,873 [a]	22,426	11,041	55,319
1985	17	30,622	35,659	30,271	15,388	53,567
1986	17	30,622	33,923	32,013	7,609	58,327
1987	17	30,622	36,770	30,261	9,953	59,255
1988	17	30,622	30,713	32,385	10,131	54,607
1989	17	30,622	34,155	31,582	10,639	56,477
1990	17	30,622	30,459	35,901	2,544	65,473

n.a. = Not available.
a. In-lieu replenishment water counted as groundwater pumped.
SOURCE: Raymond Basin Watermaster Reports, 1945–1990.

groundwater pumped and total water use. In more than forty-five years of basin self-governance, it has never been necessary to use sanctions to enforce the injunction against overpumping.

This does not mean that Raymond Basin water users have had no water supply problems, or that no overpumping to meet short-term exigencies has occurred. The limitation on pumping after the entry of the judgment in 1945 produced an acute water shortage in the Monk Hill subarea. Before the judgment, water users there had relied entirely on groundwater extractions and surface water diversions and none had access to imported water from MWD. The judgment curtailed their pumping and the drought reduced their surface water supplies, while water demands increased.

Pasadena, however, had access to imported MWD water beginning in June 1941. Pasadena and water companies in the Monk Hill subarea used the Water Exchange Agreement incorporated in the judgment to provide a supplemental supply of water indirectly. Under the Water Exchange Agreement, each party must offer to the "exchange pool" its rights to water in excess of its needs for the coming year, at a price no greater than the party's average water production cost. Parties anticipating that their access to water will be inadequate to meet their needs for the coming year submit requests to the exchange pool. The watermaster matches the offers to the requests, with the lowest priced water allocated first, then the next lowest, and so on. Actual water is not allocated, but the right to pump specific quantities. Payments are collected by the water-master and distributed to the offerers. This exchange pool arrangement allows intrabasin transfers without actual leasing or sale of parties' decreed rights and saves the costs of negotiating separate transactions between individual parties.

Pasadena imported water from MWD, refrained from pumping its full decreed right, and offered the difference to the exchange pool, from which the Monk Hill companies purchased it. Pasadena's offers peaked in 1952 at 3,929 acre-feet. There was, however, a limit to Pasadena's ability to offer exchange water. Pasadena had its own demands to meet as a water supplier and could purchase only a limited amount of imported water from MWD each year. The parties in the Monk Hill subarea agreed to form a municipal water district to annex to MWD in order to acquire their own access to imported water supplies. In the interim, the Monk Hill water producers were allowed to extract more than their allowed pumping from underground without being penalized. The Foothill Municipal Water District, covering the Monk Hill subarea, was formed in 1952, annexed to MWD in 1953, and began to receive deliveries of Colorado River water in 1955.

Water exchange purchases in the Monk Hill subarea declined after 1955, reaching zero by 1959. Use of the exchange pool throughout the basin dwindled to virtually nothing after 1959 and has been zero since 1978. Since the 1950s, decreed rights have primarily been leased or sold rather than offered for exchange.[2]

A more recent, but similar, water supply problem in the basin involves the city of Sierra Madre. Sierra Madre joined with three other San Gabriel Valley cities in 1959 to form the San Gabriel Valley Municipal Water District and contract directly with the state of California for imported water from northern California through the State Water Project. However, there are no State Water Project delivery facilities in Sierra Madre, and since the city is not a member of MWD, it lacks physical access to either MWD water or State Project water. According to the 1989–90 annual report of the Raymond Basin watermaster, Sierra Madre has recently had difficulties in meeting its water supply needs while complying with the judgment, a situation undoubtedly exacerbated, if not brought about entirely, by the recent drought. While the city's short-term and long-range water supply plans are under review, it is being allowed to temporarily over-extract its decreed right from the basin, as were the Monk Hill pumpers in the 1950s.

Another important modification to the management program had to do with recharging the basin. The original judgment made no provision for artificial replenishment of the basin with conserved or imported water supplies. However, the Los Angeles County Department of Public Works (formerly the Flood Control District) operates water-spreading grounds on each of the surface streams in Raymond Basin—the Arroyo Seco, the Eaton Wash, and Santa Anita Creek. In addition, several Raymond Basin parties conduct water-spreading operations—the Kinneloa Irrigation District, the Las Flores Water Company, the Lincoln Avenue Water Company, the Rubio Canyon Land and Water Association, and the cities of Pasadena and Sierra Madre.

Actions taken by these parties benefit all Raymond Basin water producers. In order to maintain an incentive to engage in spreading, the parties modified the Raymond Basin judgment in 1974 to allow pumping credits for spreading. The watermaster determines each year the amount of water diverted for spreading, and the county Department of Public Works provides a statement of the amounts actually spread. Each party engaged in spreading is allowed in the following year to extract up to 80 percent of the amount credited to it, in addition to its decreed right under the judgment. Extraction of spreading credits accounts for the fact that total groundwater extractions have exceeded total decreed rights in most years since 1974.

Currently, the city of Pasadena is planning a multiple-use project at Devil's Gate dam, which is operated by the county Department of Public Works. The project would impound surplus water and recirculate it through a natural stream channel. The slowly released recirculating water would recharge the groundwater supply, while supporting a several-hundred acre theme park that restores natural vegetation to the hills, floodplains, and trail areas above the city. The city would receive spreading credits for the water recharged to the basin.

A third modification to the Raymond Basin judgment, in 1984, reconstituted the basin governance system. Most monitoring and basin-management activities during the first forty years after the judgment were conducted by the Southern District office of the California Department of Water Resources, which was the Raymond Basin Watermaster. The Southern District office monitored water production in the basin, kept a water account for each producer recording extractions made and annual decreed right remaining on a monthly basis, administered the Water Exchange Agreement, and prepared and submitted an annual report on basin activities and conditions to the court and to each of the parties.

The costs of these activities were shared by the state of California and by the parties to the *Pasadena v. Alhambra* judgment. One-half of the watermaster costs were paid from the state budget, on the theory that the state had an interest in, and benefited from, the proper management of water supplies. The other half was apportioned among the parties in accordance with their decreed rights.[3]

The Southern District Office, as watermaster, was assisted and advised by the Raymond Basin Advisory Board, a group of water producer representatives chosen by the parties. Over time, the Raymond Basin Advisory Board assumed an increasingly active role in reconsidering the management program for the basin, especially in light of developments in neighboring groundwater basins. For example, in 1968 the Raymond Basin Advisory Board joined with the city of Pasadena and the California Department of Water Resources to support the development of a mathematical model of the basin, to simulate the behavior of the underground and surface supplies under various pumping and recharge plans.

The modeling study was completed in 1971, and analysis of its results led to some of the elements in the 1974 modification of judgment, such as the spreading credits. Another element was a program for the voluntary control of pumping patterns. At least twice a year, existing pumping patterns are reported to the board, with recommendations based on the model as to where greater or smaller amounts of water should be pumped. The board transmits its recommendations to the parties. The program is entirely voluntary; no party can be stopped from pumping its full decreed right. Parties are simply encouraged to reduce or increase pumping for a certain period.

Around the time of the 1974 modification of judgment, water users in the neighboring Main San Gabriel and Chino basins were developing a new form of watermaster organization. Instead of relying on the state Department of Water Resources as watermaster, users in these basins selected multimember watermasters, composed of water users or their representatives who were dedicated to a more active approach to managing basin water conditions (see Chapters 8 and 12). After several years of consideration, the parties to the Raymond Basin judgment decided to change the basin governance structure. They returned to court and obtained a modification of judgment on March 16, 1984, replacing the Department of Water Resources as watermaster with the Raymond Basin Management Board, successor to the Raymond Basin Advisory Board.

The management board is composed of ten water users' representatives and normally operates by consensus. The court retains jurisdiction to decide future controversies. The board uses the offices of the Foothill Municipal Water District in La Canada–Flintridge for meetings and as a mailing address, and the General Manager of the District serves as the assistant secretary-treasurer for the board and provides staff support. These arrangements economize on the administrative costs of the board's watermaster functions.

Although the California Department of Water Resources is no longer the Raymond Basin watermaster, the Raymond Basin Management Board has retained the services of the department under contract for the preparation of the annual report and for other support services, as required. Under this arrangement, the state of California no longer subsidizes the cost of the watermaster service. The parties to the Raymond Basin judgment pay all costs of this service, which, since the 1984 modification, have ranged from $3.50 to $3.75 per acre-foot of groundwater pumped.

In recent years, the Raymond Basin Management Board has been attempting to manage the basin with more precision and to move away from the simple, fixed safe-yield operation created in the original judgment in 1945. The board is experimenting with changes in addition to those concerned with the spreading credits and the voluntary adjustments of pumping patterns. Since 1984–85, the city of Pasadena has been allowed to experiment with a program of storing water in the basin for later withdrawal. The board monitors the effects of the storage program on the basin and must reapprove the storage program each year. Before the beginning of the current drought, Pasadena stored about 5,000 acre-feet in the basin, which it retains at this time. Also, board members have granted a waiver of the requirement of a 500-foot underground water elevation each spring at the city of Arcadia's Orange Grove wells, as part of a six-year study of the effect on pumping patterns and water levels. The cities of Arcadia and Sierra Madre are to assess and report the effects (if any) of greater drawdown of water levels in the Eastern Unit.

Analysis

Forty-five years after *Pasadena v. Alhambra*, the water producers in Raymond Basin, through the Raymond Basin Management Board, are managing the basin through a self-governing and self-financing system they developed themselves, which includes various means of checking each other's actions. As a result, compliance and cooperation have been very high. This system evolved over a period of decades, during which the producers changed the structure of rights to use, acquired access to alternative supplies, and developed a management program that they altered over time in light of new ideas about groundwater management and observed innovations in other basins. These actions were taken in the face of certain obstacles and opportunities, and with the aid of available and newly created institutional capabilities.

Eliciting Information

Raymond Basin water users were aware of receding water levels in the 1910s and 1920s, but did not know much about the basin's physical characteristics and safe yield, and did not know the extent of the overdraft. Pasadena undertook some investigations on its own. Primarily, Raymond

Basin water users employed the investigative capability of the state's Division of Water Resources, and the court reference procedure, to obtain the information needed to arrive at a common understanding of their water supply problems. That common understanding was essential to crafting an effective cooperative resolution of the overdraft.

The adjudication also elicited information from and about the water users themselves. The set of Raymond Basin pumpers was identified and bounded by the adjudication, and the parties were required to assist the Division of Water Resources by providing information about their wells and past production. The provision of information by the parties was formalized in the judgment, so in each annual report the Raymond Basin watermaster publishes and circulates the name and well locations of each party and its water production by month through the year. This institutionalized process has encouraged individual parties with water supply deficiencies to report them and engage the basin governance structure to deliberate upon and resolve them.

Institutional Design

The information elicited from parties and the Division of Water Resources was used to conceive, design, and constitute institutional arrangements to resolve the overdraft. The original institutional design was relatively simple: once it was known that the basin was being overdrafted by an estimated 31 percent, an agreement was negotiated to reduce each pumper's production by 31 percent; the equity powers of the court were employed to enjoin overproduction; and a watermaster was established to monitor pumpers' behavior. Basin governance was conducted by the parties, the court, and the watermaster, with the parties able to propose to the court alterations in the institutional arrangements over time.

Although relatively simple, this structure provided water users facing problems in other basins with a basis for developing information about, and responses to, those problems. In Raymond Basin itself, new information about basin conditions and new ideas about basin governance and management have led its users to adapt and redesign their institutional arrangements accordingly. Although the Raymond Basin governance structure and management program remain relatively simple compared with some of the others we shall review, they have been altered significantly since 1945.

Integration with Other Governance Systems

The governance system in Raymond Basin does not exist in a vacuum but is embedded in, and connected with, other water resource organizations and governance systems. Some aspects of this network were devised to avoid duplicating existing capacities. For example, the Southern District office of the Department of Water Resources already collects, analyzes, and publishes most of the data needed to manage the basin. The county Department of Public Works operates flood control and water-spreading grounds in the basin and provides information on storm flows and spreading operations. In addition, the Foothill Municipal Water District and the cities of Pasadena and San Marino are MWD member agencies with access to imported water from the Colorado River and northern California. The city of Sierra Madre joined with three other San Gabriel Valley cities to form the San Gabriel Valley Municipal Water District, a State Water Project contractor. The city of Arcadia joined with several other San Gabriel cities to form the Upper San Gabriel Valley Municipal Water District, an MWD member agency. The management program established by the Raymond Basin Management Board is subject to the continuing jurisdiction of the Superior Court, and ultimately is subject to California water law and the California constitution.

Operation and Performance of the Management Program

The governance structure established for Raymond Basin by the water users provides the decision-making framework for establishing the basin management program. That program currently consists of a fixed safe-yield operation with pumping limitations, transferable decreed rights, voluntary adjustment of pumping patterns, voluntary water spreading by parties in exchange for pumping credits, one experimental program for storing water in the basin, and importation of water supplies to meet additional needs. In addition, each party must pay its own water production, importation, and spreading costs (if any), plus its assigned share of the costs of the monitoring services provided by the watermaster (see Table 5.2).

The Raymond Basin management program has performed well with respect to most criteria. Parties have demonstrated a strong record of compliance with the management program, which has proved effective in stopping the overdraft and preserving the basin. Administrative costs of the management program have been maintained at a low level (the lowest of any of the eight cases in this study). Management costs have been apportioned equitably among parties in proportion to their use of the basin. Although the management program has not fully taken advantage of the basin's storage capacity, changes are under way to improve the efficiency of resource use by adopting some of the techniques developed in other basins. Both the basin governance structure and the management program have shown considerable adaptability to changed basin conditions and new ideas.

TABLE 5.2

Cost of Raymond Basin Watermaster Service and Amount Paid by Parties, Fiscal Years 1945–1990 (dollars)

Year	Total cost	Cost to parties	Parties' cost per acre-foot of groundwater pumped
1945	3,868.77	1,934.38	0.10
1946	4,313.10	2,156.55	0.09
1947	6,200.22	3,100.11	0.16
1948	5,941.36	2,970.68	0.12
1949	5,496.00	2,798.00	0.13
1950	4,480.11	2,240.06	0.12
1951	6,548.91	3,274.46	0.14
1952	5,268.65	2,634.33	0.14
1953	4,511.64	2,255.82	0.10
1954	5,386.55	2,693.28	0.13
1955	8,749.02	4,374.51	0.18
1956	9,102.17	4,551.09	0.18
1957	9,112.84	4,556.42	0.15
1958	9,936.48	4,968.24	0.21
1959	10,548.82	5,274.41	0.16
1960	13,666.45	6,833.23	0.23
1961	16,498.68	8,249.34	0.28
1962	16,225.51	8,112.75	0.28
1963	17,414.00	8,707.00	0.29
1964	18,070.91	9,035.46	0.30
1965	23,005.89	8,090.94 [a]	0.28
1966	24,842.56	10,189.71	0.35
1967	16,195.75	8,097.87	0.32
1968	21,209.47	10,604.73	0.31
1969	26,289.54	13,144.77	0.46
1970	24,080.38	12,040.09	0.37
1971	29,113.84	14,556.92	0.47
1972	26,739.87	13,369.94	0.44
1973	34,642.72	17,321.36	0.53
1974	35,671.48	17,835.74	0.56
1975	39,434.28	19,717.14	0.62
1976	44,460.88	22,230.44	0.61
1977	54,714.18	27,357.09	0.83
1978	57,997.73	28,998.86	1.07
1979	51,804.28	25,902.00	0.82
1980	58,082.24	29,041.04	0.73
1981	75,180.43	37,590.40	1.07
1982	94,906.08	62,925.47	1.94
1983	94,647.08	63,414.85	1.93

TABLE 5.2 (continued)

Year	Total cost	Cost to parties	Parties' cost per acre-foot of groundwater pumped
1984	106,662.81	71,108.55	1.88
1985	112,471.00	112,471.00	3.15
1986	117,510.00	117,510.00	3.46
1987	123,299.00	123,299.00	3.35
1988	115,211.00	115,211.00	3.75
1989	122,962.00	122,962.00	3.60
1990	194,029.00 [b]	194,029.00 [b]	6.37 [b]

a. Special appropriation made by state legislature.
b. Includes $66,600 in costs for administration of Title 22 water-quality sampling program.
SOURCE: Raymond Basin Watermaster Reports, 1945–1990.

NOTES

1. California-Michigan Land and Water Company petitioned the U.S. Supreme Court for a writ of certiorari to review the California Supreme Court's ruling. On April 17, 1950, the U.S. Supreme Court denied the petition, refusing to review the case (339 U.S. 937).

2. Some Raymond Basin users have acquired additional pumping rights by purchasing them from others, halting their production in the basin. The number of active pumpers has declined gradually from thirty-one at the time of the lawsuit in 1937 to twenty-five at the time of the judgment in 1945 to seventeen today.
The judgment's allocation of decreed rights and provisions for their sale has been used to block production by larger nonparties or force them to become parties. In 1960, the city of Pasadena sued the East Pasadena Water Company (which was not a party to the judgment and had no decreed rights) to enjoin it from further pumping from the basin. The suit was settled in 1965, when East Pasadena Water Company became a party to the judgment by acquiring the water rights of the California-Michigan Land and Water Company, which ceased producing groundwater from Raymond Basin fifteen years after the end of its appeals. Currently, there is one actively producing nonparty, but since its annual production is usually less than 10 acre-feet, the parties have chosen not to take action against it.

3. During fiscal years 1982–1984, the state reduced its contribution to one-third, so two-thirds of watermaster service costs were paid by the parties.

6

West Basin

Simultaneous and Sequential Problem Solving in a Coastal Basin

At the beginning of this century, West Basin's 170 square miles were devoted primarily to agricultural use. Today, this area is home to a population of three-quarters of a million and encompasses several incorporated cities, a large industrial and commercial community, the Los Angeles Harbor, and Los Angeles International Airport. West Basin's water supply problems have been as complex as its overlying urban development.

These problems were more numerous and more complicated than those in Raymond Basin. West Basin contained hundreds of water producers and wells, spread over an area nearly five times the size of Raymond Basin. West Basin depends entirely on subsurface flow for its freshwater replenishment. Being the last basin in the San Gabriel River watershed, its freshwater supplies may be adversely affected by upstream activities miles away. And as a coastal basin, it is exposed to saltwater intrusion from the ocean if water levels fall too far.

Uncovering this tangle of problems was challenging enough; unraveling and addressing them was even more demanding. Before they could concern themselves with how to use the basin and its water supplies most efficiently, West Basin water users had to work on several fronts just to keep it from being destroyed.

Groundwater Problems in West Basin

In 1905, the U.S. Geological Survey reported that the West Basin water table sloped from the Newport-Inglewood Uplift toward the coast, and that fresh underground water from the basin discharged into the ocean

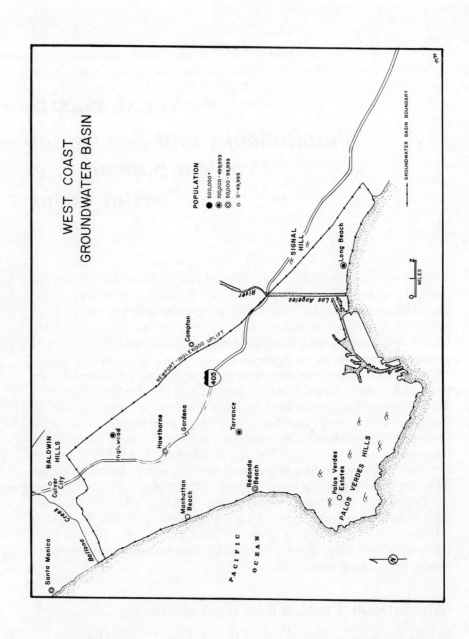

WEST COAST
GROUNDWATER BASIN

POPULATION
● 500,000 +
◉ 100,000 - 499,999
◎ 50,000 - 99,999
○ 0 - 49,999

Santa Monica

BALDWIN HILLS

Culver City

Ballona Creek

Inglewood

Hawthorne

Gardena

Manhattan Beach

Torrance

Redondo Beach

405

NEWPORT - INGLEWOOD UPLIFT

Compton

Los Angeles River

SIGNAL HILL

Long Beach

PACIFIC OCEAN

Palos Verdes Estates

PALOS VERDES HILLS

N

0   2
MILES

GROUNDWATER BASIN BOUNDARY

98

as a result of this seaward-sloping gradient. By 1912, the exchange of water with the ocean evidently had been reversed. Southern California Edison Company abandoned a well at its Redondo Steam Plant because the well was pulling saltwater.

Water levels in many parts of West Basin had fallen below sea level. By 1933, increased groundwater production in West Basin had changed the water table from seaward-sloping to concave. Water moved from all sides of the basin toward the center, where water levels were 5 to 20 feet below sea level (California DPW, 1934a: 202).

As water levels in West Basin fell, freshwater inflow across the Newport-Inglewood Uplift from Central Basin initially increased—from about 10,000 acre-feet per year in the early 1920s to about 30,000 acre-feet per year in the mid-1940s. Increases in pumping more than offset these gains in freshwater replenishment. Annual groundwater extractions in West Basin reached 40,000 acre-feet by 1930, passed 50,000 acre-feet at the end of the 1930s, 70,000 acre-feet by the mid-1940s, and 90,000 acre-feet in the early 1950s (Table 6.1). After the mid-1940s, the falling water level on the Central Basin side reduced the freshwater inflow across the uplift, and the supply-demand imbalance in West Basin grew worse. By the early 1950s, West Basin groundwater extractions were in excess of 90,000 acre-feet per year, and the annual freshwater inflow was down to about 25,000 acre-feet.

West Basin urbanized rapidly from the 1920s through the mid-1950s, and groundwater production increased. By 1950, only 10 percent of the water produced went to irrigation, whereas 48 percent went for industrial use and 42 percent for municipal use. Because urbanization reduced return flows and reuse, groundwater production grew much more rapidly than total consumptive use. Land surfaces were paved over, stream channels were lined with concrete, and wastewater and stormwater were collected by sewer and storm drainage systems and transported directly to the ocean. Wastewater export from West Basin averaged 17,067 acre-feet per year during the 1930s, 35,530 acre-feet per year during the 1940s, and 63,657 acre-feet per year in the 1950s; these figures corresponded almost to the acre-foot to the difference between groundwater extractions and freshwater replenishment.

Because of the overdraft, water levels dropped and groundwater in storage decreased, making local water supplies more costly, less reliable, and more exposed to saltwater intrusion. As underground water elevations dropped below sea level, the basin began to fill from the west, with seawater. The total accumulated overdraft in West Basin through 1957 has been estimated at 832,000 acre-feet, 50 to 75 percent of which was replaced by saltwater (California DWR, 1962: 92; Jennings, Engstrad, and Henrikson, 1963: 12). Between 400,000 and 600,000 acre-feet of saltwater

TABLE 6.1

West Basin Water Production and Total Water Use, 1933–1990 (acre-feet)

Year	Groundwater extractions	Imported water	Exported water	Total water use
1933	45,635	18,146	581	63,200
1934	49,985	17,915	600	67,300
1935	48,880	17,098	478	65,500
1936	47,152	27,758	610	74,300
1937	45,655	27,602	657	72,600
1938	46,054	27,014	668	72,400
1939	50,975	27,353	628	77,700
1940	52,024	26,953	777	78,200
1941	52,406	27,425	631	79,200
1942	52,929	31,349	678	83,600
1943	59,258	39,085	843	97,500
1944	68,062	42,379	1,041	109,400
1945	75,856	51,339	1,295	125,900
1946	75,847	52,033	1,880	126,000
1947	75,275	47,735	2,110	120,900
1948	82,138	51,455	2,193	131,400
1949	81,601	57,010	1,911	136,700
1950	81,626	60,652	1,578	140,700
1951	86,240	60,990	2,330	144,900
1952	87,490	63,150	2,600	148,040
1953	94,070	73,320	2,620	164,770
1954	86,970	84,580	2,670	168,880
1955	80,540	94,570	2,000	173,110
1956	67,650	112,870	2,214	189,086
1957	67,700	137,200	2,607	202,293
1958	67,000	135,000	3,053	198,947
1959	67,000	151,000	3,676	214,324
1960	67,000	152,000	4,089	214,911
1961	61,900	156,000	4,577	213,323
1962	58,624	165,918	7,542	215,975
1963	58,861	168,437	8,052	223,264
1964	60,842	188,877	8,873	240,846
1965	59,370	248,161	9,752	297,778
1966	60,759	237,237	10,618	287,378
1967	62,552	233,714	10,291	285,976
1968	61,554	243,184	11,445	293,293
1969	61,638	240,276	11,224	290,690
1970	62,447	257,012	13,700	305,759
1971	60,924	251,887	12,846	299,965
1972	64,733	262,633	12,868	314,498

TABLE 6.1 (continued)

Year	Groundwater extractions	Imported water	Exported water	Total water use
1973	60,478	245,857	11,323	295,012
1974	54,966	251,931	12,056	294,841
1975	56,673	244,157	11,906	288,924
1976	59,407	256,846	13,225	303,028
1977	59,882	234,168	11,820	282,229
1978	58,300	257,535	10,461	305,374
1979	58,058	242,594	10,550	290,103
1980	57,085	264,379	11,783	309,681
1981	57,700	266,071	12,527	311,244
1982	62,664	251,393	11,728	302,329
1983	57,057	268,673	12,089	314,091
1984	53,341	282,569	12,230	323,680
1985	51,450	283,764	7,779	327,435
1986	54,708	256,067	5,752	305,023
1987	48,721	295,260	11,093	332,888
1988	45,455	299,809	11,509	333,755
1989	44,538	305,054	10,974	338,618
1990	46,344	276,248	11,601	310,991

SOURCE: 1952 West Basin Referee Report; 1961 West Basin Referee Report; West Basin Watermaster Reports, 1956–1990.

entered West Basin from the 1930s through 1957 (California DWR, 1962: 99; Ostrom, 1965: 14; Fossette, 1986: 149–50).

During the 1950s, about 50,000 acre-feet per year of ocean water poured into West Basin. Along the western coastline, the line of underground water exhibiting chloride concentrations in excess of 100 parts per million moved inland at a rate of 1,100 feet per year from 1950 to 1956, advancing nearly 1.5 miles (California DWR, 1959b: 39). By 1957, nearly 12,000 acres of the western coastal area were underlain by waters with chloride concentrations in excess of 500 parts per million. As of spring 1962, seawater intrusion was 1 to 2 miles inland all along Santa Monica Bay. A second saltwater front appeared along the southern coastline of West Basin, coming in from San Pedro Bay in the vicinity of the Dominguez and Alamitos gaps. By the late 1950s, this second front had reached the Pacific Coast Highway near Wilmington, approximately 2 miles inland (California DWR, West Basin Watermaster Report, 1962: 17–18).

With water levels down 200 feet in some places, an accumulated over-draft of more than 800,000 acre-feet, and a half-million acre-feet of salt-water underlying thousands of acres of land and advancing on two fronts, the groundwater supply in West Basin was threatened with destruction. In 1959, West Basin was pronounced "one of the most critically overdrawn ground water sources in southern California" (California DWR, 1959b: 1).

Gathering Information about West Basin, and the First Basin Governance System

At first, West Basin water users had little information about the general deterioration of basin conditions. Furthermore, the more noticeable problems of water level declines and saltwater intrusion did not affect all locations within the basin equally; some water users faced severe problems while others saw only a modest lengthening of pumping lifts. But the seawater intrusion made it clear, at least along the coast, that something more than a seasonal or cyclical drop in water levels was occurring. Although the Pacific's invasion nearly destroyed West Basin, it also served as "the stimulus which evoked the efforts of entrepreneurs to seek . . . solutions to their common problem" (Ostrom, 1965: xviii).

Water engineers in industrial firms along the coast were among the first to become concerned, but at that time there was little the industrial firms could do other than shut down brackish wells and construct new ones in other locations (Ostrom, 1965: 222). Water department personnel in some of the beach cities also grew uneasy. Because of its interest in Coastal Plain water supply and conservation, the Los Angeles County Flood Control District (LACFCD) began keeping track of the emerging problems in West Basin.

In July 1942, LACFCD Chief Engineer Paul Baumann wrote to Manhattan Beach City Engineer O. A. Gierlach that the district was interested in investigating the cause of the increased salinity of water in the Manhattan Beach area. Both then contacted other producers. Baumann wrote to several pumpers alerting them to the possibility of contamination from seawater intrusion, and Gierlach invited representatives from other West Basin cities to a meeting to discuss the possible problem. There was no response.

In March 1943, LACFCD hosted a conference for all West Basin cities and chambers of commerce, and this time enough people showed up to form a survey committee to organize and fund an investigation of the area's problems (Ostrom, 1965: 222; Fossette, 1986: 7). In 1944, the West Basin Survey Committee sponsored a series of meetings with represen-tatives of local industries, private water companies, and public agencies, leading to the formation of a broader group, the West Basin Ground Water Conservation Group, to replace the survey committee.

This group appointed a Ways and Means Committee to produce a report on West Basin water problems. The committee's September 1945 report, which was distributed throughout the basin, incorporated data from federal, state, and county investigations and contained a map of West Basin. The report's findings were alarming: the West Basin overdraft was close to 37,000 acre-feet per year and rising, a landward-sloping hydraulic gradient had been created within the basin, and saltwater could be expected to flow into the basin in increasing quantities. The report warned that remedial measures would involve considerable time, effort, and money and that West Basin needed a supplemental supply of water immediately.

The report of the Ways and Means Committee recommended that West Basin water users organize an effort to address the overdraft problem. In February 1946, the Ground Water Conservation Group disbanded, and the West Basin Water Association (WBWA) was formed. The WBWA had twenty charter members, including the beach cities, oil companies, and private water companies. The cities of Hawthorne, Inglewood, and Torrance—all located farther inland—did not join at first. The WBWA's articles of association were drafted by attorney Kenneth Wright, whose services were retained by the California Water Service Company. Wright had been the attorney for several of the parties in the recently completed Raymond Basin adjudication.

The association appointed a nine-member executive committee composed of three representatives each from industry, the cities, and private water companies. The association also hired a paid executive secretary who, along with one part-time clerical assistant, conducted its daily affairs from a small office throughout the period that West Basin's problems were being resolved. Association members paid dues based on their groundwater production. Members' statements of their own production were used for apportioning dues. The incentive to understate production was offset by the fact that votes within the association also were apportioned on the basis of stated groundwater production. If members understated production, they lost votes; if they overstated production, they lost money.

The association represented the first governance system for West Basin. It operated on two principles: all decisions were to be made by consensus, and all members should continue to derive benefit from the basin (Ostrom, 1965: 31; Fossette, 1986: 16–17). Most important, the association "provided a means whereby people representing conflicting interests could discuss mutual problems and search for satisfactory solutions . . . [and] insured the continuation of sustained negotiation and communication by all affected parties" (Ostrom, 1965: 80).

For each member, continuing to mine the basin yielded a short-run payoff. Yet each also had significant investments in West Basin and anticipated a long future need for water. A greater long-run advantage could be gained if some other water source were used for a base supply and the groundwater reserved for peaking use. This would require reduced pumping from the basin, but that was not necessarily the first step to be taken. Members felt that securing an additional water supply had to come first, since water users would not likely cooperate in reducing withdrawals from the basin until they had an alternative source of supply.

Securing an Additional Supply

In the late 1940s, MWD was about the only source of an additional supply in West Basin. However, the cities of Long Beach and Torrance were the only MWD members in West Basin at the time. Basinwide access to MWD imports would require annexation to MWD, since MWD was financed primarily by property taxes. MWD was also interested in having more customers; it needed taxpayers and water buyers to meet its financial obligations and perfect its claim to a million acre-feet per year of Colorado River water. As of 1945, MWD was selling less than 3 percent of its claim.

MWD was not interested in having several West Basin cities annex one at a time, however.[1] A public water district would have to be created covering the West Basin area to be annexed to MWD, but such a district could not be formed without a vote of the residents—who would then have to vote to annex to MWD, which in turn would have to approve the annexation. In the process, West Basin voters would have to agree to pay additional taxes, to the local water district that joined MWD and purchased water from it, and to MWD as well.

West Basin Water Association members believed they would be unable to persuade residents to take these steps without educating voters and building a consensus on the gravity of West Basin's problems. But there was no time for such action. As the WBWA was preparing its strategy, Los Angeles County Supervisor Raymond Darby seized on the water issue and organized the Southwest Water Fact-Finding Committee. In the summer of 1946, Darby's committee proposed that a municipal water district be created for the entire West Basin area. By September, the committee had been reorganized and renamed the West Basin Campaign Committee, and it organized a special election to form the West Basin Municipal Water District.

The special election was scheduled for January 14, 1947, less than a year after the WBWA had been formed. The WBWA reluctantly agreed to support the Darby effort, even though the needed consensus had not been developed and the election seemed highly problematic. Inland communities not yet affected by saltwater intrusion were not ready to be taxed for what they perceived as a benefit to the coastal towns. Political leaders of inland cities, such as the mayor and council of Inglewood, campaigned in opposition to district formation. The inland communities voted against the proposed West Basin Municipal Water District, and the beach communities voted for it. The "no" votes prevailed, and district formation was defeated.

Recognizing the heavy support in the beach communities for the formation of a municipal water district, the association began to work on a new district and a new election. WBWA members drew boundaries for a West Basin Municipal Water District that included El Segundo, Manhattan Beach, Hermosa Beach, Redondo Beach, Palos Verdes Estates, and thirteen unincorporated areas while excluding inland communities such as Inglewood, Hawthorne, and Gardena. Petitions again were circulated and signatures collected, and a second special election was scheduled for November 25, 1947. The smaller district received 8-to-1 voter support.

The newly formed West Basin Municipal Water District (WBMWD) petitioned MWD for approval of annexation and organized another special election to obtain the voters' approval of annexation to MWD. MWD's board voted unanimously to grant annexation on March 26, 1948, provided that voter approval within the district was secured by the end of the year. The special election for annexation to MWD was held on June 8, 1948. Residents voted 15 to 1 in favor of annexation. Annexation proceedings were formally completed on July 23, 1948. Colorado River water deliveries began in 1949. Part of West Basin had secured a supplemental supply.

The inland cities soon recognized their own need for an additional water supply. Gardena requested annexation to the WBMWD almost immediately and was annexed by special election on November 15, 1948. At the beginning of 1949, the mayor of Inglewood, who had campaigned against the formation of the original district in 1947, asked the WBMWD to annex Inglewood so it could have access to MWD water. Annexation of Inglewood was completed in June of 1952, and the city also joined the West Basin Water Association. The city of Hawthorne annexed to the district on October 23, 1953. By the end of 1953, the West Basin Municipal Water District included essentially the area originally proposed in January 1947. Virtually all of West Basin had access to a supplemental supply of water.

Curtailing Demand: The West Basin Adjudication

In addition to acquiring a supplemental water supply, the 1945 report of the Ways and Means Committee had recommended curtailing the demand on West Basin groundwater through an adjudication of rights similar to the one just completed and pending appeal in Raymond Basin. Even before the report was issued, the California Water Service Company informed its attorney, Kenneth Wright, that it was interested in initiating a Raymond-type adjudication in West Basin. Wright, having observed the energy and money spent by Pasadena as sole plaintiff in the Raymond Basin case, advised the company not to go it alone (Ostrom, 1965: 303).

California Water Service Company found two other West Basin appropriators, the Palos Verdes Water Company and the city of Torrance, to join as plaintiffs. On October 24, 1945, one month after the publication of the Ways and Means Committee Report and before the formation of the West Basin Water Association or the West Basin Municipal Water District, the three plaintiffs filed a complaint seeking an adjudication and limitation of groundwater rights against 151 named and several hundred unnamed defendants in West Basin. The case of *California Water Service Company et al. v. City of Compton et al.* occupied the California Superior Court docket for the next sixteen years.

Once again, before the West Basin Water Association was even off the ground, action had been started to which it had to respond. The association decided to support the adjudication and in early 1946 organized a seventeen-member engineering advisory committee to help collect the necessary data. Judge Arnold Praeger ordered a reference of the physical facts in the case to the Division of Water Resources on July 26, 1946. On the basis of the preliminary findings reported by the division, Judge Praeger issued an order on November 9, 1949, to add 340 more named parties to the suit, bringing the total to about 500.

A draft referee report was issued to the parties and filed with the court in February 1952; a final version was filed in September. It found that continuous overdraft had begun in West Basin in 1920 and grown worse since then, and that the basin faced substantial and irreparable injury as a result. Aggregate groundwater extractions had reached 90,000 acre-feet per year, while freshwater replenishment had averaged 24,400 acre-feet per year from 1930 through 1949. The report recommended that groundwater production be limited to 30,000 acre-feet per year initially, with adjustments to that amount from time to time as basin conditions warranted. This represented a reduction of groundwater pumping by two-thirds, a far more drastic cutback than the one in the Raymond Basin case. Finally, the report dispelled earlier hopes that an impermeable "clay cap" covered West Basin and would block the spread of saltwater intrusion. The main water-producing aquifers in West Basin were in hydrologic contact with the ocean, and nothing stood in the way of further degradation of basin water quality.

The referee report "was a great motivator" (Fossette, 1986: 95; Ostrom, 1965: 33). Most large water producers were alarmed at the prospect of reducing pumping by two-thirds. They voiced their concerns within

the West Basin Water Association, which voted to form a legal settlement committee to negotiate a settlement that would be more generally
acceptable to water users. If they did not work out a settlement, the
judge might adopt the referee's recommendation and order a two-thirds
reduction in pumping.

The Legal Settlement Committee drafted a stipulation and circulated
it among the major water producers, with a revised draft submitted in May
1954. At its July 14, 1954 meeting, the committee decided to propose the
revised draft to the parties as an interim agreement to reduce pumping for
the duration of the litigation. This agreement provided for a 25 percent cutback in groundwater extractions, and defined for each party a "Prescriptive Right, 1949," totaling 67,789 acre-feet for the 472 remaining litigants.

The agreement was a contingent contract (Blomquist and Ostrom, 1985)
that would take effect only if signatures were obtained from parties with
70 percent of the total "Prescriptive Right, 1949." No one who signed committed to a cutback unless there would be enough other such commitments
to actually improve basin conditions. Parties were also more willing to sign
because a California Water Code provision adopted in 1951 with the
WBWA's support declared that groundwater users would not forfeit their
rights by reducing pumping and using an imported supply instead.

Under those conditions, signatures were gained fairly rapidly. On
February 16, 1955, Judge Praeger approved the interim agreement and
ordered the fifty signers, who had more than 80 percent of the prescriptive rights as defined in the agreement, to abide by it for the duration
of the litigation. He appointed the Division of Water Resources as watermaster to monitor compliance, maintain production records, issue reports,
and administer a water exchange pool.[2] Costs of the watermaster service
were apportioned among the signers.

Compliance with the interim agreement was high. As a group, the
signers consistently extracted less than their total prescriptive rights, and
only one signer overextracted its right by more than the allowed 10 percent without making it up the next year. The signers increased their
purchases of imported water to make up the difference between their
reduced pumping and their water needs.

The interim agreement was also effective in improving basin water
conditions. After the first full year under the agreement, the Department
of Water Resources reported that the water level had risen 5 to 15 feet
in the southern, southwestern, and southeastern parts of the basin. These
improvements were sustained throughout the period of the interim agreement, despite the drought cycle that had begun in 1945.

By 1956, the data in the original referee report were six years old,
and several parties remained concerned about having to reduce pumping
to 30,000 acre-feet per year. In addition, signers of the interim agreement

were worried about the behavior of new pumpers and nonsigners. If non-signers had increased pumping since 1949 and the judge chose some other year as the benchmark for determining rights, they might have enlarged their rights. If the judge did choose 1949 as the benchmark, new pumpers might have acquired prescriptive rights. Late in 1956, a majority of the larger pumpers persuaded Judge Praeger to order a second reference in the case, while the seven largest producers initiated a second lawsuit to prevent new pumpers from gaining prescriptive rights.

That action named 120 producers who had not been included in *California Water Service Co. v. City of Compton.*[3] Most of them were small producers, and many with connections to other water sources dropped out rather than pay the costs of defending their right to a small amount of groundwater production. By 1963, only twelve of the defendants in the second suit were still active pumpers and their total annual production was only 300 acre-feet. The second suit was settled by a stipulated judgment in 1966.

In 1957, the action in the two West Basin suits was suddenly suspended when Judge Praeger disqualified himself upon discovering that he owned stock in one of the parties. All of his standing orders were declared void, including those governing the interim agreement and providing for the second reference. The Judicial Council and the parties' attorneys searched for a new judge. In May 1958, Judge George Francis of Alpine County took over the cases, and by the end of July had reinstated all of Judge Praeger's orders. Work on the adjudication resumed, but everyone had been reminded of the fragility of the process.

The first draft of the second referee report was presented to the parties and the court on June 2, 1959. It did not contain a recommendation to cut pumping to 30,000 acre-feet. In fact, the draft report did not even contain an estimate of West Basin's safe yield, although another department publication later reported the basin's 1957 safe yield as approximately 36,100 acre-feet per year (California DWR, 1962: 121). Instead, the draft report essentially ratified the provisions of the interim agreement, recommending curtailment of pumping to the 1949 prescriptive rights defined therein.

With the second reference concluded and the case now fourteen years old, work began in earnest on a final settlement. The Legal Settlement Committee presented a final draft of a stipulated judgment at the West Basin Water Association's February 1960 meeting. This stipulation was to be presented to the court and was to take effect once signed by parties with 75 percent of the 1949 prescriptive rights. By May 1960, twenty parties with 33 percent of the rights had signed. By February 1961, thirty parties with 65 percent of the rights had signed, and by June 1961, fifty-six parties with 82 percent of the rights had signed the stipulation. It was filed with the court on July 21, 1961, and a trial lasting a few hours was held the same day.

On August 18, 1961, Judge Francis signed the West Basin judgment, which ratified in all particulars the parties' stipulation. It gave ninety-nine parties transferable "adjudicated rights" totaling 64,064.09 acre-feet. Watermaster service by the Department of Water Resources was continued, including administration of the exchange pool.

There were three appeals from the judgment. The first was settled within a year by an upward adjustment in the adjudicated right of Chandler's Palos Verdes Sand and Gravel Company. An appeal by Edward Sidebotham and Son, Inc., was consolidated with a more serious appeal by the city of Hawthorne, a major West Basin water user.[4] An inland city, Hawthorne had not yet felt the effects of saltwater intrusion, and since reluctantly joining the West Basin Municipal Water District in 1953 had access to both West Basin groundwater and MWD Colorado River water. Hawthorne had pursued a noncooperative strategy throughout the adjudication, refusing to participate with the other major producers in negotiating the interim agreement (which it never signed), or in negotiating the stipulated judgment (which it also did not sign). Now, Hawthorne challenged the judgment. Hawthorne's appeal raised the key issue left unaddressed by the Raymond Basin case, that of Civil Code Section 1007, which prohibited the acquisition of prescriptive rights against public entities. By prevailing on appeal, Hawthorne might unravel the carefully negotiated judgment put together by the other parties.

Hawthorne raised its Section 1007 argument in a peculiar way, however, arguing first that the city's prescriptive right had vested in 1937 rather than 1949, and second, that the city was by prescription entitled to the *share* of the groundwater production in the basin it had in 1937. The city contended that Section 1007 meant that its *share* of West Basin groundwater production could not be decreased, so that as total production increased, so did its entitlement. Therefore, Hawthorne's 1937 prescriptive right of 1,674 acre-feet should have been 3,170 acre-feet as of the first limitation of production in 1955. Presented this way, Hawthorne's appeal was dismissed out of hand by the District Court of Appeal, which found it "well settled" that prescriptive water rights are calculated on a quantitative rather than a proportionate basis. The District Court of Appeal affirmed Judge Francis's decision on February 17, 1964. On April 15, 1964, the California Supreme Court denied a petition to review the appellate court decision, and the appeals ended, nineteen years after *California Water Service Company et al. v. City of Compton et al.* began.[5]

With the adjudication completed, West Basin water users had added important elements to the basin's governance structure and had used that structure to design and implement the first phase of a basin management program. The West Basin Water Association clearly remained the centerpiece of basin governance, as the principal forum for water users' discussions, negotiations, dissemination of information, and the taking of collective decisions. To the association was added the court, with the authority to establish and enforce rules for all water users in the basin (including those not in WBWA). Through the continuing jurisdiction retained by the court, water users could also seek changes in the formal rules if needed. The adjudication also added the Southern District office of the state Department of Water Resources, monitoring and reporting on water users' behavior under the interim agreement and then under the judgment.

This basin governance system produced West Basin's first management program. The adjudication had defined and limited the set of authorized basin users and assigned them legally enforceable and transferable rights to specific quantities of groundwater. Like the original management program in Raymond Basin, the initial approach in West Basin was to manage only the "demand side" of the water equation. The adjudication did not include any collective effort to augment the supply of water in the basin, and the basin was not geologically suited to direct replenishment by water spreading. Individual users were responsible for acquiring their own additional supplies for direct use. Basin conditions were to be improved by reducing the demand on the basin to a fixed amount every year. Unlike the water users in Raymond Basin, however, those in West Basin did not fix annual pumping equal to the basin's estimated safe yield. Indeed, authorized pumping from West Basin was nearly double most estimates of the safe yield. In an already overdrafted basin, that sort of "demand-side" management program clearly would not suffice to keep the ocean back and water levels up, especially if the freshwater supply to the basin kept dwindling.

Problems Upstream: Replenishment Lost and Regained

The reduction of pumping under the interim agreement and the judgment had produced a mild recovery of water levels. In another basin, that might be an unmixed blessing, but in West Basin it further reduced freshwater replenishment from Central Basin. Increased water production upstream in the Central and Main San Gabriel basins had lowered underground water levels there. As the levels on the Central Basin side of the Newport-Inglewood Uplift fell and those on the West Basin side rose, the water level differential across the uplift decreased, and so did the freshwater inflow to West Basin.

Subsurface inflow from Central Basin had peaked at 30,683 acre-feet in water year 1947–48. By 1955–56, the first year of operation of the interim agreement in West Basin, the estimated freshwater replenishment to West Basin was down to 17,970 acre-feet. In 1958, the Department of Water Resources noted in its annual West Basin Watermaster Report that the water level differential between Central and West Basins had been completely eliminated and even reversed in some places along the uplift. At some locations, groundwater was actually moving across the uplift from West Basin into Central Basin.

West Basin water users regarded their position as untenable: they had reduced their use of the less expensive groundwater underlying their lands, were purchasing increasing amounts of more expensive Colorado River water to meet their needs, were paying taxes to WBMWD and MWD for the dubious privilege of doing so, and were paying for watermaster service to monitor their demand curtailment, while watching their own basin conditions continue to deteriorate as their upstream neighbors pumped more groundwater. Once again, the West Basin Water Association was the focus of activity. Members realized that action within West Basin alone was insufficient. Although they had no control over Central Basin, they did have two experiences on which to build: (1) their working relationship with the Los Angeles County Flood Control District, which operated water-spreading facilities in the Montebello Forebay of Central Basin, and (2) the activities of their neighbors in Orange County, who in 1949 had begun a program of artificial replenishment of their groundwater supply by spreading untreated imported MWD water. The WBWA pursued the possibility of increasing the freshwater inflow to West Basin by means of an artificial replenishment program in the Montebello Forebay.

The LACFCD had spread floodwaters in the Montebello Forebay since 1938. With the drought that began in 1945, however, there was little local runoff or storm flow to conserve. The challenge was to devise an institutional means of purchasing and controlling quantities of imported water to be spread for basin recharge. After the creation of the Central Basin Water Association (see Chapter 7), the WBWA joined with it and the LACFCD to obtain an amendment to the Los Angeles County Flood Control District Act to allow the establishment of "conservation zones" within the district. These zones would be special taxing districts to finance projects beneficial to part but not all of LACFCD's jurisdiction. Such zones would allow Central and West Basin residents to be taxed for an artificial replenishment program at the LACFCD spreading grounds to recharge Central Basin, and through it, West Basin.

Legislation passed by the state legislature and signed by the governor in the spring of 1950 authorized the creation of temporary "zones of benefit" within the Los Angeles County Flood Control District for the financing of special projects. In 1952, the Los Angeles County Board of Supervisors created Conservation Zone I encompassing Central and West basins, with an ad valorem tax rate of two cents per $100 of assessed valuation, and the statutory maximum life of five years. The zone was reauthorized by the county in 1957. Zone I funds were used to purchase and spread imported water at Montebello Forebay. The Flood Control District purchased and spread 478,000 acre-feet of untreated Colorado River water in the Montebello Forebay area from July 1, 1953, through June 30, 1961, with Zone I funds.

Seeing that an artificial replenishment program could work, the associations contemplated establishing a permanent funding base for it. In 1953, the Orange County Water District had switched the funding base for its artificial replenishment program to a pump tax. A fee on ground-water production—in other words, a tax on use of the basin—financed purchases of replenishment water. This scheme showed promise as a permanent funding base, and seemed fairer, too: the water users who benefited from replenishment most directly paid its costs.

However, the Central and West basins lacked a public jurisdiction coinciding with basin boundaries and authorized to impose such a tax. Since another legislative change would be necessary to authorize taxing groundwater production, members of the two water associations decided that it may as well include the creation of a permanent agency to operate the replenishment program. The associations and a drafting committee of twelve men representing water users worked on two fronts in the state legislature in 1954 and 1955, seeking authorization for the creation of a special water replenishment district, and a legislative mandate that groundwater producers record their production (Krieger, 1955: 2).

In June 1955, the legislature passed and the governor signed the Water Replenishment District Act. Replenishment districts could be formed in seven southern California counties (Los Angeles, Riverside, San Bernardino, Kern, Ventura, San Diego, and Imperial) with the authority to raise funds for replenishment operations through ad valorem property taxes, pump taxes, and water sales. Proposed district boundaries would be checked by the state engineer to ensure that those included in such a district would in fact benefit directly from its activities. The act also required a replenishment district to determine whether other existing agencies could do any part of its work; if so, the district had to contract the work to that other agency, rather than establish its own facilities or operations.

Taxing groundwater production would require groundwater production records. West Basin pumpers already recorded and reported their extractions because of the adjudication. Central Basin pumpers did not. The proposed Water Recordation Act was promoted not only as a means of acquiring the Central Basin data, but as a way of reducing the time and expense of future basin adjudications in southern California. The act, which also passed in June 1955, required entities withdrawing 25 acre-feet or more per year in the four southern counties of Los Angeles, Riverside, San Bernardino, and Ventura to record and report their production to the State Water Rights Board.

With the recordation and replenishment district acts approved, the West Basin Water Association and the Central Basin Water Association formed the Joint Committee on the Water Replenishment District. The joint committee worked on the boundaries of a replenishment district and arrived at a proposed district of about 420 square miles, encompassing all of West Basin and nearly all of Central Basin. The committee also recommended keeping the Conservation Zone I property tax in place and using Zone I funds to purchase replenishment water to make up the accumulated overdraft in the two basins, since all property owners had benefited from the development of the area that had produced the accumulated overdraft. The proposed replenishment district would fund annual replenishment through the pump tax, thereby placing the cost of maintaining the replenishment program on the water users within the district. Since nearly all of the area of the proposed replenishment district was already annexed to MWD, the joint committee did not propose to annex the replenishment district to MWD. The replenishment district could purchase MWD replenishment water through the existing MWD members in the area, such as the municipal water districts.

The water associations began a drive to collect petition signatures to allow a special election on the proposed replenishment district. More than 100,000 signatures were presented to the county board of supervisors on June 9, 1959. The signatures were forwarded to the Department of Water Resources and the state engineer for determination of the appropriateness of the proposed district's boundaries. The department endorsed the proposed boundaries on July 17. The county board of supervisors set November 17, 1959, for a special election on the formation of the Central and West Basin Water Replenishment District (CWBWRD). It received 4-to-1 support from the voters.

A five-member board of directors representing five divisions within the district was elected to govern it, setting policy and establishing tax rates. The board appointed a general manager to conduct day-to-day operations, and established a first-year pump tax rate of $3.19 per acre-foot of groundwater production. The amount of the CWBWRD pump tax for each year and the MWD price per acre-foot of replenishment water are shown in Table 6.2.

The Los Angeles County Board of Supervisors renewed Conservation Zone I in 1962 and 1967, but not in 1972, leaving the replenishment district as the sole source of financing for the replenishment program thereafter. The replenishment district has operated mainly as a financier of the replenishment program rather than as a central manager of the basins, or even as the direct operator of the replenishment program. The district purchases most of its imported replenishment water through the Central Basin Municipal Water District, with which the district until recently shared an office in Downey.[6] The replenishment water is conveyed to the San Gabriel River channel at Whittier Narrows, where the county Department of Public Works (formerly the LACFCD) conducts the actual spreading operation.

TABLE 6.2

Amount of CWBWRD Pump Tax and Price of MWD Replenishment Water, 1961–1990 (dollars per acre-foot)

Year	CWBWRD pump tax	Cost of MWD water for replenishment
1961	3.19	12.75
1962	5.75	13.50
1963	6.63	14.25
1964	6.58	15.00
1965	7.36	15.25
1966	7.31	16.00
1967	6.20	17.00
1968	6.11	18.00
1969	6.00	19.00
1970	6.00	20.00
1971	6.00	22.00
1972	6.00	24.00
1973	9.00	27.00
1974	11.00	30.00
1975	14.00	30.00
1976	21.00	32.00/42.00 [a]
1977	21.00	36.00/42.00 [a]
1978	24.00	41.00
1979	24.00	48.00
1980	24.00	53.00
1981	16.00	53.00
1982	16.00	61.00
1983	16.00	79.00
1984	27.00	100.00/153.00 [b]
1985	41.00	153.00
1986	70.00	172.00
1987	70.00	153.00
1988	70.00	153.00
1989	61.00	153.00
1990	51.00	115.00/153.00 [c]

a. Two-price system: higher price for State Project water.
b. MWD price changed in middle of fiscal year.
c. MWD Seasonal Storage Program offers lower price for untreated replenishment water during the winter months.
SOURCE: Central and West Basin Water Replenishment District Annual Survey Reports, 1961–1990.

The artificial replenishment program added a "supply-side" component to the management program in West Basin, attempting to improve conditions by augmenting the supply of water to the basin. The replenishment program also added an important element to the basin governance system, the Central and West Basin Water Replenishment District. The replenishment district levies the tax on groundwater pumping in both basins and finances and makes decisions about the replenishment program that benefits both basins.

The Central and West Basin Water Replenishment District and the county Department of Public Works are key elements of another part of the basin management program. The replenishment district finances and the Department of Public Works operates West Basin's fight against the sea.

Fighting Back the Sea

Since the 1950s, it has been understood that West Basin is fully exposed to saltwater intrusion. It has also been understood that maximizing freshwater inflow from Central Basin to West Basin requires keeping West Basin water levels below sea level. Such levels, however, expose West Basin to the threat of destruction by saltwater intrusion.

Ideas about how to keep the ocean out of West Basin had begun circulating within the West Basin Ground Water Conservation Group in 1945. There the idea of creating a freshwater mound below the ground surface and parallel to the coast first emerged. J. F. Poland of the U.S. Geological Survey, who had been engaged by the West Basin Survey Committee, supported the idea, as did the Los Angeles County Flood Control District engineers who had met with the Survey Committee and then the Ground Water Conservation Group (Fossette, 1986: 52–53).

The chairman of the West Basin Ground Water Conservation Group, Manhattan Beach City Engineer O. A. Gierlach, and LACFCD Chief Engineer Paul Baumann convinced the city and the district to try an experiment in Manhattan Beach. LACFCD engineers converted one of the city's seven abandoned wells to work in reverse, and freshwater was injected underground through this well. Measurements were taken at the other six wells, 300 to 600 feet away. There was a noticeable rise in water level; a tiny freshwater mound apparently had been created.

The West Basin Water Association successfully appealed to the state of California to finance a mile-long prototype injection barrier in the Manhattan Beach area. If it worked, the freshwater barrier idea could benefit other coastal California basins, as well as West Basin. Funds were appropriated to the State Water Resources Board, which contracted with LACFCD to install and operate the prototype barrier. Construction began in January 1952 on a series of nine injection wells approximately 500 feet apart and parallel to the coast about 2,000 feet inland. In February 1953, LACFCD began injecting treated MWD Colorado River water imported via the West Basin Municipal Water District into the wells.

Again, the injection worked—observation wells nearby showed increased water levels and decreased salinity.

The state funds were exhausted by November 1953, and there remained ten miles of exposed West Basin coastline. The LACFCD kept the prototype barrier in operation with its own funds while the WBWA sought a means of funding its extension along the coast. The WBWA drafted an ordinance authorizing the creation of another LACFCD Conservation Zone, known as Zone II, which coincided with the boundaries of West Basin. The county board of supervisors approved the creation of Zone II in January 1954, with an ad valorem tax rate of five cents per $100 of assessed valuation.

This funding sufficed to maintain the prototype barrier and some extension through 1959, but constructing and operating a full barrier would exceed Zone II's temporary revenue-generating capacity. Furthermore, discussion had begun about constructing a similar barrier along San Pedro Bay to stop saltwater intrusion along the basin's southern boundary, and Zone II could not possibly support that additional project.

The financing of the barrier became another reason for the establishment of the water replenishment district with its pump-tax authority. The replenishment district could use pump-tax money to purchase imported water for the barrier at the same time that it purchased water for spreading. After the formation of the replenishment district, a new financing arrangement was developed similar to that for funding the spreading operation. Zone II revenues generated from West Basin property owners would be used to meet capital costs of barrier construction. The replenishment district would use pump-tax revenue from Central and West Basin water users to pay the costs of operating and maintaining the barriers (Ostrom, 1965: 44–45).

After the barrier projects were completed, the county terminated Zone II. The replenishment district now finances the water purchases and maintenance costs of the barriers, while county Department of Public Works personnel actually operate the injection wells. The West Basin Barrier Project, along the basin's western coastline, now has 144 injection wells. The Dominguez Gap Barrier Project facing San Pedro Bay began operation in February 1971, and now has 41 injection wells.

Operation of the barriers is expensive. Treated MWD water injected at the barriers currently costs about $250.00 per acre-foot, so injecting 40,000 acre-feet of water at the three barriers costs about $10,000,000. Nevertheless, studies undertaken by the Department of Water Resources and the county Department of Public Works find the barrier program financially preferable to alternatives such as mining the basin and replacing it completely with surface water storage and distribution, or trying to fill the basin from upstream through an enlarged spreading program.

At the time of the expansion of the West Basin Barrier Project, for example, the Los Angeles County Flood Control District estimated that the average annual cost of building and maintaining surface storage facilities to match the underground aquifers' capacity for meeting peak demands was nearly three times greater than the average annual cost of building and operating the barrier projects (Ostrom, 1965: 528).

The barrier projects were responsible for another essential feature of the West Basin management program. The barriers have created a freshwater wall against the ocean. Water levels along the coast in West Basin are maintained above sea level to keep additional seawater from entering the basin, while water levels farther inland are maintained below sea level to maximize freshwater inflow from Central Basin. In combination with the artificial replenishment program, the barriers allow West Basin pumpers to extract 64,000 acre-feet annually from a coastal basin with an estimated safe yield of about 30,000 acre-feet.

Modifications to the Basin Management Program

Although the essential features of the West Basin management program were in place by 1970, water users have modified particular aspects of basin management methods in response to challenges that have arisen or been recognized during the past two decades.

On the demand side of the management program, West Basin users have altered the judgment to create "nonconsumptive water rights." In recent years, some industrial water users, particularly oil and aircraft companies, have needed to perform cleanup operations to remove contaminants or old refined oil from beneath their land. They have engaged in intensive pumping for short periods in excess of their adjudicated rights, after which the water with the contaminants removed is returned. Because the water is returned underground and the removal of contaminants benefits all parties, West Basin users did not want to penalize these overextractions. In 1984, the parties and the court amended the West Basin judgment to recognize nonconsumptive water rights and authorize the watermaster to issue orders permitting parties to exercise such rights when needed.

The Central and West Basin Water Replenishment District has also attempted to encourage groundwater users to use more imported water for direct use when available. MWD has a compatible interest in maximizing sales of imported water when available. As a result, MWD and the replenishment district have entered into arrangements with pumpers in certain years to replace groundwater with direct use of imported water. These are known as "in-lieu" replenishment programs, because basin replenishment occurs by leaving water in the ground, instead of pumping it out and then replacing it. The replenishment district identifies groundwater users with the facilities to take either groundwater or imported water and reimburses them for the difference in cost between pumping groundwater and using treated MWD water. At a proper reimbursement rate, the user receives imported water at the same cost per acre-foot as incurred from pumping groundwater (or even slightly less, to provide an incentive for participation). The replenishment district keeps groundwater in the ground at 100 percent replacement (which is more efficient than spreading) and pays only the difference between groundwater production and the treated imported water (which is normally less than the full cost of replenishment water), and the MWD sells more water.

More often in recent years, however, MWD has not had much additional water to sell. Competition throughout southern California for imported water supplies intensified through the 1970s and 1980s, again raising concern about their availability for replenishment. As explained in Chapter 1, MWD's supplies have been threatened by a combination of recent developments, and replenishment water has lower priority in times of shortage than water for direct use.

On the supply side of the West Basin management program, the Central and West Basin Water Replenishment District has responded in large measure by developing a local source of replenishment water. It has executed contracts with two Los Angeles County Sanitation Districts reclamation plants to supply reclaimed wastewater for spreading. The locally produced reclaimed wastewater is by far the district's cheapest and most reliable source of replenishment water. As of 1990, untreated MWD replenishment water cost $153.00 per acre-foot, whereas reclaimed water from the Whittier Narrows Reclamation Plant cost $7 per acre-foot, and reclaimed water from the San Jose Creek Reclamation Plant $9.37 per acre-foot (CWBWRD Annual Survey Report, 1990).

The replenishment district generally uses all the reclaimed wastewater it can each year. Limits on the amount of reclaimed wastewater it can spread are imposed by the Regional Water Quality Control Board and the state Department of Health Services. Relatively conservative limits were set initially until the effects of spreading reclaimed water could be studied over a number of years. Recently, the Regional Water Quality Control Board and the Department of Health Services have approved a series of increases in the allowed amounts of reclaimed water for spreading, so the district is now able to use up to 50,000 acre-feet of reclaimed water per year. Increased use of reclaimed water allowed the replenishment district to reduce its pump tax from $70 per acre-foot in fiscal 1988 to $51 per acre-foot in fiscal 1990. The district's replenishment program now relies on the conservation of local runoff, the spreading of reclaimed water, and the spreading of imported MWD water in roughly equal proportions in an average year. In 1991, the West Basin Municipal Water District and the city of Los Angeles signed an agreement to build a $200 million water reclamation facility in El Segundo to take more than 100,000 acre-feet per year of treated wastewater from the Los Angeles Hyperion Treatment Plant and reclaim it for irrigation, industrial use, and basin replenishment.

The saltwater intrusion barriers have also had an unanticipated benefit as an additional source of freshwater replenishment. The water injected in the barriers not only resists seawater encroachment, but eventually moves inland into the basin. At the same time, this inland movement of freshwater from the barriers has created a new problem.

The course of the West Basin Barrier Project ran directly through the area of intruded seawater. When injection began and a freshwater mound formed along the coast, a large area of saltwater was trapped on the inland side of the freshwater mound. This trapped seawater underlies about 10 square miles of the basin and amounts to about 600,000 acre-feet of water, or about 20 percent of the basin's usable storage volume. Pushed by freshwater injected at the barrier, the seawater wedge moves inland at a rate of about 300 feet per year (CWBWRD, 1986: 42). It has reached West Torrance and will reach Torrance by 1995. The replenishment district, the West Basin Municipal Water District, the West Basin Water Association, and the county Department of Public Works studied the problem and discussed ideas for addressing it. The WBMWD has organized a $3.5 million desalination plant project to be located in Torrance to treat the brackish water after its extraction. In the meantime, the county Department of Public Works completed a $10 million upgrading of the injection barriers to prevent seawater from intruding farther.

Analysis

Problems in West Basin have been complex, interrelated, and continuing. A solution worked out for one problem in some instances created or compounded another. It took considerable institutional innovation to organize a governance system that could develop and implement a basin management program to establish and maintain water level patterns that will bring freshwater into the basin while keeping saltwater out. Ideas also were adapted from other southern California basins: users drew heavily on the Raymond Basin adjudication to curtail demand and adopted the pump tax from Orange County as a means of financing replenishment. Adapting these ideas from other basins to the particular circumstances of West Basin, and fitting them together with original arrangements to achieve a coherent basin management program was a substantial achievement in entrepreneurship.

The governance structure in West Basin, however, is not built around a single entrepreneur. Under West Basin's complex polycentric system, decisions are not made by a basin "manager," but by an array of water users and their association, the court, the Southern District office of the Department of Water Resources, the replenishment district, the municipal water district, and the county Department of Public Works. Elements of this governance system interact with and must take into account the actions of other entities that are not part of West Basin's governance structure per se, such as the MWD, the Central Basin Water Association, and the Los Angeles County Sanitation Districts. These polycentric arrangements took time to develop and weave together. In doing so, West Basin water users relied on a rich supporting institutional structure that enabled them to gather the information they needed, to design and create new institutional arrangements, and to implement and adapt a management program.

Eliciting Information

Even the complex problems of West Basin can be perceived relatively clearly today with the benefit of hindsight and all the information about the basin and its problems that has been gathered since 1905. Many of the organized efforts of water users had to be devoted to obtaining that information, however.

The West Basin Survey Committee was established by a small number of West Basin users in 1943 to investigate these problems. The West Basin Ground Water Conservation Group directed its Ways and Means Committee to produce a report on the basin in 1945, which provided not only a common picture of the basin and its conditions, but recommendations for a basin governance system and the first elements of a management program. The West Basin Water Association's rules for voting and assessing dues elicited information from members about groundwater production. During the adjudication, the collection and dissemination of information about groundwater production and total water use were formalized with the designation of the watermaster as monitor for the basin. At the same time, the West Basin Water Association helped secure legislative approval of the Water Recordation Act, which provided information about the groundwater production necessary for the assessment of a pump tax in a nonadjudicated basin.

Institutional Design

In addition to developing their understanding of West Basin water problems, water users designed and established a governance system for the basin to devise and implement a basin management program. These institutional design activities were akin to fitting together the pieces of a puzzle, only without a picture of what the completed puzzle should look like.

Water users created several organizations, including the West Basin Survey Committee, the West Basin Ground Water Conservation Group, the West Basin Water Association, the West Basin Municipal Water District, and the Central and West Basin Water Replenishment District. They took action in Sacramento to amend the Flood Control District Act and the California Water Code, and to pass the Water Recordation Act and the Water Replenishment District Act. They persuaded the Los Angeles County Board of Supervisors to authorize the creation of Flood Control District Conservation Zones I and II. Through the adjudication, they used the court system to develop additional information about the basin and to establish a set of rules governing use of the basin (including the establishment of firm, transferable pumping rights). In establishing the replenishment district, they developed arrangements for taxing groundwater production and augmenting the supply of water to the basin. And in cooperation with the Los Angeles County Flood Control District (now the Department of Public Works), they designed a successful experiment for a freshwater barrier against the sea and developed the institutional arrangements to finance and operate it.

Integration with Other Governance Systems

Governance systems and management programs as complex as those in West Basin do not exist in isolation. Water users in West Basin have had to integrate their institutional arrangements with other sets of rules and organizations, including the MWD, the state, and the county. In addition, the governance system in West Basin is integrated with the governance system devised for the San Gabriel River watershed (see Chapter 7).

Interorganizational arrangements have been developed to keep the number of duplicated functions in the West Basin management program to a minimum. Elements of the governance structure in West Basin rely on each other and on other organizations to perform specialized functions. Some monitor basin conditions and water production and use, for example, and others provide supplemental water supplies or operate physical facilities such as the spreading grounds and the barrier injection wells.

Operation and Performance of the Management Program

West Basin is managed with both demand and supply in mind. There are provisions for limiting pumping, on one hand, and for augmenting water supply and protecting against saltwater intrusion, on the other. West Basin is now part of a conjunctive-use system. Groundwater accounts for only about 15 percent of total water use. The cities, water districts, private water companies, and industrial users who do most of the ground-water pumping in the basin rely on imported water for the greater part of their base supply. West Basin is drawn on for peaking and emergency purposes, as well as a small share of the area's freshwater supply. This system reserves West Basin for its more valuable uses.

Compliance with the management program has been high. Users have observed the pumping limitations and have contributed to basin gover-nance and management through the payment of dues and pump taxes. Groundwater production has remained near or below the total adjudicated right since 1961 (see Table 6.1). Overextractions in excess of the emergency provisions of the judgment have been few and isolated, and no West Basin parties have been subject to sanctions for repeated violations of the pro-visions of the judgment. There have been no sanctionable failures to pay pump taxes or association dues in a timely fashion.

The management program has been effective to date in improving and maintaining basin water conditions. Water elevations in most of the basin have stabilized at the levels to which they recovered after the interim agreement took effect in 1955, with additional increases in some parts of the basin and decreases in the Hawthorne area.

The lowest underground water levels in West Basin today (70–80 feet below sea level) are maintained along the uplift to restore and maintain the water level differential across that divide. The restoration of that dif-ferential suggests that freshwater replenishment to West Basin probably has been restored to the amounts present in the 1940s—approximately 30,000 acre-feet per year.

The basin management program has been operated with low adminis-trative costs. Watermaster service costs have been kept to less than one dollar per acre-foot of water used in West Basin (Table 6.3). Only one dollar of the pump-tax rate per acre-foot shown in Table 6.2 goes to the replenishment district's general fund for administrative expenses; the remainder is used for water purchases.

With respect to fiscal equity, program costs have been allocated among water users primarily on the basis of water production from the basin. Some administrative costs of the municipal water districts and the replen-ishment district, as well as the MWD, have been met from property taxes, which are not as directly related to benefits from the management program. At the same time, the portion of costs paid by these districts from property taxes instead of water sales or pump taxes has decreased over time.

As for distributional equity, the West Basin adjudication undoubtedly drove some smaller pumpers out of groundwater production between 1945 and 1965. There also are fewer parties and active pumpers today than in 1965 (see Table 6.4). As of 1990, there were seventy-three parties to watermaster service, only thirty-two of which are active pumpers. Since

TABLE 6.3
West Basin Watermaster Expenditures, 1956–1990 (dollars)

Year	Total watermaster expenditures	Amount paid by parties	Expenditures per acre-foot of groundwater extractions[a]	Expenditures per acre-foot of total water use[a]
1956	19,722	9,861	0.37	0.12
1957	n.a.	n.a.	n.a.	n.a.
1958	17,114	8,557	0.33	0.09
1959	17,620	8,810	0.34	0.09
1960	16,507	8,254	0.31	0.08
1961	23,123	11,562	0.43	0.11
1962	34,180	17,090	0.58	0.16
1963	24,784	12,392	0.42	0.11
1964	25,403	12,702	0.42	0.11
1965	39,143	19,572	0.66	0.13
1966	39,707	19,854	0.65	0.14
1967	26,644	13,322	0.43	0.09
1968	39,620	19,810	0.64	0.14
1969	26,971	13,486	0.44	0.09
1970	34,810	17,405	0.56	0.11
1971	42,275	21,138	0.69	0.14
1972	47,547	23,774	0.73	0.15
1973	44,947	22,474	0.74	0.15
1974	45,406	22,703	0.83	0.15
1975	49,821	24,911	0.88	0.17
1976	61,819	30,910	1.04	0.20
1977	59,942	29,971	1.00	0.21
1978	68,038	45,585	1.17	0.24
1979	72,942	48,871	1.26	0.25
1980	79,032	52,951	1.38	0.26
1981	103,075	69,060	1.79	0.33
1982	118,998	59,499	2.07	0.39
1983	120,099	60,050	2.09	0.38
1984	127,794	63,897	2.40	0.39
1985	157,101	78,551	3.05	0.48
1986	186,346	93,173	3.41	0.61
1987	189,597	94,799	3.89	0.57
1988	195,713	97,857	4.31	0.59
1989	179,829	89,915	4.04	0.53
1990	208,298	104,149	4.49	0.67

n.a. = Not available.
a. By parties to watermaster service.
SOURCE: West Basin Watermaster Reports, 1956–1990.

TABLE 6.4

West Basin Parties to Watermaster Service, Adjudicated Rights, and Active Pumpers and Nonparties, 1956–1990

Year	Parties to watermaster service[a]	Groundwater rights[a]	Active pumpers	Active nonparties
1956	46	56,963	38	n.a.
1957	44	56,491	39	n.a.
1958	44	56,491	37	n.a.
1959	44	56,527	36	n.a.
1960	43	56,767	34	n.a.
1961	42	56,985	32	n.a.
1962	92	64,042	67	13
1963	95	64,138	64	12
1964	94	64,138	58	11
1965	95	64,138	55	10
1966	79	64,138	48	7
1967	88	64,469	54	5
1968	88	64,469	51	5
1969	82	64,468	49	4
1970	81	64,468	48	4
1971	80	64,468	48	4
1972	79	64,468	45	5
1973	77	64,468	43	5
1974	76	64,468	42	4
1975	76	64,468	40	4
1976	76	64,468	40	4
1977	76	64,468	40	4
1978	76	64,468	40	4
1979	76	64,468	40	4
1980	75	64,468	42	4
1981	74	64,468	35	4
1982	78	64,468	36	3
1983	76	64,468	36	3
1984	74	64,468	37	2
1985	74	64,468	37	2
1986	73	64,468	37	3
1987	73	64,468	35	1
1988	73	64,468	33	1
1989	73	64,468	32	1
1990	73	64,468	32	1

n.a. = Not available.
a. Under Interim Agreement, 1956–1961; under West Basin Judgment, 1962–1990.
SOURCE: West Basin Watermaster Reports, 1956–1990.

the entry of the West Basin judgment, several small West Basin water users have abandoned production, most selling their adjudicated rights to other water users. Other owners of small adjudicated rights retain them but lease them to larger producers. Perhaps surprisingly, the reduction in the number of water rights owners and active pumpers has not markedly increased the concentration of West Basin water production, which was highly concentrated before the adjudication of rights and the curtailment of pumping.[7]

This is not to say that West Basin has been perfectly preserved and managed. Litigation dragged on for sixteen years and cost millions of dollars before a stipulated judgment was finally attained, and even that judgment was appealed. In the time that passed, lasting damage was done to the basin. Today, the trapped seawater wedge and the instability of imported water supplies present West Basin users with new problems to solve. And, despite its demonstrated ability to adapt to changes in basin conditions, the basin management program has not incorporated some new ideas about basin operation. For example, little use is made of West Basin's available storage capacity, so the basin may not be used as efficiently as it could.

Nevertheless, a stable, self-governing system manages West Basin today as part of a conjunctive-use program tied in with imported water supplies. The Department of Water Resources no longer considers the basin to be critically overdrafted, new seawater intrusion has effectively been halted, and replenishment has been placed on a permanent, efficient, and equitable basis. Those achievements represent a long step back from the brink since 1945.

NOTES

1. Because each MWD member agency receives a weighted representation on the district's board in proportion to its share of water sales, MWD directors were not interested in adding members representing relatively tiny constituencies, although they were interested in annexations by larger areas such as the West Basin. MWD Director Franklin Thomas testified before the California Joint Legislative Committee on Water Problems in 1948:

> In general the policy with reference to annexation has been that an area seeking admission should be of such size that it would make a significant addition to the Metropolitan Water District and preferably it should overlie in a comprehensive way an underground water basin. Then annexation of that area would not leave islands or fringes of area, which might benefit by the adoption of the burden by a portion of the area of the cost of the imported water, thereby easing the drain on the underground water so that the area which did not come into the district might, as the term has been used so frequently, "hitchhike" to water without paying its portion of the cost.

2. In the West Basin exchange pool, parties were required to offer the amount of water by which their rights to groundwater exceeded one-half their estimated total water need in the coming fiscal year, provided they could replace that amount from some other source. Water was to be offered at the replacement cost or less. Parties could voluntarily offer more water at a cost not exceeding WBMWD's cost for imported water. Parties without connections to a supplemental supply, or whose needs exceeded their rights plus the availability to them of imported supplies, could request additional pumping rights through the exchange pool. Through its thirty-five years of operation to date, receipts of exchange water rights have averaged about 500 acre-feet per year and have ranged from slightly less than 100 acre-feet to 800 acre-feet in any year. The market for water rights leases has been more active than the exchange pool, largely because such leases negotiated between parties can extend for more than one year and can include the lessor's carryover right as well as the decreed pumping right. In 1990, 184 acre-feet of exchange water were sold, and there were nineteen water rights leases totaling 9,472.4 acre-feet.

3. *Dominguez Water Corporation et al. v. American Plant Growers Association et al.*, Case 668965 in the Superior Court of the State of California in and for the County of Los Angeles.

4. *California Water Service Company et al. v. Edward Sidebotham and Son et al.*, 224 C.A.2d 715, 37 Cal. Rptr. 1 (1964). The Sidebotham appeal charged that the proceedings against it had been void since the death of its attorney in 1951, since it had never filed an appointment of a new attorney and allegedly had not received the written notices filed in the case subsequent to that date. The appellate court refused to overturn the trial judge's evaluation of the evidence, which showed, among other things, that Sidebotham had responded to a 1958 order for payment of its proportion of the referee's expenses, despite the fact that its attorney had been dead for seven years.

5. Hawthorne's "holdout" strategy allowed it temporarily to pump less expensive groundwater and avoid purchasing more expensive imported water, but this short-term benefit came at a long-term price. While water levels elsewhere in the basin rose, levels in the Hawthorne area fell during the interim agreement and after the judgment and appeal; the pumping trough this created in the Hawthorne area is still there. Since it lost its appeal, Hawthorne has had to reduce its extractions and replace them with imported water anyway and continues to experience the longest pumping lifts and highest groundwater production costs in the basin.

6. From 1961 through 1990, the general manager of the replenishment district served also as general manager of the Central Basin Municipal Water District. In 1990, the Replenishment District Board appointed a separate general manager, and in 1991, the Central and West Basin Water Replenishment District moved into its own office in Cerritos.

7. In 1950, there were 232 small pumpers (100 acre-feet per year or less), who accounted for 5 percent of groundwater production, and 19 large producers (1,000 acre-feet per year or more), who accounted for 84 percent of groundwater production. After the West Basin judgment was entered in 1961, there were 16 producers of 1,000 acre-feet or more, who accounted for 87 percent of total production. As of 1990, there were 11 producers of 1,000 acre-feet or more (five oil companies, three private water companies, and three cities), whose groundwater production was 95 percent of the total. The reduction in the number of active pumpers has been more dramatic than the increase in the concentration of West Basin water production.

7

Central Basin
Developing a Polycentric Public Enterprise System in the Middle of a Watershed

As West Basin water users learned, West and Central basins are so closely related that it is nearly impossible to address problems in one without involving the other. Important aspects of collective action and institutional development in Central Basin were instigated by water users in West Basin. Several individuals and water users in West Basin also played a vital role in Central Basin. This does not mean that Central Basin water users did not attempt to develop their own solutions; they tried in particular to avoid an adjudication of water rights within the basin by improving the available supply of water. When an adjudication was deemed necessary, Central Basin users made improvements in the process using lessons learned in Raymond and West basins.

Problems in Central Basin

Like West Basin, Central Basin initially was developed for agriculture, then underwent rapid urbanization during the first half of this century. Today, its 277 square miles contain twenty-three cities and more than a million residents. Population growth and urbanization brought increased groundwater production and wastewater export, and the loss of return flows, water reuse, and natural replenishment. Urbanization left the Los Angeles Forebay paved over and the Los Angeles River channel lined with concrete, eliminating one of the two major recharge zones for Central Basin aquifers and one of the two main stream channels through which water might percolate underground. With the development of the San Gabriel Valley upstream from Central Basin, there was also less water

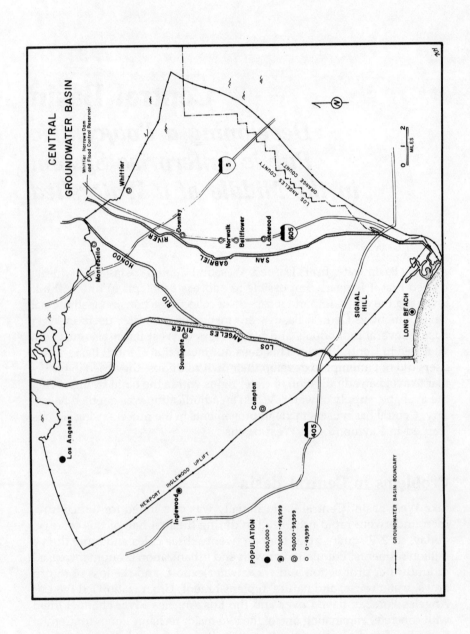

128

flowing out of the valley into the Montebello Forebay, the other important recharge zone for Central Basin aquifers.

Interestingly, the estimated consumptive use of water in Central Basin actually declined during urbanization, from an annual average of 281,193 acre-feet through the 1930s to 265,420 acre-feet through the 1940s and 265,971 acre-feet through the 1950s. Groundwater extractions, however, rose from slightly more than 150,000 acre-feet in the mid-1930s to nearly 300,000 acre-feet at the end of the 1950s (California DWR, 1962: 78). Wastewater exports increased during this period, averaging 112,250 acre-feet per year during the 1930s, 160,930 acre-feet per year during the 1940s, and 235,029 acre-feet per year in the 1950s (California DWR, 1962: 87). The Department of Water Resources calculated that Central Basin's annual overdraft under 1957 conditions was about 103,200 acre-feet, a little less than the difference between wastewater exports in the 1930s and wastewater exports in the 1950s.

Some of the increase in groundwater production in Central Basin can be traced to the Raymond and West Basin adjudications in the 1940s and 1950s. Under Raymond Basin's mutual-prescription solution, if a basin was adjudicated, the size of the users' groundwater rights would depend on their history of production. Water users in Central Basin and elsewhere in southern California responded to this new set of rules by pumping as much water as they could use.

Once begun, overdraft in Central Basin increased rapidly. The overdraft for 1945 was close to 12,270 acre-feet. The annual overdraft in 1950 was 77,000 acre-feet, and in 1960, it was 149,200 acre-feet (CWBWRD, 1960: 19). In the Central Basin pressure area, water levels fell 100 feet through the 1940s and 1950s. By 1960, the accumulated overdraft in Central Basin totaled about one million acre-feet, which meant that 10 percent of the basin's storage capacity had been emptied. Along with West Basin, Central Basin was placed on the state's "critical overdraft" list.

By 1950, groundwater levels in the Alamitos Gap at the southern tip of Central Basin were 30 feet below sea level. Saltwater had begun to flow up the gap into Central Basin (Fossette, 1986: 125). By the spring of 1962, seawater intrusion had proceeded more than 3 miles up Alamitos Gap and threatened to invade Central Basin's major water-bearing aquifers.

Developing an Association and Launching an Investigation

In 1950, there were about 750 well owners in Central Basin, but only a handful of these—fewer than twenty—accounted for most of the groundwater production. These large pumpers were primarily cities and water companies whose continued prosperity depended heavily on a secure supply of water. The first efforts to understand and respond to Central Basin problems began within this small band of water suppliers.

The city of Compton—a water producer in both Central and West basins and a defendant in the West Basin adjudication—invited representatives of Central Basin cities to a meeting in August 1949, along with the executive secretary and the Executive Committee chairman from the West Basin Water Association, and attorney Kenneth Wright. This meeting was the first forum at which the major users of Central Basin water aired their problems. They discussed possibilities that included adjudicating water rights and acquiring an imported water supply. The participants from West Basin offered their insights as "old hands at this sort of thing" (Fossette, 1986: 71).

Shortly after this meeting, the city of Long Beach reported the first evidence of saltwater in Central Basin, on the inland side of the Newport-Inglewood Uplift. This shocked many Central Basin water users, who thought their basin was protected from the sea by the fault zone.

After additional meetings over the next several months, Central Basin water users formed the Central Basin Water Association (CBWA) on June 1, 1950. Structured and funded in much the same way as the West Basin Water Association, the CBWA provided the first forum for investigation, communication, and collective decision making in Central Basin. The CBWA's seventeen original members accounted for about half of Central Basin groundwater extractions. The new association hired Carl Fossette as its executive secretary. He was also the executive secretary of the West Basin Water Association. Serving in both positions for several years, Fossette was "an essential communications link between the two associations" (Ostrom, 1965: 43n).

One of the CBWA's first actions was to ask the State Water Resources Board for an investigation, to get "an authoritative and unbiased statement of water conditions within Central Basin" (Fossette, 1986: 109). The report, published in 1952, indicated that basin water conditions were significantly worse than expected. The association distributed copies of that report to Central Basin water producers immediately.

The first referee report in the West Basin adjudication also appeared in 1952 and was eagerly reviewed by Central Basin users, who gleaned three important lessons from it. First, the referee had recommended a two-thirds reduction in groundwater extractions, which meant that the outcome of adjudication could be much more restrictive than in the Raymond Basin case. Second, it had taken the referee six years to compile its report, and a similarly detailed history of Central Basin was bound to take even longer, since it was larger and had more producers. Third, the entire cost of the investigation was being charged to the parties, which could add hundreds of thousands of dollars to the litigation costs (Fossette, 1986: 107).

Central Basin water producers concluded that they had little to gain and much to lose from adjudication. The strategy of the Central Basin Water Association was to try to avoid an adjudication. Instead, the CBWA decided to try increasing the available water supply in the basin. Members believed that they could avoid an adjudication through this action (Fossette, 1986: 107-8).

Supplemental Supplies and Artificial Replenishment

In the early 1950s, CBWA members believed that if water users had direct service connections to imported water from MWD, they would reduce their pumping (CBWA, 1961: 4). Members did not yet recognize that the sequence of cause and effect ran in the opposite direction. In the Raymond and West basins, it was reduction of pumping that led to increased use of imported water, not the other way around. Nevertheless, association members were correct about the timing of these matters: they first had to acquire imported water supplies before they could achieve any widespread reduction of pumping.

The 1952 investigation by the State Water Resources Board concluded that, at 1950 demand levels, the Central Basin overdraft could be alleviated by importing for direct use up to 77,000 acre-feet of water per year, in addition to supplies already being imported by MWD members Compton, Long Beach, and Los Angeles. Before that much imported water could be acquired, however, the remainder of Central Basin would have to be annexed to MWD. As in West Basin, MWD preferred to annex the entire area rather than the individual communities. The CBWA planned to form a municipal water district for this purpose. With the participation and advice of the "old hands" from West Basin, the CBWA collected signatures on petitions calling for the formation of the Central Basin Municipal Water District (CBMWD).

A special election on the district's formation was set for December 15, 1952, five years after the successful election to form the West Basin Municipal Water District. In Central Basin, a consensus about the need for the district had already been achieved among the cities and other major water users, and there was no organized opposition by the time the election was held. Residents voted 6 to 1 for a Central Basin Municipal Water District.

After the MWD Board approved the annexation of the CBMWD, the issue of annexation was placed before the voters. After another petition drive, another special election was scheduled on annexation to MWD. This election was held on September 21, 1954, and favorable votes prevailed by a 3-to-1 margin. The Central Basin Municipal Water District became the second largest member of MWD, entitled to four directors on the thirty-six-member board. Colorado River water began to flow to Central Basin water suppliers in 1955.

Central Basin water users had access to imported water, but groundwater production continued to expand and basin water supply conditions did not improve. Still hoping to avoid an adjudication and limitation of pumping rights, and spurred by the desire of West Basin water users to increase the freshwater inflow to their basin, Central Basin water users worked during the remainder of the 1950s to further improve their water supplies.

As explained in Chapter 6, the concern of West Basin water users over the loss of freshwater replenishment from Central Basin provided the impetus for a program of artificial replenishment at the Montebello Forebay in Central Basin. The construction of the Whittier Narrows Dam and the Los Angeles County Flood Control District (LACFCD) waterspreading grounds adjacent to the Rio Hondo and the San Gabriel rivers in the forebay area provided the physical facilities for a program of water impoundment, controlled release, and spreading for maximum percolation and minimum waste. Conditions in Central Basin were ripe for such an undertaking; the falling water level in the Central Basin pressure area had created a sharp enough hydraulic gradient to allow groundwater to move rapidly from Montebello Forebay to the pressure area.

The artificial replenishment program was initiated with funds from LACFCD Conservation Zone I. From 1953–54 through 1962–63, the Zone I program purchased and spread more than 500,000 acre-feet of imported water in the Montebello Forebay (Table 7.1). Thereafter, the water associations in Central and West basins jointly designed and secured voter approval for the Central and West Basin Replenishment District to take over the artificial replenishment program.

The artificial replenishment programs of Zone I and the replenishment district significantly offset the loss of freshwater supplies to Central and West basins and reduced the accumulated overdraft in Central Basin from more than 1 million acre-feet in 1960 to less than 600,000 acre-feet in 1965. Despite these measures of effectiveness, however, the association's supply-oriented program remained incomplete.

The San Gabriel River Adjudication

An equally important source of freshwater supply to Central Basin was the flow from the San Gabriel Valley into Central Basin through Whittier Narrows. Central Basin users viewed the loss of this supply as a serious threat to the viability of the basin. Yet, through the 1950s rapid development and population growth in the upper part of the San Gabriel Valley brought increased groundwater production there, while reducing the

TABLE 7.1
Water Spreading at Montebello Forebay, 1954–1990 (acre-feet)

Year	Local runoff	Imported water purchased by LACFCD	Imported water purchased by CWBWRD	Reclaimed water	Makeup water from San Gabriel	CBMWD	Total
1954	n.a.	30,000					n.a.
1955	n.a.	24,800					n.a.
1956	n.a.	54,500					n.a.
1957	n.a.	50,000					n.a.
1958	n.a.	105,100					n.a.
1959	n.a.	54,400					n.a.
1960	n.a.	80,900					n.a.
1961	n.a.	80,800	66,400				n.a.
1962	n.a.	39,500	168,600	1,178			n.a.
1963	4,520	4,800	75,800	12,405			97,525
1964	5,609	0	104,902	13,258			123,769
1965	8,301	75,456	84,672	14,548			182,977
1966	46,779	67,812	53,847	15,056	6,500		189,994
1967	60,971	74,060	10,180	16,224	0		161,435
1968	40,390	66,592	28,799	18,275	0		154,056
1969	104,222	12,529	5,251	13,877	0		135,879
1970	55,440	26,651	43,100	17,158	0		142,349
1971	41,781	46,714	25,420	19,495	0		133,410
1972	23,778	0	34,400	17,543	0		75,721

(continued)

133

TABLE 7.1 (continued)

Year	Local runoff	Imported water purchased by LACFCD	Imported water purchased by CWBWRD	Reclaimed water	Makeup water from San Gabriel	CBMWD	Total
1973	44,835	0	71,900	21,949	0	20,000	158,684
1974	29,796	0	68,200	21,393	0	23,900	143,289
1975	29,665	0	71,900	21,884	0	0	123,449
1976	23,551	0	50,783	21,466	0	0	95,800
1977	26,309	0	9,300	22,863	14,500	6,900	79,872
1978	114,400	0	39,900	19,252	0	0	173,552
1979	68,600	0	66,351	22,457	0	0	157,408
1980	78,633	0	10,200	24,383	10,900	0	124,116
1981	35,120	3,300	28,700	26,109	31,500	0	121,759
1982	39,980	0	29,999	29,418	30,900	0	130,297
1983	102,713	0	39,751	17,035	8,900	0	168,399
1984	70,067	0	1,500	27,784	20,800	0	120,151
1985	47,310	0	40,600	26,998	0	0	114,908
1986	55,256	0	21,500	25,314	0	0	102,070
1987	27,086	0	44,468	34,321	0	0	105,875
1988	37,811	0	40,276	39,946	0	0	118,033
1989	9,575	0	49,052	50,522	0	0	109,149
1990	2,098	0	56,611	47,054	0	0	105,763

n.a. = Not available.
SOURCE: Central Basin Watermaster Reports, 1963–1990.

inflow to Central Basin. Rising water passing from the Main San Gabriel Basin to the Central Basin at Whittier Narrows decreased from an average of 74,557 acre-feet per year during the 1940s to an average of 15,164 acre-feet per year during the 1950s.

In the late 1950s, water users in the Main San Gabriel Basin still had not gained access to a supplemental water supply. This displeased water users in the Lower Area of the San Gabriel River watershed (Central and West basins): The Lower Area had acquired a supplemental water supply by joining MWD at a cost of approximately $76 million, and Lower Area water users resented their Upper Area counterparts for using all of the local water and not paying for a supplemental source (Jorgensen, 1967: 58).

Using a combination of encouragement and threats, Lower Area water users tried to induce those upstream in the Main San Gabriel Basin to follow the process used twice in the Lower Area: namely, to organize a water association, form a municipal water district, annex to MWD, and contribute to the cost of supplying the region with supplemental water. After the Central Basin Municipal Water District annexed to MWD in 1954, the CBWA invited major Upper Area water users to a luncheon meeting in the Upper Area, at the Rainbow Angling Club in Azusa, on January 22, 1955.[1] The meeting was attended by about forty producers, including representatives of the Upper Area cities of Alhambra, Arcadia, Azusa, Covina, Duarte, El Monte, La Puente, Monrovia, Monterey Park, and Sierra Madre.

Robert J. Furlong, mayor of Vernon and CBWA president, presided at the meeting. He and the other CBWA directors shared accounts of their experiences in the Lower Area. They recommended that a discussion be opened between the two areas concerning the water supply of the San Gabriel River system. They recommended that the Upper Area producers form a representative water association to facilitate that discussion. And they hinted that the probable alternative to such action by the Upper Area would be a lawsuit by Lower Area producers to settle the issue of rights to water supplies in the San Gabriel River watershed.

The Upper Area producers formed the Upper San Gabriel Valley Water Association. They, too, hired Carl Fossette as their executive secretary. As described in Chapter 8, they discussed organizing a water district to annex to MWD. Chapter 8 describes their deliberations. Eventually, Lower Area water users grew impatient with the pace of action in the Main San Gabriel Basin. On October 16, 1958, Brennan Thomas, general manager and chief engineer of the Long Beach Water Department and a member of the CBWA Executive Committee, issued a press release through the *Whittier News* announcing that the city of Long Beach intended to seek an injunction to restrain Upper Area pumping.

The Board of Water Commissioners of the city of Long Beach directed Thomas to line up other Lower Area parties as co-plaintiffs for future legal action against the Upper Area. In the Spring of 1959, the city of Compton and the Central Basin Municipal Water District agreed to join Long Beach in an action against the Upper Area producers. The original complaint in the case of *Board of Water Commissioners of the City of Long Beach et al. v. San Gabriel Valley Water Company et al.* was filed in Superior Court on May 12, 1959. It named twenty-five defendants (nine cities, fourteen private water companies, and two county water districts), all of which were known major water producers in the Upper Area, and who accounted for about 75 percent of total water production above Whittier Narrows (Jorgensen, 1967: 65). The complaint alleged that increased water production by these defendants had led to the removal of more water from the Upper Area than was being replenished annually, thereby causing harm to the Lower Area. The plaintiffs requested a determination of the Upper Area parties' water rights, and an injunction restraining them from interfering with the rights of the Lower Area to San Gabriel River system water.[2] The case was assigned to Judge Virgil Airola.

The Upper San Gabriel Valley Water Association had begun to organize a joint defense for Upper Area pumpers even before the complaint was filed. The association's Executive Committee chose a special attorneys' committee composed of existing counsel for many of the Upper Area producers and directed the committee to select a chief counsel. As recalled by a participant observer, the selection of chief counsel reflected the attitude of the defendants on their approach to the case:

> Attorney John B. Surr, of the firm of Surr & Hellyer, San Bernardino, was selected unanimously. Mr. Surr was asked during the interview how many court cases he had won. He replied that he had not won any court cases involving water disputes—all had been settled out of court! (Jorgensen, 1967: 67)

Surr was authorized to appoint engineers and geologists to assist him. Thomas Stetson was selected as consulting engineer for the defendants, and Dr. John F. Mann as consulting geologist. In the Lower Area, the plaintiffs retained the legal services of the firm of Burris and Lagerlof, with Stanley Lagerlof as chief counsel, and the engineering services of Bookman, Edmonston, and Gianelli, with Max Bookman as the principal consulting engineer. Elmer Marliave was consulting geologist.

Once the complaint was filed, settlement negotiations began. Early meetings of the professional staffs for the Lower and Upper areas proved unfruitful. In May 1960, Brennan Thomas suggested that the Upper and Lower areas appoint five-member lay negotiating committees. Thomas became chairman of the plaintiffs' negotiating committee, which also included Hilton Harris from the city of Compton, and Marshall Bowen, Milo Dellman, and Hamilton Robinson representing the Central Basin

Municipal Water District. The Upper San Gabriel Valley Water Association directed Chief Counsel John Surr to appoint a defendants' negotiating committee. Surr appointed David Fiscus from the California Water and Telephone Company (chairman), M. E. Moseley from the San Gabriel Valley Water Company, Ira Calvert from the Azusa Valley Water Company, J. Ercel Cleminson of the city of El Monte, and Alfred W. Jorgensen of the city of Monrovia.

The ten members of the lay negotiating committees were no strangers. As Alfred Jorgensen of the defendants' committee recalled:

> All ten of the committee members were active in the Southern California Water Utilities Association, which met monthly; the American Water Works Association, which had two or three meetings a year; the Irrigation Districts Association which met twice a year; the California Municipal Utilities Association which met annually, as well as other special water organizations.
>
> Many conversations about this lawsuit took place at these meetings. (Jorgensen, 1967: 92–93)

The first joint meeting of the lay negotiating committees occurred on July 6, 1960, at the Central Basin Municipal Water District offices in Downey. That meeting had three important outcomes. First, according to Jorgensen (1967: 70), "both sides earnestly stated that they did desire to reach a settlement and not go to court. Brennan Thomas suggested that a solution might be either a guaranteed flow through the Narrows (which was used ultimately for the basis of settlement), or a production limit on the defendants."

Second, only the lay committee members were present; the professional staffs were not invited. The lay negotiators mutually agreed to leave the lawyers and engineers out of their direct negotiations at joint meetings. Only occasionally were professional staff invited to attend, and then usually with a "speak only when spoken to" condition.

Third, the negotiating committees agreed to have their respective consulting engineers, Bookman and Stetson, perform a joint engineering reconnaissance study. They were instructed to investigate and agree upon engineering data concerning the water flow from the Upper Area to the Lower Area through Whittier Narrows, and quantities of water produced on each side of the Narrows. This early move ensured a shared picture of the interbasin water supply situation. There were no joint negotiating committee meetings from October 1960 through March 1961 while the engineers worked on the study.

The Bookman-Stetson Joint Engineering Reconnaissance Study was completed in March 1961. It "became the basic reference book throughout the negotiations" (Jorgensen, 1967: 76; see also Fossette, 1986: 190). After four more joint negotiating committee meetings in April, May, and June, a breakthrough occurred at a joint meeting on July 11, 1961, where the defendants' committee presented what became known as the "usable water" plan. The defendants proposed to guarantee a certain flow of water to the plaintiffs through Whittier Narrows. The amount initially discussed was 99,900 acre-feet per year, composed of any combination of surface water, subsurface water, and rising water.

There were significant advantages to the usable water plan. First and foremost, it did not require a water rights adjudication among the individual upstream defendants in order to satisfy the downstream plaintiffs' needs. Their needs were met as long as the Lower Area received its guaranteed flow from the Upper Area. Second, the plan was relatively simple and unambiguous. Measurable quantities of water would be promised to the Lower Area, and measurements could be made at just a few locations to determine whether the promised amount had passed through the Narrows. Third, the plan encouraged the Upper Area parties to work with the flood control district to conserve as much stormwater as possible, in order to maximize natural flows to the Lower Area and keep large and unusable storm flows from rushing through the Narrows and wasting to the ocean.

At the next joint meeting, on July 26, the negotiating committee members agreed to the usable water approach. The plaintiffs' committee undertook a first draft of a Statement of Principles for Settlement. The statement was reviewed at the next joint meeting, on September 19, 1961. After a few modifications, on September 26, 1961, the members of the negotiating committees signed the Statement of Principles for Settlement.

Early progress of the negotiating committees had been swift, but they had agreed only to the barest of principles on which to base a settlement. Most of the details remained to be determined. That process consumed another four years. During 1962 and the first half of 1963, the details of determining what would count as usable water, what would count as unusable water, how to calculate the amounts of each, how deficiencies would be made up, who would pay for them, and so on, emerged at meeting after meeting, slowing the negotiating process to a crawl.

The question of making up deficiencies involved the new Upper San Gabriel Valley Municipal Water District (USGVMWD), which covered most of the Main San Gabriel Basin. The USGVMWD had been annexed to MWD, and therefore became an important element in the negotiations between the Upper and Lower areas.

The USGVMWD also had some important connections with the Lower Area. The general manager of the district was Carl Fossette. Fossette was also general manager of the Lower Area co-plaintiff, Central

Basin Municipal Water District, general manager of the West Basin Municipal Water District, general manager of the new Central and West Basin Water Replenishment District, and executive secretary for the West Basin, Central Basin, and Upper San Gabriel Valley Water associations. Ralph Helm was the attorney for the USGVMWD. He was also attorney for the Central Basin Municipal Water District. Thus, Fossette and Helm were employed by both the Lower Area plaintiffs and (most of) the Upper Area defendants throughout the San Gabriel River litigation.

The Upper Area chief counsel, John Surr, invited Carl Fossette to a defendants' negotiating committee meeting on May 29, 1963. At that meeting, the committee agreed to involve Fossette, who worked for and had the trust of both sides, in a new push toward a settlement. At the next joint negotiating committees' meeting, on June 6, the participants agreed to bring Fossette into the negotiations as a neutral and well-regarded middleman. Fossette was assigned to draft a new settlement agreement, incorporating points of agreement reached so far, and devising language to resolve the remaining differences.

Fossette worked on the draft for the remainder of the summer of 1963. At the end of the summer, he suggested—and the negotiating committees agreed to engage in—one "prolonged, uninterrupted effort" to reach an agreement.[3] The committee members and their professional staffs of attorneys, engineers, and geologists went into a "lock-up session." On Wednesday, September 11, 1963, they arrived at the Edgewater Inn in Long Beach and announced their intention to "stay there until we reach agreement" (Fossette, 1986: 191).

The first full day of the session was difficult: Brennan Thomas, chairman of the plaintiffs' negotiating committee, walked out of the afternoon session. Everyone reconvened on the morning of the second day, however, and over the next several days they settled into a pattern, described by Fossette:

> After early breakfasts, talks extended until lunch, followed by sessions until dinner hour. Even at the dinner hour, the participants were busy discussing strategy. This schedule of negotiating and wrestling with problems continued for several days. After each session, it was necessary for Fossette and [secretary Ruth] Getches to redraft and retype the documents which had been amended, or simply reworded, and agreed upon. The next day, fresh documents were supplied for reconsideration. (Fossette, 1986: 191–92)

In the last afternoon session of the fourth day, the negotiating committees agreed to split the difference in the alternative proposals for the amount of the Lower Area's total usable water entitlement. After one more day was spent on the language, the parties and staff left the Edgewater Inn on Sunday, September 15, 1963, with a settlement agreement.

A stipulation for judgment and form of judgment were drafted. Two engineering exhibits were included: a map of Whittier Narrows prepared by Max Bookman's firm, and the information compiled by Bookman and Thomas Stetson during the joint engineering reconnaissance study in 1961. At three joint meetings in January and February 1964, some remaining language problems were resolved and the settlement documents and engineering exhibits were agreed to by March. All documents were agreed upon in final form by the two negotiating committees by the time of a joint meeting held on July 6.

Meetings in the spring and summer of 1964 turned to two issues: the need for a validation lawsuit to ensure the legality of the settlement reached by the parties, and the possibility of setting up a reimbursement contract among the Upper Area parties that would identify the Upper San Gabriel Valley Municipal Water District as the guarantor of "makeup water" to the Lower Area. The upper district was the logical choice, but it did not include all upstream water producers, most notably the cities of Alhambra, Azusa, and Monterey Park. Furthermore, the Lower Area's complaint had not included all Upper Area water producers and water rights owners, and the named defendants were reluctant to commit themselves to delivering usable water to the Lower Area on behalf of the entire Upper Area. Also, the upper district was not authorized to collect a pump tax, which would have been the fairest means of collecting funds from Upper Area water users for makeup water purchases. Finally, since the upper district was not itself a water producer, it had not been named in the plaintiffs' complaint and was not a party to the suit.

On August 24, 1964, the upper district was brought into the Long Beach case as an intervener, by and on behalf of all owners of water rights and land within its boundaries, save for those named defendants who were representing themselves. This allowed commitments between the upper district and the Lower Area to become part of the judgment.

The upper district and the Upper San Gabriel Valley Water Association successfully appealed to the state legislature to give the upper district authority to levy a pump tax on upper district water production. The Municipal Water District Act of 1911 was amended, effective September 17, 1965, to authorize the collection of a pump tax by any municipal water district in the state of California that had an obligation to deliver makeup water to downstream users under the provisions of a court judgment. That amendment, of course, defined a set with only one member: the Upper San Gabriel Valley Municipal Water District.

With these changes, the parties in the Upper Area had worked out a set of institutional arrangements for meeting their obligations to the Lower Area. The parties proceeded quickly to a signing of the settlement documents on September 15, 1964. At the last joint negotiating committee meeting, on December 7, 1964, everyone agreed that the language in the settlement documents was final (Jorgensen, 1967: 103).

Through the winter months of December 1964 and January and February 1965, meetings were held in various locations along the San Gabriel River system to explain the judgment and the various arrangements it entailed. The settlement documents were filed with the Superior Court on February 10, 1965. Judge Airola had been succeeded on the case by Judge Edmund Moor, who signed and entered the stipulated judgment. On May 21, 1965, a validation case, *Central Basin Municipal Water District v. Fossette*, 235 C.A.2d 689, 45 Cal.Rptr. 651 (1965), was filed with the District Court of Appeal. On September 24, 1965, the stipulated judgment in the San Gabriel River adjudication was ruled valid, bringing the proceedings to an end.

More than ten years had passed since the original Azusa meeting called by the Central Basin water users. The San Gabriel River judgment had been reached at the end of about six and a half years of legal proceedings, with a total cost of about $585,000 ($192,000 plaintiffs' costs, and about $392,000 defendants' costs; see Jorgensen, 1967: 57).

The San Gabriel River Judgment

The Long Beach judgment, as it is known, has operated without formal modification since 1965. It has provided a representative structure for self-governance of the San Gabriel River watershed. It also has provided a stable and effective program for managing the allocation of San Gabriel River water supplies between the Upper and Lower areas. In 1975, the San Gabriel River Watermaster reported, "Experience gained under the Judgment indicates that the objectives sought are being realized" (San Gabriel River Watermaster, 1975: 2). After nineteen years of operation, watermaster member Thomas Stetson wrote, "We are now completing the nineteenth water year under the Watermaster service with no significant problems in its operations" (Stetson, 1985: 8).

The San Gabriel River Watermaster

The judgment is administered by the court-appointed San Gabriel River Watermaster. This time, the watermaster was not the Southern District office of the state Department of Water Resources. The water users along the San Gabriel River system wanted to administer their division of the waters themselves. They also wanted a structure that would provide for representation of, and decision making by, both the Upper and Lower areas. They agreed on a three-member watermaster, with a representative chosen by the Upper Area, one chosen by the Lower Area, and one chosen by both areas.

The original San Gabriel River Watermaster was composed of Max Bookman, representing the Lower Area, Thomas Stetson, representing the Upper Area, and M. E. Salsbury, representing both. The selection of these three men lent continuity and stability to the operations under the judgment. Bookman and Stetson had been the Lower Area and Upper Area engineers and were familiar with the physical solution prescribed in the judgment. Salsbury was the chief engineer of the Los Angeles County Flood Control District, which provides most of the data used to determine the quantities of water delivered under the judgment and owns and operates most of the spreading grounds and water impoundment facilities in the Upper Area.[4] Salsbury had extensive knowledge of the San Gabriel River system, as well as the trust and regard of water users above and below Whittier Narrows. The San Gabriel River Watermaster has used the office of Bookman-Edmonston Engineering on North Brand Boulevard in Glendale for a mailing address and meeting place since 1965.

These three original members served together as the San Gabriel River Watermaster for nineteen years. In 1985, M. E. Salsbury (who had long since retired from the flood control district) retired from his watermaster duties and was replaced by Howard Haile, another former chief engineer for the flood control district. In 1986, Max Bookman retired and was replaced by Richard Rhone, an engineer with Bookman's firm, Bookman-Edmonston Engineering. Stetson, Haile, and Rhone continue to serve as the San Gabriel River Watermaster, so the three-person watermaster has had only five members since 1965.

Costs of the San Gabriel River Watermaster are distributed by formula among Upper and Lower area parties. The Upper Area bears half of the costs (billed to the upper district; now reimbursed by the Main San Gabriel Basin Watermaster). The Lower Area bears the other 50 percent, apportioned among the three Lower Area plaintiffs as follows: Central Basin Municipal Water District, 41.2 percent; Long Beach, 7.125 percent; and Compton, 1.675 percent. San Gabriel River Watermaster expenditures for the administration of the Long Beach judgment have ranged from 7 to 33 cents per acre-foot of usable water entitlement since 1965 (Table 7.2).

Usable Water

The amount of usable water to which the Lower Area is entitled under the Long Beach judgment in any given year depends on rainfall conditions

TABLE 7.2
San Gabriel River Watermaster Budget and Expenditures (dollars)

Water year	Budget	Expenditures
1966	15,000.00	11,564.82
1967	12,500.00	10,959.17
1968	14,500.00	9,004.48
1969	14,500.00	9,462.41
1970	14,000.00	13,423.23
1971	13,000.00	13,439.20
1972	13,000.00	6,890.78
1973	12,000.00	6,434.77
1974	12,800.00	9,878.32
1975	14,700.00	14,752.60
1976	17,900.00	16,358.76
1977	22,000.00	20,085.05
1978	22,000.00	17,671.41
1979	23,000.00	25,443.24
1980	27,000.00	18,285.37
1981	32,000.00	22,125.67
1982	40,000.00	23,041.84
1983	31,000.00	27,012.73
1984	36,000.00	36,519.23
1985	40,000.00	35,944.89
1986	44,000.00	40,709.25
1987	48,000.00	32,779.73
1988	48,000.00	44,140.47
1989	52,000.00	47,954.44

SOURCE: San Gabriel River Watermaster Annual Reports.

in the San Gabriel Valley. The Lower Area is entitled to a long-term average of 98,415 acre-feet of usable water per year, which is keyed to the long-term average annual rainfall in the San Gabriel Valley of 18.5 inches. Using those averages as midpoints, annual usable water entitlement amounts were calculated for rainfall amounts from 14.0 to 25.0 inches, in increments of one-tenth of an inch. A table incorporated with the judgment lists the Lower Area entitlement for each rainfall amount. Thus, once the rainfall figure for a given year is arrived at, any party can look up the Lower Area's water entitlement for that year in the table in the judgment.

Rainfall is measured at four precipitation stations in the San Gabriel Valley. The amounts recorded at these four stations are averaged to obtain a rainfall figure for the valley as a whole. To reduce the variability from year to year, that rainfall average is combined with the rainfall averages for the previous nine years to obtain a moving average. This moving average is the rainfall amount used to calculate the Lower Area's usable water entitlement.

This entitlement is compared with the amount actually received across Whittier Narrows from the Upper Area. Usable water is calculated from measurements of surface and subsurface flow, water exported to the Lower Area, replenishment water, reclaimed water, and makeup water and estimates of unusable surface flows and recirculation of measured water. In all, more than twenty measurements and variables are calculated.

The judgment also provides a system of accrued debits and credits to account for differences between the annual entitlements and the amounts of usable water received by the Lower Area. The Upper Area is credited for amounts of usable water received by the Lower Area in excess of the annual entitlement and debited for amounts by which it falls short. Accrued credits are simply maintained "on the books" from year to year until used up by subsequent debits; however, accrued debits must be acted upon by the Upper Area's provision of makeup water to the Lower Area.

Makeup Water

When a water year results in an accrued debit, the Upper Area must supply makeup water to the Lower Area in the following water year. Makeup water must be of usable quality and can consist of surface deliveries of supplemental imported water or reclaimed water. The Upper Area's makeup water obligation for a given water year is either one-third of the accrued debit, or enough to reduce the accrued debit to no more than 25,000 acre-feet, whichever is greater. Lower Area entitlements, usable water received, accrued debits and credits, and makeup water received are shown in Table 7.3. Because of its low cost and high quality compared with other local or imported water sources, reclaimed water from the Whittier Narrows or San Jose Creek reclamation plants is purchased by the Upper Area whenever possible for delivery as makeup water to the Lower Area.

Long-Term Accounting

The judgment also provides for a long-term accounting procedure, which represents an attempt to keep the average amount of usable water supplied to the Lower Area close to the long-term average of 98,415 acre-feet per year. A long-term accounting must be made each fifteen to twenty-five years. The particular year the accounting occurs depends on rainfall conditions.

TABLE 7.3

Lower Area Annual Entitlement, Usable Water, and Makeup Water Received by Lower Area, and Accrued Credit or Debit of Upper Area, 1963–64 through 1988–89 (acre-feet)

Year	Lower Area annual entitlement	Usable water received by Lower Area	Makeup water received by Lower Area	Accrued credit or debit (+/−) of Upper Area
1964	67,200	40,975	0	−26,225
1965	68,000	34,743	13,257	−46,227
1966	70,300	71,272	21,017	−24,238
1967	78,700	80,653	14,735	−7,550
1968	67,200	61,728	7,425	−5,597
1969	84,000	162,228	5,597	+78,228
1970	84,000	86,761	0	+80,989
1971	90,200	71,922	0	+62,711
1972	79,500	53,989	0	+37,080
1973	87,100	78,475	0	+28,455
1974	92,500	57,369	0	−6,676
1975	92,500	58,779	2,834	−37,563
1976	87,100	58,687	14,637	−51,339
1977	78,700	70,116	26,901	−33,022
1978	96,200	153,864	18,002	+42,664
1979[a]	91,500	110,226	0	n.a.
1980	107,600	137,175	21,559[b]	+29,575
1981	105,700	85,917	45,809[b]	+9,792
1982	111,900	94,823	42,180[b]	−7,285
1983	122,200	185,014	32,089[c]	+62,814
1984	118,600	99,725	33,589[b]	+43,939
1985	118,100	90,965	0	+16,804
1986	123,900	119,457	0	+12,361
1987	121,000	63,192	0	−45,477
1988	106,300	85,251	20,477	−46,049
1989	98,800	70,280	21,190	−53,379

a. Lower Area annual entitlement for water year 1979 calculated by the author; not reported in the Watermaster Annual Report, owing to long-term accounting period.

b. Makeup water deliveries made to satisfy long-term accounting requirements; not accounted in calculation of accrued debit or credit, which is based on annual data.

c. Makeup water received by the Lower Area to satisfy long-term accounting requirements amounted to 24,804 acre-feet; the remaining 7,285 acre-feet were received by the Lower Area to satisfy the accrued debit from water year 1981–82.

SOURCE: San Gabriel River Watermaster Annual Reports.

A long-term accounting compares the total usable water received by the Lower Area during the accounting period with the Lower Area's entitlement over that period. If the comparison reveals a deficiency, the Upper Area is obliged to redress that deficiency with additional makeup water over a three-year period. The first long-term accounting was triggered in water year 1978–79, the fifteenth year of operation under the judgment, which also marked the end of a fifteen-year period of near-normal average annual rainfall.[5]

The "California Solution" Meets the "Dismal Science": Adjudication in the Central Basin

By 1961, Central Basin water users had secured access to imported water supplies, instituted an artificial replenishment program, and initiated a lawsuit against Upper Area producers that would guarantee them a minimum annual supply of water from upstream. Although these steps were vital for ensuring the adequacy of basin water supplies, they nevertheless failed to curb the pumping race.

Central Basin water users had pursued the "California solution," which is that the way to solve a water problem is to pour water on it (Trelease, 1980: 865). They learned, however, that water problems are not solved by more water if the cost differences between the local and supplemental supplies still encourage users to exploit the local supplies. The CBWA's actions to augment basin water supplies, especially through the artificial replenishment program, had actually made more groundwater available to pumpers. They weighed the costs of using MWD imports or pumped groundwater, and responded not as had been hoped, but as would be expected. They pumped more groundwater. Indeed, imported water for direct use went largely untouched. Before long, groundwater extractions reached 300,000 acre-feet per year, and Central Basin water suppliers were using less than 20 percent of the capacity of their MWD service connections (Ostrom, 1965: 494).

CBWA members reluctantly conceded that merely increasing water supplies would not overcome the overdraft problem. Some enforceable reduction in pumping would be necessary to restore a supply-demand balance to the basin. Increased use of MWD imports would have to follow an adjudication rather than prevent it (CBWA, 1961: 5–6). In 1961, groundwater conditions in Central Basin reached an all-time low, and the CBWA began the step it had hoped to avoid. The Executive Committee recommended, and the Board of Directors adopted, a resolution expressing the association's support for an adjudication of groundwater rights in Central Basin.

The Central and West Basin Water Replenishment District provided a means for pursuing the adjudication. The replenishment district could initiate the suit as plaintiff and incur the costs of information gathering and the negotiation of a stipulation. Revenues collected by taxing ground-water production could be used to prosecute a legal action against Central Basin pumpers for a determination of rights to future production. This had been anticipated during the process of district formation, as West Basin users sought assurance that increased freshwater replenishment in Central Basin would not simply be pumped out by Central Basin users before it could reach West Basin (California DWR, 1959b: 74; Krieger, 1961: 7).

The replenishment district was also used to develop a consensus that the adjudication was indeed necessary. It was hoped that such a consensus would speed the negotiation process after the suit was initiated. The replenishment district commissioned a report, performed by its consulting engineers, Bookman and Edmonston. The presentation of that report, "Control and Reduction of Ground Water Pumping in the Central Basin," in October 1961, combined with the CBWA's resolution endorsing the adjudication produced the needed consensus. On January 2, 1962, the Central and West Basin Water Replenishment District filed suit against 750 well owners in Central Basin.

The case of *Central and West Basin Water Replenishment District v. Charles E. Adams et al.* was assigned to Superior Court Judge Edmund Moor, also presiding over the San Gabriel River adjudication between the Upper and Lower areas.[6] The complaint stated that as a result of the continued over-draft, water levels were below sea level in approximately 80 percent of Central Basin. The complaint alleged that this lowering of water levels had damaged basin water users through increased costs and growing saltwater intrusion, and that these occurrences resulted from the mutual prescripting of pumpers extracting nonsurplus water from the basin. The relief requested was an adjudication of the respective claims of the defen-dants, control and reduction of groundwater extractions, and retention of jurisdiction by the court for such modifications as might become necessary.

Settlement negotiations were under way even as the suit was being filed. Experience gained during the West Basin adjudication aided the negotiations in Central Basin.

Because the Water Recordation Act of 1955 required groundwater pro-ducers to record and report their groundwater production, the parties were able swiftly to compile a recent history of withdrawals from the basin, from which their relative rights could be ascertained (Fossette, 1986: 182). The CBWA sent a questionnaire to its members requesting data on the quantity of water produced since 1950. These data were verified by the replenishment district engineers, to form the sort of record that would other-wise have been compiled by a court-ordered reference. As a result, a court-appointed reference was avoided altogether in the Central Basin case.

A settlement committee was appointed by the CBWA to draft an interim agreement for the reduction of pumping. The settlement committee worked with the replenishment district's attorney and engineers to develop a formula for calculating the prescriptive rights acquired in the basin. The committee met every month, and presented a draft of an interim agreement to the Central Basin Water Association on May 3, 1962, just four months after the filing of the complaint. Included as Exhibit A were the engineer's verifications of pumping records to date, which already had accounted for 93 percent of the production from the basin. Meetings with water producers began immediately thereafter to explain the interim agreement and encourage them to sign.

Those who signed the interim agreement would be required after October 31, 1962, to reduce their groundwater production to an "agreed pumping allocation" that was 80 percent of their "assumed relative right." The agreement listed the parties' assumed relative rights, based on their groundwater production and imports of water (which under the Water Code were preserved as rights for producers who had substituted imported water for groundwater). The interim agreement would be presented to the court when parties representing 75 percent of the assumed relative rights had signed.

Signatures were collected within a few months from forty-eight parties with approximately 78 percent of the assumed relative rights, who agreed to reduce their pumping to a total of 166,917 acre-feet. The interim agreement was presented to Judge Moor on September 28, 1962. He accepted it, ordered the signers to comply with it, and appointed the Department of Water Resources as watermaster to oversee its operation. The number of parties under watermaster service and their agreed pumping allocations are shown in Table 7.4.

The settlement committee and the attorney for the replenishment district set to work on a stipulation for judgment. A draft was completed by the end of 1964. It involved all defendants, from individual homeowners to the city of Los Angeles. The assumed relative rights totaled 271,650 acre-feet, and the agreed pumping allocation 217,367 acre-feet. The stipulation also provided for an exchange pool and the continuing jurisdiction of the court. The stipulation would be presented to the court once signatures had been obtained from parties with 75 percent of the assumed relative rights.

The stipulation was presented to Judge Moor at a formal hearing on May 7, 1965. A short trial was held in August. On October 11, Judge Moor signed the Central Basin judgment, incorporating all provisions of the stipulation. The judgment became effective at the beginning of the next fiscal year, on October 1, 1966.

Like the West Basin judgment, the Central Basin judgment avoided a statement of the basin's safe yield. A Department of Water Resources estimate of the 1957 safe yield was 137,300 acre-feet (California DWR,

TABLE 7.4

Central Basin Parties to Watermaster Service, Agreed Pumping Allocation, and Active Pumpers and Nonparties, 1963–1990

Year	Parties to watermaster service[a]	Agreed pumping allocation[a]	Active pumpers	Active nonparties
1963	47	166,917	46	NA
1964	78	181,497	74	NA
1965	88	186,620	85	NA
1966	91	189,450	86	NA
1967	508	217,367	462	34
1968	488	217,367	437	38
1969	451	217,367	389	37
1970	402	217,367	368	30
1971	363	217,367	299	25
1972	327	217,367	269	20
1973	312	217,367	247	19
1974	292	217,367	228	19
1975	282	217,367	219	18
1976	279	217,367	202	17
1977	278	217,367	188	22
1978	257	217,367	169	14
1979	226	217,367	222	13
1980	220	217,367	173	14
1981	206	217,367	140	13
1982	198	217,367	135	12
1983	191	217,367	128	11
1984	181	217,367	124	10
1985	184	217,367	116	10
1986	187	217,367	124	10
1987	182	217,367	104	10
1988	179	217,367	100	9
1989	177	217,367	97	7
1990	174	217,367	97	8

NA = Not applicable.
a. Under Interim Agreement, 1963–1966; Under Central Basin Judgment, 1967–1985.
SOURCE: Central Basin Watermaster Reports, 1963–1990.

1962: 121). Reducing pumping to that amount would have required a 50 percent cut, rather than the 20 percent decrease the parties negotiated. Central Basin water users chose instead to attempt to restore a balance to the basin by relying on a combination of a 20 percent reduction in groundwater extractions, a guaranteed minimum inflow from the Upper Area, and the artificial replenishment program.

The Central Basin negotiators placed some provisions in their stipulation that differed from those in West Basin. Exchange pool water prices were calculated by a different formula, which made prices significantly higher in Central Basin. As a result, an active market in water right leases emerged in Central Basin, since lease prices negotiated between lessor and lessee were usually lower than exchange pool prices.[7] Watermaster service costs, too, were allocated differently in Central Basin. In the Raymond and West basins, watermaster service costs are apportioned among the parties according to their groundwater rights, which means, for some parties, issuing invoices and collecting payments that are so small the cost of billing them exceeds the amount collected. In Central Basin, a minimum charge of $5.00 is assessed every party; any remaining watermaster service costs are apportioned among parties according to their agreed pumping allocation. If the total cost of watermaster service works out to less than $5.00 per party, each party is assessed that lesser amount equally.

Central Basin's Fight against the Sea

Water levels in the Central Basin pressure area have recovered significantly, but remain below sea level. In the southern reaches of the basin, water levels are deliberately retained below sea level in order to increase the hydraulic gradient between the Montebello Forebay and the pressure area. Maintaining this gradient facilitates the transmission of water from the spreading grounds through the aquifers to the Newport-Inglewood Uplift. As in West Basin, however, maintaining underground water elevations below sea level in this part of Central Basin leaves the groundwater supply vulnerable to further saltwater encroachment up the Alamitos Gap. In order to take maximum advantage of their replenishment program, Central Basin water users needed to create their own wall against the sea.

The institutional arrangements for constructing a freshwater injection barrier in the Alamitos Gap were patterned after those created by West Basin water users. In West Basin, LACFCD Conservation Zone II was used to fund the extension and operation of the West Basin Barrier Project. Conservation Zone I covered both Central and West basins to begin the artificial replenishment program through spreading in the Montebello Forebay. With the establishment of the replenishment district, Zone I funds were devoted to purchasing replenishment water to offset the accumulated overdraft. In addition, Central Basin water producers used some Zone I funds to construct a barrier project in Alamitos Gap. In reauthorizing Zone I in 1962, the Los Angeles County Board of Supervisors authorized LACFCD to use the funds for the construction of the Alamitos barrier in addition to purchasing replenishment water.

The flood control district was also authorized to negotiate with the Orange County Water District for joint construction and operation of the Alamitos barrier, which straddles the boundary between Los Angeles and Orange counties. During the fiscal 1962–63 and 1963–64, $1.75 million of Zone I funds were used for the construction of the Alamitos barrier. Barrier operation began in 1965, with fourteen injection wells; it has since been expanded to twenty-six wells. Barrier operation remains a joint project of the Los Angeles County Department of Public Works and the Orange County Water District. Since the expiration of Zone I in 1972, all water purchases for injection at Alamitos have been made by the replenishment district and the Orange County Water District. An average of 4,000 acre-feet of treated MWD water has been injected at the Alamitos Barrier each year; this injected water does not significantly replenish the Central or Orange County basins. The barrier has halted saltwater intrusion in Central Basin, protecting the basin from further degradation while allowing the replenishment program to recharge Central and West basins at the highest rate attainable.

Analysis

Central Basin's short history of institutional development has nonetheless been eventful—the basin has been able to recover from "critical overdraft" condition since 1960. Between 1950 and 1965, Central Basin water users adapted experiences of Raymond, West, and Orange County basin users in constituting a governance system for Central Basin and developing a basin management program. Today, Central Basin is governed by a polycentric system that includes the water users and their association, the court, the municipal water district, the replenishment district, the Southern District office of the Department of Water Resources, the county Department of Public Works, and the San Gabriel River Watermaster.

Central Basin water users did not have to design basin governance or management from scratch. Some of them, such as the city of Compton, also pumped from West Basin and had been involved in the development of basin governance and management there. Key personnel—attorneys and engineers, staff of the Department of Water Resources and county Department of Public Works, and individuals such as Carl Fossette (executive secretary of the West Basin, Central Basin, and Upper San Gabriel Valley water associations and general manager of the West Basin,

Central Basin, and Upper San Gabriel Valley municipal water districts as well as the Central and West Basin Water Replenishment District)— brought experienced entrepreneurship to these tasks. In Fossette's words, they were "old hands at this sort of thing."

Central Basin water users, whether old hands or new, also had to develop some new institutional arrangements for a basin with such an unusual combination of physical characteristics (it is a coastal basin with both forebay and pressure zones) and position within the watershed (both upstream and downstream). There are delicate balances to maintain in Central Basin. The ocean must be kept from flowing up Alamitos Gap, but water levels in the pressure zone must be kept low enough to draw water into and through the basin from Montebello Forebay; however, water levels in the pressure zone cannot be kept so low that water no longer moves across the Newport-Inglewood Uplift into West Basin. An important task of the management program here has been to maintain these flow directions and water-level differentials while attempting to return water to storage and raise water levels throughout the basin.

Eliciting Information

One of the Central Basin Water Association's first actions was to sponsor an investigation of Central Basin by the State Water Resources Board and then disseminate its report to all known pumpers in the basin. That 1952 investigation supplied users with a shared picture of the basin and its water supply characteristics. The CBWA, structured like the West Basin Water Association, also elicited information about groundwater production from its members. During the Central Basin adjudication, this information plus information gathered through the 1955 Water Recordation Act provided pumping histories from which rights could be determined.

In the San Gabriel River adjudication, Central Basin and San Gabriel Valley water users agreed first on the institutional means of gathering information about water supplies along the river—the joint engineering reconnaissance study conducted by Max Bookman and Thomas Stetson, which in turn relied heavily on data provided by the county flood control district. Once engineers from the Upper and Lower areas agreed on the water supply data, it was easier for the parties to negotiate a division of the waters. Since the San Gabriel River and Central Basin adjudications were concluded in 1965, information gathering and dissemination have been formalized and performed by their respective watermasters.

Institutional Design

Central Basin water users relied heavily on West Basin experience in designing and implementing their basin governance system and acquiring a supplemental supply of water. Their institutional arrangements consisted of the Central Basin Water Association and the Central Basin Municipal Water District, and together with West Basin users they established Conservation Zone I and the Central and West Basin Water Replenishment District.

Central Basin water users also improved upon the intrabasin adjudication process used in Raymond and West basins and designed the institutional arrangements for the division of San Gabriel River water supplies between the Upper Area and Lower Area. Together with Upper Area water users, they fashioned the usable water and makeup water rules and established the San Gabriel River Watermaster as a multimember, representative body to monitor the implementation of those rules.

The result of these institutional design activities in Central Basin has been a polycentric system of public enterprises. Those enterprises, through their relationships with one another, accomplish replenishment and protection of the basin, monitoring and enforcement of rules governing its use, and the maintenance of delicate balances for a water supply system on which more than a million southern Californians depend.

Integration with Other Governance Systems

Because of its position within the watershed, Central Basin's governance structure and management program are linked with many of the other water resources governance structures in southern California. The governance system for the San Gabriel River watershed developed by the water users' committees during the adjudication is the best example. The Central Basin Municipal Water District, acting as the representative of Central Basin water users, shares the costs and participates in choosing two of the three members of the San Gabriel River Watermaster.

Central Basin governance is also connected with the MWD, the county Department of Public Works, and the Los Angeles County Sanitation Districts. The Central Basin Municipal Water District holds a significant share of seats on the MWD Board of Directors, which sets policies and prices for the importation of Colorado River and northern California water to the San Gabriel River watershed. Decisions about the operation of the county's flood control and water conservation facilities at Whittier Narrows and in the Montebello Forebay are affected by the needs of the Central and West Basin Water Replenishment District's replenishment program, and vice versa. Similarly, the output and pricing of the reclaimed wastewater produced at the sanitation districts' Whittier Narrows and San Jose Creek reclamation plants affect both the replenishment district's program and the delivery of makeup water to the Lower Area under the Long Beach judgment, and vice versa.

Operation and Performance of the Management Program

The management program in Central Basin has operated without significant change since 1965. The court's continuing jurisdiction provides for
alterations, however, and one may be under way at this time. In 1991,
the Central and West Basin Water Replenishment District returned to
Superior Court with a motion to amend the Central Basin judgment to
authorize the directors of the replenishment district to declare a "water
emergency," during which the judgment's provisions allowing the carryover of unused pumping rights would be liberalized to encourage groundwater conservation. The amendments also would raise the ceiling on
carryover rights during normal years to give the parties more flexibility
in deciding between current and future pumping. In addition, the amendments would contain provisions similar to those adopted in West Basin
in 1984 allowing increased pumping by users attempting to remove contaminated groundwater from the basin.

Neither the Central Basin judgment nor these proposed amendments
provide for parties or the overlying districts to store water in Central Basin,
so one valuable characteristic of the resource is not being used under the
current management program. The basin management program has performed well with respect to all other criteria, however. Compliance with
the management program has been high, and it has been effective in
restoring a balance between water supply and demand in the basin.
Groundwater extractions have been restrained to the amounts provided
in the judgment, and it has not yet been necessary to sanction any pumper
for overproduction. Total pumping in Central Basin declined from 248,800
acre-feet in 1962 to 211,600 acre-feet in 1965 and has remained below the
total agreed pumping allocation in every year but two, despite the fact
that total water use in the basin has increased by more than 100,000 acre-
feet since 1965 (see Table 7.5). Parties have increased their use of imported
water to make up the difference; in recent years, imported water use has
surpassed groundwater withdrawals.

With the successful reduction in pumping, combined with the artificial
replenishment program and the guaranteed minimum inflow from upstream, water levels in wells have risen and the accumulated overdraft
has been reduced. By 1964, water elevations in the pressure zone had
recovered to 1950 levels; by 1966, water levels in much of the basin were
roughly equivalent to those of the late 1940s. These increases indicate the
return of almost 700,000 acre-feet of groundwater to storage.

Basin management costs have been kept low and are borne by the
parties roughly according to their share of production from the basin. Central Basin watermaster service costs borne by the parties are shown in
Table 7.6; they have yet to exceed a dollar per acre-foot of water used

TABLE 7.5

Central Basin Water Production and Total Water Use, 1962–1990 (acre-feet)

Year	Groundwater extractions	Imported water	Exported water	Total water use
1962	248,800	52,392	33,479	267,713
1963	225,400	70,079	32,960	262,519
1964	219,100	87,919	31,308	275,711
1965	211,600	87,161	32,767	265,994
1966	222,800	124,414	32,986	314,228
1967	206,591	129,424	35,160	300,855
1968	219,945	140,362	37,011	323,296
1969	213,598	157,496	37,805	333,289
1970	221,998	173,599	40,509	355,088
1971	211,443	190,750	35,822	366,371
1972	215,913	196,619	35,400	377,162
1973	205,503	182,331	34,887	352,947
1974	211,274	187,430	33,853	364,851
1975	213,092	163,802	33,024	343,870
1976	215,979	175,843	33,231	358,591
1977	211,537	147,747	29,593	329,691
1978	196,532	160,392	48,743	308,181
1979	206,990	166,204	32,560	340,634
1980	209,513	168,678	40,081	338,110
1981	210,600	184,794	38,442	356,952
1982	205,576	174,597	38,705	341,467
1983	194,550	178,260	42,261	330,549
1984	194,079	176,150	43,109	327,120
1985	195,349	222,916	47,640	370,625
1986	198,783	215,318	44,137	369,964
1987	194,901	227,529	44,049	378,381
1988	197,870	223,170	43,866	377,172
1989	198,038	205,070	44,401	358,707
1990	194,403	214,888	42,855	366,436

SOURCE: Central Basin Watermaster Reports, 1963–1990.

in the basin. As noted earlier, San Gabriel River watermaster costs (which, unlike the West Basin or Central Basin watermaster costs, are not split with the state) have been even lower (Table 7.2).

Many of the original 750 well owners in the Central Basin adjudication dropped out during the suit; the 1965 Central Basin judgment covered

TABLE 7.6

Central Basin Watermaster Expenditures, 1963–1990 (dollars)

Year	Total watermaster expenditures	Amount paid by parties	Cost of parties per acre-foot of groundwater extractions[a]	Cost to parties per acre-foot of total water use[a]
1963	30,289	15,145	0.18	0.15
1964	45,586	22,793	0.26	0.20
1965	44,135	22,068	0.25	0.20
1966	62,976	31,488	0.33	0.25
1967	57,464	28,732	0.28	0.19
1968	45,123	22,562	0.21	0.14
1969	49,571	24,789	0.23	0.16
1970	66,943	33,472	0.30	0.20
1971	73,462	36,731	0.35	0.21
1972	58,289	29,145	0.27	0.15
1973	69,293	34,647	0.34	0.20
1974	80,895	40,448	0.38	0.22
1975	80,293	40,147	0.38	0.23
1976	84,311	42,156	0.39	0.24
1977	93,352	46,676	0.44	0.28
1978	104,391	69,942	0.53	0.34
1979	111,353	74,607	0.54	0.33
1980	118,695	79,526	0.57	0.35
1981	131,156	87,875	0.62	0.37
1982	181,111	90,556	0.88	0.53
1983	201,026	100,513	1.03	0.61
1984	186,074	93,037	0.96	0.57
1985	226,412	113,206	1.16	0.61
1986	263,094	123,064	1.32	0.71
1987	285,384	142,692	1.46	0.75
1988	260,773	130,387	1.32	0.69
1989	325,609	162,805	1.64	0.91
1990	328,609	164,305	1.69	0.90

a. By parties to Watermaster Service.
SOURCE: Central Basin Watermaster Reports, 1963–1990.

508 parties. As in the Raymond and West basins, the number of parties and active pumpers has declined further since the judgment, although Central Basin retains many more pumpers than either Raymond or West basin. As of 1990, 174 parties were still under watermaster service, of

whom 97 remained active pumpers, including many small ones. Of the 97 active pumpers, the 33 largest (pumping more than 1,000 acre-feet per year) accounted for 93 percent of basin production; this means 64 remain active in the basin but together pump only 7 percent of basin production. Most of the other small water rights owners originally covered by the judgment have sold their rights; the city of Cerritos has been especially active in acquiring pumping rights within the basin.

Central Basin water users learned from the examples provided by water users in other basins, but they also contributed their own examples. The San Gabriel River adjudication initiated by Central Basin users against the Upper Area producers was mirrored in the Santa Ana River watershed. Central Basin users originally hoped to avoid an intrabasin adjudication of rights, because of the time and costs involved. In the end, they recognized that an adjudication would be necessary and focused on improving the process. In just a few years, Central Basin water users adapted the adjudication process in ways that made theirs the fastest and least expensive (per acre-foot) of the basin adjudications. Their handling of the adjudication provided an example for water users in the Main San Gabriel Basin.

NOTES

1. This meeting is vividly recounted by a number of participants and contemporaries. See, for example, Fossette, 1986: 185–86; Jorgensen, 1967: 58–59; and Stetson, 1985: 3.

2. Stetson (1985: 4–5) points out that, technically, the theory of the complaint was mistaken, since increased pumping in the Upper Area had not changed Lower Area water conditions as much as the rapid increase in wastewater exports.

3. Fossette's account (Fossette, 1986: 191) merely states that "the two committees decided" on the need for a final effort. Jorgensen (1967: 98), a member of the defendants' negotiating committee, recalls that the suggestion was Fossette's.

4. The county flood control district (now part of the Los Angeles County Department of Public Works) plays an important role in the successful operation of the Long Beach judgment. The department collects at least seven types of data that are used in administering the judgment. The San Gabriel River Watermaster's annual reports to the parties and the public "are based largely on data compiled and recorded by the Los Angeles County Flood Control District." (Stetson, 1985: 7). Also, the Upper Area uses county flood control channels and spreading grounds to deliver required makeup water to the Lower Area under the judgment.

5. The Upper and Lower area parties executed a memorandum of understanding in 1982 that does not modify the judgment's requirements, but allows more flexible means for the Upper Area parties to meet those requirements. The

memorandum was developed in response to problems that arose after the first long-term accounting.

The first long-term accounting by the San Gabriel River Watermaster revealed a deficiency in the amount of water received by the Lower Area of nearly 170,000 acre-feet. This quantity of additional supplemental water was not immediately available, however, and even later was extremely expensive to acquire. In addition, in one of the years during which the Upper Area attempted to deliver long-term accounting water to the Lower Area, the county flood control district was reconstructing the channels in the Whittier Narrows area, making the delivery of the water physically impossible.

In light of these difficulties, the parties developed a number of "practical accommodations" for adhering to the requirements of the judgment. The 1982 memorandum of understanding commits the Upper Area to attempt to protect the Lower Area's rights in years of shortages in replenishment water, allows the Upper Area to make payments to the Lower Area in lieu of water deliveries in years when it is impossible to deliver makeup water, and allows the Upper Area to pay for reclaimed water as makeup water up to the limits in the judgment, provided excess capacity exists in the Whittier Narrows reclamation plant.

6. Case 786656 in the Superior Court of the State of California in and for the County of Los Angeles.

7. In 1985, the Central Basin judgment was modified to direct the watermaster to fill exchange pool requests from voluntary offers first, whereas the original judgment instructed the watermaster to fill requests from mandatory offers first. A very active market for water-rights leases continues to operate in Central Basin. In water year 1989–90, there were sixty-nine water rights leases totaling 17,527 acre-feet.

8

Main San Gabriel Basin
Adaptation, Innovation, and Learning

Like water users in many other areas, those in the Main San Gabriel Basin adapted institutional arrangements from other basins to their own needs. They began with basin water users' associations and municipal water districts and then turned to supplemental water supplies and artificial replenishment, a pump tax, and adjudication and limitation of ground-water rights. They also designed new arrangements, some of which have since been adopted in other basins. With respect to basin governance, they set up the multimember San Gabriel River Watermaster, along with Central Basin water users, and created the multimember Main San Gabriel Basin Watermaster to govern their own basin. With respect to basin management, they agreed on a single measure of basin water supply conditions, combined rights to surface water diversions and groundwater extractions, based allowable extractions on a variable "operating safe yield," and provided for the use of the basin's valuable underground storage space.

Problems in the Main San Gabriel Basin

Groundwater problems appeared somewhat later in the Main San Gabriel Basin, because of its upstream position and its more recent urbanization (Fossette, 1986: 4–5). A serious and continuing groundwater overdraft did not occur until the 1945–65 drought, and it was during this period that the basin also began to urbanize (see Table 8.1). Earlier water disputes and institutional development in the basin revolved around the surface flows of the San Gabriel River (see Chapter 4).

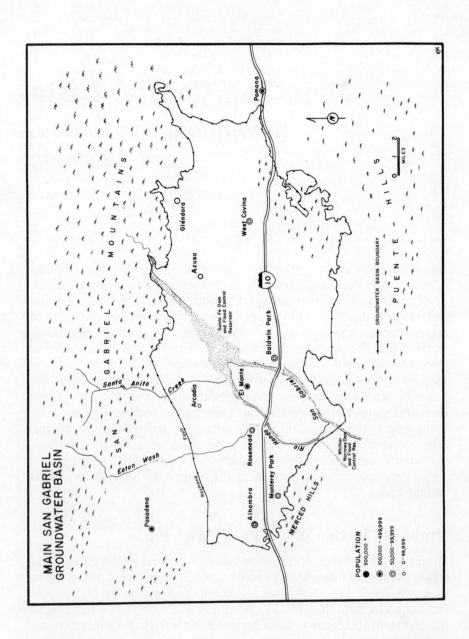

MAIN SAN GABRIEL
GROUNDWATER BASIN

SAN GABRIEL MOUNTAINS

PUENTE HILLS

MERCED HILLS

Pomona

Glendora

West Covina

Azusa

Santa Fe Dam
and Flood Control
Reservoir

Baldwin Park

Santa Anita Creek

Arcadia

El Monte

Eaton Wash

Rosemead

Monterey Park

Alhambra

Pasadena

Rio Hondo

San Gabriel River

Whittier Narrows Dam
and Flood Control Res.

10

GROUNDWATER BASIN BOUNDARY

N

0 1 2
MILES

POPULATION
● 500,000 +
◉ 100,000 - 499,999
◎ 50,000 - 99,999
○ 0 - 49,999

TABLE 8.1

Groundwater Production and Overdraft in the Main San Gabriel Basin, 1934–1972 (acre-feet)

Year	Groundwater extractions	Estimated water supply surplus or deficiency	Estimated change in groundwater in storage	Annual overdraft	Accumulated overdraft
1934	160,600	−36,300	−18,000		
1935	119,800	+79,700	+118,100		
1936	153,300	−48,900	−79,000		
1937	146,300	+156,600	+181,100		
1938	153,500	+130,600	+94,500		
1939	129,300	−26,200	−2,900		
1940	135,700	−52,400	−39,400		
1941	125,600	+250,000	+228,100		
1942	134,900	−85,800	−139,400		
1943	138,800	+106,500	+114,600		
1944	132,100	+38,800	+26,300		
1945	145,100	−42,100	−60,500		
1946	148,300	−46,700	−55,500		
1947	146,300	−45,700	−98,800		
1948	160,000	−116,600	−89,900		
1949	175,300	−124,300	−108,700		
1950	170,900	−94,400	−102,200		
1951	177,800	−126,400	−103,800		
1952	151,000	+119,300	+176,100		
1953	168,600	−65,000	−110,400		
1954	173,300	−19,600	−13,900		
1955	168,200	−71,800	−22,500		
1956	166,500	−19,100	−57,200		
1957	164,700	−55,400	−40,500		
1958	181,200	+196,000	+248,500		
1959	200,495	−92,500	−142,300		
1960	196,260	−111,000	−105,100		
1961	215,828	NA	NA		
1962	198,757	NA	NA		
1964	213,471	NA	NA		
1965	208,846	NA	−24,000	69,400	912,000
1966	217,298	NA	+194,000	0	779,400
1967	217,506	NA	+230,000	0	532,529
1968	228,748	NA	−69,000	91,000	709,000
1969	209,436	NA	+224,000	0	398,000
1970	226,502	NA	−130,000	130,000	525,000

(continued)

161

TABLE 8.1 (continued)

Year	Groundwater extractions	Estimated water supply surplus or deficiency	Estimated change in groundwater in storage	Annual overdraft	Accumulated overdraft
1971	223,487	NA	−99,400	99,400	643,000
1972	247,687	NA	−154,100	157,000	825,000

NA = Not applicable.
SOURCE: The figures in the first three columns are from California Department of Water Resources, Bulletin 104-2, Appendix A (1966b). The figures in the last two columns are from Stetson (1966–1973); there are no Stetson data before 1965.

During one of those disputes, however, water users and agencies agreed on an institutional arrangement that marked an important step for monitoring groundwater conditions in the basin: they established the Baldwin Park Key Well in the center of the Main San Gabriel Basin. Pasadena, the San Gabriel Valley Protective Association, the Los Angeles County Flood Control District (LACFCD), the U.S. Geological Survey, and the U.S. Department of Agriculture's Bureau of Agricultural Engineering collaborated on this project during the resolution of the controversy over Pasadena's attempt to build a dam in San Gabriel Canyon in the early 1930s.

An agreement signed by these parties on December 7, 1931, expressed their interest ''in increasing the storage of underground waters in the San Gabriel Valley.'' The San Gabriel Valley Protective Association furnished the plot of ground for the well, transferring title to the flood control district. Pasadena committed up to $1,000 for the cost of the well. The flood control district agreed to contract out and oversee well construction and to pay any remaining construction costs. The U.S. Geological Survey agreed to equip the well with accurate measuring devices and to keep the water level records and distribute them to the parties to the agreement. The bureau agreed to install equipment at the well site for measuring evaporation ''and other data having a bearing upon the water supply in said area.'' The Baldwin Park Key Well has provided Main San Gabriel Basin water users and agencies with a simple shared picture of basin conditions for sixty years.

As part of the endeavor to increase the groundwater supply in the basin, the LACFCD constructed several channel improvements and water impoundments during the 1930s and 1940s, including spreading grounds into which conserved flood flows could be diverted to recharge the groundwater supply. With above-normal rainfall through the 1930s and early 1940s, water elevations in Main San Gabriel Basin wells reached record levels by 1943–44. Near Whittier Narrows, the water table rose sufficiently near the land surface to cause swampy conditions (Koebig and Koebig, 1961: S-3).

Groundwater supply problems began in earnest after 1945. The drought caused surface water supplies in the Main San Gabriel Basin virtually to disappear. The drought also coincided with the period of most intensive urbanization of the San Gabriel Valley. From 1940 to 1960, the number of people living in the valley more than tripled, from 192,100 to 690,200. Urban and suburban land uses rose from 30,000 acres in 1942 to 105,100 acres in 1960, while agricultural acreage dropped from 52,000 acres to 15,800.[1] The valley developed an active water supply industry, and by 1960, sixty-three large agencies were pumping from the Main San Gabriel Basin, including an increased number of public water districts and municipalities, as well as private and mutual water companies (California DWR, 1966b: 17).

While consumptive use of water within the basin remained fairly stable, wastewater exports and groundwater extractions increased rapidly. Groundwater extractions rose from 150,000 acre-feet or less per year through 1944 to 175,000 acre-feet by 1949, 200,000 acre-feet by 1959, and 215,000 acre-feet in 1961 (Table 8.1). The basin, which supplied 90 percent of the water used in the area, lost groundwater from storage nearly every year. Underground water levels dropped at an average rate of 6 feet per year. The Baldwin Park Key Well dropped from a peak of 325 feet above sea level in 1944 to 209 feet above sea level in 1965. In its 1966 report, the California Department of Water Resources described the Main San Gabriel Basin as "one of the most heavily developed" in California (California DWR, 1966b: 7).

The San Gabriel River Adjudication and the Acquisition of a Supplemental Water Supply

As pointed out in Chapter 7, these changes in the Main San Gabriel Basin reduced the flow of freshwater through Whittier Narrows to the Central Basin. Central Basin water users saw little prospect for improvement as long as the population and groundwater extractions in the Main San Gabriel Basin continued to increase and the area remained without access to additional sources of water supply. In 1954 it was the only part of the San Gabriel River watershed that had not annexed to Metropolitan Water District of Southern California (MWD) to obtain access to Colorado River water (except for its easternmost section, which was included in the Pomona Valley Municipal Water District). Pressure from Central Basin contributed to the development of a water users' association in the Main San Gabriel Basin and eventually, access to supplemental water supplies.

The Upper San Gabriel Valley Water Association

At the Azusa meeting of Central and Main San Gabriel basin water users in January 1955, Mayor Robert Furlong of the Central Basin city of Vernon nominated Mayor Robert Radford of the Main San Gabriel Basin city of Monrovia to try to form a water users' association for the Upper Area. Radford, a "valley water authority for 30 years" (Fossette, 1986: 186) recruited eight other men to make up a formation committee.

The committee called a general meeting of Upper Area water users at Arcadia City Hall on June 15, 1955. Representatives attended from eleven cities, thirty-seven private and mutual water companies, and two county water districts (Jorgensen, 1967: 59). They voted to form an association patterned after the water associations in Central and West basins and invited Carl Fossette to serve as its executive secretary. The Upper San Gabriel Valley Water Association (USGVWA) was officially formed on January 16, 1956, with seventy members representing the vast majority of basin water production. This association provided the first governance structure for groundwater users in the Main San Gabriel Basin.

The USGVWA established a program for the regular collection of water production data from members, a step made considerably easier by the 1955 Water Recordation Act. The association also distributed a newly published LACFCD study of basin water supplies. At a USGVWA meeting on July 25, 1957, Mayor Radford spoke about the falling water levels in the basin and about the options for redressing the situation, including the possibility of acquiring access to imported water as a supplemental water supply source. A resolution was adopted to study the feasibility of forming a municipal water district. At the next meeting, on August 19, an even stronger resolution was adopted ordering the preparation of a plan for the formation of a municipal water district to obtain supplemental water for the basin. At the November meeting, USGVWA members agreed to assess themselves to create a $20,000 campaign fund for a special election to form a municipal water district (Jorgensen, 1967: 62).

The San Gabriel Valley Municipal Water District

The majority of USGVWA members had pushed rapidly toward a municipal water district in the latter half of 1957, but without a consensus. Four Upper Area cities—Alhambra, Azusa, Monterey Park, and Sierra Madre—objected strenuously to annexing to MWD. Their opposition was potentially significant. Alhambra, Azusa, and Monterey Park were major Main San Gabriel Basin pumpers. (Sierra Madre overlies and pumps from the Raymond Basin, and had avoided being included in the Foothill Municipal Water District.)

As movement toward a municipal water district and annexation to MWD quickened, representatives of these four cities met in secret to review their opposition and their alternatives. In September 1958, the four cities announced their joint decision to secede from the USGVWA, to oppose any attempt to include them in the proposed municipal water district, to form instead their own municipal water district, and to provide for their own future water supply. In particular, they contemplated the planned importation of northern California water through the State Water Project as an alternative to MWD; State Project water was expected to reach the area by about 1970.

The other USGVWA members were stunned and disturbed. The Executive Committee sent a letter to the four cities on October 6, 1958, expressing disappointment and regret at their announcement, as well as the association's view that a single municipal water district for the remaining Upper Area water users would be most practical and economical. The committee expressed its belief that the cities' announcement had increased the likelihood of litigation over San Gabriel River system water rights, and urged them to reconsider their decision (Jorgensen, 1967: 63).

Lower Area reaction followed within days. On October 16, Brennan Thomas of the Long Beach Water Department and Central Basin Water Association issued a press release noting that it appeared to the Lower Area that the Upper Area was not in agreement on the question of whether to form a water district and annex to MWD. He urged the four cities to reconsider their stated intentions and announced that Long Beach would go to court if necessary to restrain Upper Area pumping.

Efforts to persuade the four cities to change their position failed. They proceeded with a special election, and on July 29, 1959, a majority of voters in the four cities agreed to the formation of the San Gabriel Valley Municipal Water District (SGVMWD). The SGVMWD lies in three non-contiguous parcels on the western (Alhambra/Monterey Park), northwest (Sierra Madre), and northern (Azusa) sides of the Main San Gabriel Basin. Three years later, in November 1962, the SGVMWD Board of Directors signed a contract with the California Department of Water Resources for 25,000 acre-feet per year of northern California water from the State Water Project (the contract amount was later increased to 28,800 acre-feet per year). The SGVMWD has maintained its policy of not annexing to MWD.

The Upper San Gabriel Valley Municipal Water District

In response to these developments, the Lower Area went to court, producing the San Gabriel River adjudication described in Chapter 7. The lawsuit, and the incorporation of the SGVMWD out of three pieces of the Main San Gabriel Basin, lent urgency to the USGVWA's plan to form a municipal water district for the rest of the basin.

Boundaries were established, petition signatures were collected, and a special election was set for December 8, 1959, over the remainder of the Main San Gabriel Basin plus some communities on the Raymond Basin–Main San Gabriel Basin boundary that were not in either the Foothill Municipal Water District or the San Gabriel Valley Municipal Water District. Formation of the Upper San Gabriel Valley Municipal Water District (USGVMWD) was approved overwhelmingly, 14,443 to 2,901. The district is governed by a five-member board of directors elected from divisions within the district and maintains an office in El Monte. At the first board meeting on January 11, 1960, the directors appointed Carl Fossette as general manager and Ralph Helm as attorney for the district.

The USGVMWD board commissioned a study of water supply conditions and the projected need for supplemental water. The report to the district in 1961 by Koebig and Koebig, Inc., contained mixed signals. It documented the falling water levels and observed that they had reached "troublesome" levels in some areas. Projections of water demands through 1990 indicated that supplemental water would be urgently needed. Adding in a projection of the Upper Area's water obligation to the Lower Area as a result of the San Gabriel River suit, the report predicted that an additional 131,000 acre-feet of water per year would be needed in the USGVMWD by 1990, and an additional 202,000 acre-feet per year in the Main San Gabriel Basin as a whole (Koebig and Koebig, 1961: S-5; Berlien, 1988: 3).

At the same time, the report estimated the basin's safe yield based on 1960 conditions at 205,000 acre-feet per year and suggested that the sole culprit behind the falling water levels was the drought:

> A hydrologic balance of the various items of water supply and water disposal affecting the valley in 1960 showed that if the area were now experiencing long-time precipitation and runoff; that is, if the "normal" water supply conditions were in effect at present instead of the drought, then the Valley would be experiencing no appreciable surplus or deficiency of water. (Koebig and Koebig, 1961: S-4)

That conclusion provided hope that the end of the drought could bring recovery to the basin. This was encouraging, because water users did not want to be forced into an adjudication and limitation of water rights in the Main San Gabriel Basin. After hearing the conclusion, users were all the more eager to negotiate the interbasin adjudication to a successful conclusion without embarking upon an intrabasin adjudication.

In the view of the USGVMWD board, a contract with the State Water Project or annexation to MWD were the real alternatives for a supplemental water supply. The board then contracted with the engineering firm of Stetson, Strauss, and Dresselhaus for a report on the most practical and economic means of obtaining supplemental water. The firm found northern California water from the State Water Project preferable in quality and future reliability, but MWD water preferable in immediate availability and accessibility (the MWD middle feeder runs through the USGVMWD, and MWD's planned upper feeder would run along the district's northern boundary). Once MWD contracted with the state for a share of northern California water, so that both northern California and Colorado River water would be available from MWD, the conclusion seemed clear. The final report of Stetson, Strauss, and Dresselhaus, received in October 1962, recommended that USGVMWD annex to MWD.

The USGVWA and USGVMWD campaigned to persuade residents to support annexation to MWD. At a special election on March 12, 1963, voters approved annexation to MWD by a vote of 27,506 to 6,476 (Berlien, 1988: 4). By 1965, the USGVMWD had begun an artificial replenishment program, spreading MWD Colorado River water through a contract with the Los Angeles County Flood Control District at its spreading grounds in the basin. A supply-enhancement component of a basin management program had been established in the Main San Gabriel Basin.

The Main San Gabriel Basin Adjudication

The Long Beach judgment ending the San Gabriel River adjudication was finalized and validated in September 1965. Its "usable water" approach had allowed Upper and Lower area water users to reach an accord concerning the San Gabriel River system without adjudicating the water rights of the Main San Gabriel Basin defendants.

Also in September 1965, however, the water level in the Baldwin Park Key Well reached a record low of 209 feet above sea level. In 1966, a Department of Water Resources report estimated the Main San Gabriel Basin's safe yield under 1960 conditions to be 166,100 acre-feet per year, nearly 40,000 acre-feet less than the 1961 Koebig and Koebig estimate. In a 1966 report to the USGVWA, Thomas Stetson estimated that total water demand in the basin exceeded total water supply (including both natural replenishment and imported water) by 40,000 acre-feet per year (Stetson, 1966: I-5). He further reported that overdrafting of the basin had probably begun in or around 1950 and probably had been continuous since 1953.

These discouraging reports coincided with the end of the twenty-year drought cycle. By then, however, the race to the pumphouse was on in earnest. One certainly would not have noticed the end of the drought by looking at groundwater extractions in the Main San Gabriel Basin, which continued to rise (Table 8.1). As water users scrambled to maximize their potential rights, water levels dropped again. From 1968–69 through 1971–72, underground water elevations fell 10 to 20 feet per year. Enhanced supplies were not enough; demand upon the basin would have to be reduced. Once again, the USGVWA, the USGVMWD, and key personnel such as Stetson, Fossette, and Helm, led the effort to find a solution.

"A Basin Particularly Suited to Management"

Although basin conditions deteriorated rapidly through the 1960s, the task of restoration was made somewhat easier by the fact that Main San Gabriel Basin was "particularly suited to management" (Lipson, 1978: 46). As an unconfined basin bisected by a major stream channel, which by 1960 contained fourteen spreading grounds, it was especially well situated for artificial replenishment. Furthermore, a significant amount of the basin's storage space had been dewatered as a result of the accumulated overdraft, leaving available storage capacity for water storage and low-cost water transmission.

In 1962, Thomas Stetson suggested that the basin already was being used in this manner:

> The ground water basin underlying San Gabriel Valley has been used for many years as a water storage reservoir and as a water transmission system. As quantities of recharge and extraction have varied, water levels have fluctuated in order to balance the difference between inflow and outflow with change in ground water storage. In other words, the ground water basin has been "operated" in a manner very similar to a surface reservoir. The main difference is that the ground water basin has been operated unintentionally to a far greater extent than are most surface reservoirs. As more expensive supplemental water is brought into San Gabriel Valley it will be important that the basin be operated more intentionally than in the past so that neither the local water nor the supplemental water is wasted from the area. The operation of the basin is also important to downstream users. (Stetson, Strauss, and Dresselhaus, 1962a: VI-1)

The Position of the Upper District in the Aftermath of the San Gabriel River Adjudication

Shifting to intentional operation of the basin in conjunction with local and imported surface water supplies would require a basin governance structure that could assess information about basin conditions and take collective decisions about water use and water storage. Could the USGVMWD provide such governance? In the aftermath of the San Gabriel River adjudication, attention turned to the USGVMWD's situation within the Main San Gabriel Basin. Several perceived problems related to the fact that the district did not cover the entire basin:

- Compliance with the Long Beach judgment increased USGVMWD's administrative workload, yet its administrative costs were supported by property taxes paid by property owners within its territory, and not by property owners within the San Gabriel Valley Municipal Water District or the Pomona Valley Municipal Water District.

- Although the upper district was given pump tax authority by a 1965 amendment to the Municipal Water District Act, the tax could be applied only to pumping within its territory and not to pumping by other basin water producers.

- The pump tax USGVMWD was authorized to levy was a "gross pump tax," assessed equally against all water production within its territory. This was perceived as unfair by water users who had not increased their pumping. They felt that the water problems in the basin and the Lower Area had been caused to a greater degree by water users who had been increasing production from the basin. In this view, a fairer pump tax would be assessed against pumping in excess of the basin's safe yield, matching assignment of costs with the imposition of harm.

- Supplemental water supplies are not unlimited; any MWD member or State Water Project contractor has available to it in any year only a certain quantity of imported water. Some considered it unfair to ask the USGVMWD to use its imported water supplies to meet obligations of the Upper Area under the Long Beach judgment while the other two municipal water districts in the basin were allowed to use their supplemental water supplies for direct delivery to resident water consumers.

- The fact that USGVMWD did not cover the whole basin also led some to question whether it was able to function as a policy-making organization for the whole basin. If there were to be such an entity in Main San Gabriel Basin, it would have to be created.

People began to think that the Main San Gabriel Basin needed a governance structure with the authority to develop and implement a basinwide management program. (Fossette, 1986: 194).

Designing Basin Governance and Management

In light of the problems facing USGVMWD, the USGVWA commissioned consulting engineer Stetson to review water production within the basin and recommend a management program, while the association members weighed organizational and institutional alternatives for a basin governance structure.

As in the San Gabriel River adjudication, water users in the Main San Gabriel Basin did not want to rely on the state as watermaster. They preferred a local monitor, but they did not want to lay yet another special district over the Main San Gabriel Basin. This attitude, combined with the objections to using a gross pump tax for financing, largely ruled out the replenishment-district approach of the Central and West basins and Orange County. Instead, the idea of a multimember, representative watermaster like the San Gabriel River Watermaster emerged as the desired alternative. A local watermaster made up of water users' representatives could provide a basinwide decision-making and monitoring mechanism without creating another special water district (Stetson, 1982: 9).

Stetson's May 1966 proposal recommended managing the basin to a "safe-yield" status, using a mutual-prescription determination of water production rights as had been done in the Raymond, West, and Central basins. USGVWA members were not completely averse to the idea: they wanted to protect the value of water rights, and they wanted to assign the costs of acquiring supplemental water and replenishing the basin on pumping in excess of the basin's safe yield. Those goals seemed almost certainly to require an adjudication.

At the same time, they wanted to avoid the expense and delay involved in such an adjudication. The recently completed Central Basin adjudication seemed encouraging. A "friendly" basin adjudication could be conducted more quickly and less expensively by working out a pre-negotiated settlement, and by avoiding the appointment of an outside referee. The 1955 Water Recordation Act and the production data collected by the association would help. Decade-long water production histories could be assembled for the larger water producers.

Stetson's report already included production data supplied by water users from 1953 through 1964. Total production exceeded the estimated annual basin safe yield of 175,000 acre-feet. Stetson therefore recommended assigning each water rights owner "adjusted rights" totaling that amount. These adjusted rights would be a little more than 5 percent less than the probable prescriptive rights, and about 20 percent lower than 1964 production (Stetson, 1966: V-5).

The USGVWA and its Executive Committee and Water Users' Committee drafted a statement titled "Principles of Management of the San Gabriel Basin as an Adjudicated Area," which was redrafted nineteen times from mid-1966 through mid-1967. On August 9, 1967, the statement was brought before the full association for a vote. There were two abstentions, but no one voted against it (Stetson, 1985: 8). Believing a negotiated settlement to be close, the association asked the USGVMWD to act as plaintiff and file a complaint to begin an adjudication of the water rights within the Main San Gabriel Basin. Attorney Helm filed the complaint on January 2, 1968, beginning the case of *Upper San Gabriel Valley Municipal Water District v. City of Alhambra et al.*[2] The original complaint named 132 defendants; subsequent amendments brought the total number of named parties to 190.

As in the San Gabriel River adjudication, early optimism and a quick agreement on principles were followed by five years of negotiation over details.[3] Not long after the complaint was filed, the subject of surface water diversions arose. Stetson and others had urged that the influence of surface water supplies and diversions on groundwater conditions in the Main San Gabriel Basin be included by adjudicating "rights to water production in the Basin and Relevant Watershed." The complaint was amended on August 14, 1970, to add surface water diversions. Although the total number of surface diverters was small, including them increased the complexity of the negotiations.

Verifying production data also impeded quick progress. Recordation Act filings did not cover some producers (particularly the many smaller producers), and in several cases production reports were unreliable. As in the Central Basin adjudication, production data had to be verified, a task assigned to Stetson. Parties were unexpectedly slow in submitting data and it was not until 1971 that he could announce verification was "virtually completed."

Another delay arose because the SGVMWD cities of Alhambra, Azusa, and Monterey Park had no access to supplemental water supplies until State Water Project deliveries began in 1972. Until they could be sure of their supplies, they were reluctant to agree to reduce their pumping.

From 1968 through 1972, negotiations were directed by a committee of producer representatives working with attorneys and engineers who met monthly (usually in the conference room at the USGVMWD offices) to discuss problems and work on stipulation drafts. Although there were no "lock-up" sessions, in a few cases the water producers asked the attorneys and engineers to leave so the parties could discuss the issues directly.

A settlement was reached near the end of 1972. After a brief trial in October, a stipulation for judgment and a judgment were filed with Judge John Shea on December 29, 1972. Judgment was entered on January 4, 1973, and the physical solution it contained was made retroactive to July 1, 1972. The Main San Gabriel Basin adjudication cost the plaintiff USGVMWD about $424,000, roughly equally divided between engineering costs and legal fees. The total cost of the adjudication to all parties was somewhere between $750,000 and $1 million (Lipson, 1978: 55). All parties were ordered to pay their own costs.

The Main San Gabriel Basin Judgment

The Main San Gabriel Basin judgment defined the rights of 190 parties in five different categories, created a new basin governance entity, and described a management program involving several elements developed just for this basin. The judgment is essentially a constitution for the Main San Gabriel Basin.

The judgment declares that rights to the use and storage of water in the Main San Gabriel Basin belong to the parties, subject to the control of the watermaster and the physical solution contained in the judgment. The overriding theme of the physical solution is that the basin is a resource to be used to its fullest extent by the water rights owners, and that costs of overuse of the basin should fall upon those whose production exceeds their share. Those who produce excessive amounts of water from the basin are assessed an amount sufficient to replace their excess production.

Pumper's Shares, Operating Safe Yield, and Assessments

Adjudicated rights fall into five categories: (1) base annual diversion rights, for surface water diverters who do not also pump groundwater; (2) prescriptive pumping rights, for groundwater pumpers who do not also divert surface water; (3) integrated production rights, for water producers who both divert surface water and pump groundwater; (4) special category rights, for the storage of water in surface reservoirs; and (5) nonconsumptive user rights, primarily for water-spreading operations and temporary storage of storm flows. A party's unused production rights may be carried over to the next year. "Minimal producers" (who produce 5 acre-feet per year or less) are exempted from the provisions of the physical solution, but they can be required to submit production reports.

Groundwater rights are determined on the basis of mutual prescription. The parties stipulated that the basin's "natural safe yield" under 1967 conditions was 152,700 acre-feet and that it had been in overdraft each year since 1953. Instead of converting each party's prescriptive pumping rights to adjusted rights totaling the safe yield, however, the judgment converts each party's prescriptive pumping right into a "pumper's share." For example, the judgment defines the city of Alhambra's prescriptive pumping right as 8,812.05 acre-feet per year, which translates into a pumper's share of 4.45876 percent. All pumper's shares total 100 percent.

Each year, the watermaster establishes the basin's operating safe yield, with a view to preventing long-term damage to the basin and its water users. Harm to the basin and its users from continued overdraft can be avoided by setting a fixed safe-yield figure for every year regardless of water supply and storage conditions. Over the long term, years of above-normal and below-normal water supply and storage should offset one another. Continued overdraft may also be avoided by varying the draft on the basin each year in accordance with variations in the water supply.

Main San Gabriel Basin negotiators preferred the second approach, for three main reasons: it gave them more flexibility, enabled them to make maximum safe use each year of basin water supplies, and paid due attention to the amount of underground water storage in the basin. Main San Gabriel Basin water users viewed the fixed safe-yield operation of the Raymond, West, and Central basins as too rigid: even in years when the natural water supply is fairly abundant, pumpers there must hold back on their production of water from the basin and purchase more expensive supplemental water.

Concern was also voiced about water storage in the basin. Under a fixed safe-yield operation, years of abundant recharge refill the basin and raise underground water levels. In an unconfined groundwater basin such as the Main San Gabriel Basin, increased groundwater in storage brings the water table closer to the land surface. Up to a limit, this is desirable: a higher water table reduces pumping lifts and costs. A series of wet years can bring the water table too high, however, as occurred in 1943.

The Main San Gabriel Basin judgment therefore provides for a variable operating safe yield, set each year by the watermaster on the basis of the water supply and water storage conditions in the basin. Periods of abundance should be accompanied by higher operating safe yields, permitting water producers to produce all or nearly all of their water requirements from the basin. When water is in short supply, the operating safe yield can be lowered to induce pumpers to place fewer demands on the basin.

The judgment specifies that, in setting the operating safe yield, the watermaster is to ensure that there is enough groundwater in storage to keep the water at the Baldwin Park Key Well 200 to 250 feet above sea level. The judgment further calls upon the watermaster to refrain from ordering replenishment water to be spread when the level of Key Well exceeds 250 feet, and will order imported water to be purchased and spread to keep it above 200 feet, to the extent possible.

The operating safe yield and the pumper's share are combined to arrive at a party's allowed pumping for the year. A pumper may extract up to its pumper's share of the operating safe yield for a given year without paying the net pump tax, referred to as the replacement water assessment. Production in excess of the pumper's share of the operating safe yield is subject to the replacement water assessment, so the pumper pays to replace the excess production, acre-foot for acre-foot.

The replacement water assessment is collected to purchase supplemental water to restore to the basin water produced in excess of the operating safe yield. Two other assessments on water production fund parts of the basin governance system and management program. A gross pump tax, called the administrative assessment, is levied on all water production to provide funds for the administration of the judgment. This assessment supports data collection, meter testing, report preparation, compensation of the watermaster, and other such activities. A makeup water assessment is collected as necessary, in order to meet the Upper Area's obligation to the Lower Area under the Long Beach judgment. This assessment is levied on all water production that does not bear a replacement water assessment, that is, on production of the pumper's shares of the operating safe yield.

The Main San Gabriel Basin judgment does not enjoin new water users from producing water from the basin. It allows new parties to acquire nonprescriptive production rights. These nonprescriptive rights do not entitle a new party to a share of the basin's safe yield, however, so all production by the new party would be considered production in excess of safe yield and would bear both an administrative assessment and a replacement water assessment. This procedure makes new production from the basin possible, but it is so expensive that new producers have not followed this approach. Instead, new producers have generally acquired production rights by purchase or lease from existing rights owners.

The Main San Gabriel Basin Watermaster

Main San Gabriel Basin users combined basin policy-making and monitoring functions into one representative body, the Main San Gabriel Basin Watermaster. It is composed of nine members, each of whom serves a one-year term. Six members are directly elected by water producers, two members are appointed by the Board of Directors of the USGVMWD, and the remaining member is appointed by the Board of Directors of the SGVMWD.[4] Each year, the watermaster sets the operating safe yield and the three assessment rates for the coming year.

The Main San Gabriel Watermaster does not maintain a separate office or separate staff. It meets monthly in the USGVMWD offices in El Monte and uses the district office address as its mailing address. Staff work is contracted out. Engineering and legal services have been provided by Thomas Stetson and Ralph Helm, respectively, since the 1973 judgment. Other staff services (such as preparing the annual reports and maintaining financial accounts) are performed by the USGVMWD. Watermaster payments to USGVMWD for these services come from the Watermaster's Administrative Fund supported by administrative assessments against all water production in the basin. Replacement water is purchased by the watermaster through the USGVMWD and the SGVMWD and is spread by the Los Angeles County Department of Public Works (previously the Los Angeles County Flood Control District).

The judgment confers the Upper Area's obligations under the Long Beach judgment on the Main San Gabriel Basin Watermaster. This has relieved the USGVMWD of primary responsibility for those obligations. The watermaster raises funds for makeup water purchases as required and allocates the responsibility for making those purchases between the USGVMWD and the SGVMWD.

The judgment also authorizes the watermaster to enter into court-approved contracts for the storage of water in the basin. The watermaster has entered into cyclic storage agreements with the USGVMWD and the SGVMWD, which have responsibility under the judgment for providing replacement water when ordered by the watermaster. Under the cyclic storage agreements, the districts can purchase supplemental water from MWD or the state when it is available in greater quantities and at lower cost and store it underground. The districts then "deliver" the water to the watermaster in later years—that is, it is made available for pumping. The availability of cyclic storage assures the watermaster and basin users that replacement water will be available when needed. There is no charge to store water in the basin, or any credit or liability for benefiting or harming other basin users if the stored water raises water levels.

New Challenges for Basin Governance and Management

Through the adjudication and judgment, Main San Gabriel Basin water users constructed a basin governance structure that they controlled, subject to the court's continuing jurisdiction, and a flexible basin management program. Developments since 1973 have presented new challenges to both, particularly in the matter of water quality. The judgment charged the watermaster to assume concern for the quality of water in the basin, but this responsibility has changed the role and workload of the watermaster in ways that could not have been foreseen during the adjudication.

In 1972, amendments to the California Administrative Code required water suppliers serving domestic consumers to institute adequate water-quality monitoring programs. The California Department of Health Services suggested that producers within common hydrologic units avoid duplicating their efforts by forming programs to monitor water quality on a regional basis. The USGVMWD and the SGVMWD proposed to undertake an areawide water-quality monitoring program on behalf of water suppliers in the Main San Gabriel Basin.

Subsequently, the Main San Gabriel Basin Watermaster assumed responsibility for the basin's areawide Water Quality Monitoring Program.

The cost of the Areawide Water Quality Monitoring Program has become the largest, and most rapidly growing, portion of the Watermaster's Administrative Fund Budget. The Administrative Assessment has risen since 1973, and escalated rapidly during the 1980s, reflecting the Watermaster's increased involvement with serious water-quality problems uncovered in the basin (Table 8.2).

The first area water-quality monitoring report for the Main San Gabriel Basin, filed on September 1, 1974, revealed excessive concentrations of nitrates in drinking water, especially in the eastern part of the basin.[5] The USGVMWD and SGVMWD commissioned a study of the nitrate problem, the goal of which was to identify its possible sources and recommend ways to correct it. The study, completed in 1976, found that the source of the nitrate problem could not be pinned down precisely, but possible causes were domestic sewage that had reached groundwater supplies decades earlier through septic tank leachates, fertilizers on agricultural

TABLE 8.2
Main San Gabriel Watermaster Assessment Rates (dollars per acre-foot)

Year	Administrative	Makeup water	Replacement water
1972	0.20	0.00	0.00
1973	0.35	0.00	0.00
1974	0.33	0.05	30.00
1975	0.33	0.45	43.00
1976	0.45	2.30	42.00
1977	0.45	7.50	41.00
1978	0.45	3.50	48.00
1979	0.90	3.50	48.00
1980	1.10	12.00[a]	53.00
1981	1.27	10.00[a]	60.00
1982	1.27	10.00[a]	61.00
1983	1.27	9.00[a]	100.00
1984	2.57	9.00[a]	153.00
1985	2.00	5.00	148.00
1986	2.42	1.00	153.00
1987	2.00	0.50	153.00
1988	2.50	2.00	153.00
1989	6.00	3.00	153.00

a. Years in which additional makeup water purchases were made in order to meet obligations under long-term accounting provisions of Long Beach judgment.
SOURCE: Main San Gabriel Basin Watermaster Annual Reports.

lands in the first half of the century, and vegetation buried as lands were cleared for urbanization (Stetson, 1986b: 13). The study recommended nitrate dilution to be accomplished by spreading imported water of lower nitrate concentrations in the eastern part of the basin. Dilution did not begin for several years because imported water was unavailable during the critically dry years of 1976 and 1977 and then it was discovered that the basin had more widespread contamination problems. The watermaster approved a nitrate dilution program for the eastern part of the basin during the 1985–86 water year.

Another water-quality concern has been the siting of municipal waste landfills on lands overlying the basin. The watermaster has published conditions for landfill-use permits for landfills that are somewhat more stringent than those imposed by existing regulatory agencies. Watermaster staff also now regularly inspect all active landfills within the Main San Gabriel Basin. These inspections augment the inspection programs of the Regional Water Quality Control Board and the county Department of Health Services.

The watermaster successfully opposed plans to expand landfills in Irwindale in 1985 and in Azusa in 1991, although the effort to block the Azusa expansion failed initially. The State Water Resources Control Board had rejected the watermaster's objections in 1989, and a Superior Court judge refused to set aside the board's ruling. In January 1991, however, the watermaster and local environmental groups persuaded the District Court of Appeal to block the further expansion of the Azusa landfill, and the California Supreme Court refused to review the Court of Appeal's decision.

The Problem of Volatile Organics

In 1979, the basin water-quality monitoring program revealed relatively high concentrations of trichloroethylene (TCE), a volatile organic chemical, in a Valley County Water District well. Several nearby wells were tested and found to have varying concentrations of TCE and other volatile organics, predominantly tetrachloroethylene (PCE) and carbon tetrachloride (CCl_4), all suspected carcinogens. California Department of Health Services and Regional Water Quality Control Board preliminary investigations concluded that basin groundwater supplies were potentially in jeopardy (Stetson, 1986b: 13).

On January 4, 1980, the affected water producers met in the USGVMWD offices with representatives of the state and county health departments, the Regional Water Quality Control Board, and the county flood control district. State and county health officials announced that they had closed four wells because of high TCE concentrations and would begin an intensive well-testing program to determine the areal extent and size of

TCE concentrations. The flood control district would provide groundwater contour maps with which to plot the movement of TCE concentrations. The Regional Water Quality Control Board would attempt to identify the source or sources and recommend steps to prevent further contamination. Possible remedial measures were discussed, such as aeration, water blending, and replacement of groundwater use via direct connections to imported water supplies. The Main San Gabriel Basin Watermaster held a special meeting on January 8, 1980, at which attorney Ralph Helm reviewed the results of the January 4 meeting for the watermaster and staff.

Monitoring programs continued, and wells with concentrations of TCE, PCE, CCl_4, or other hazardous organic chemicals were closed, or water from them was treated or blended with clean water to reduce contaminant concentrations to below state action levels. By 1985, 88 wells operated by thirty-three different producers in the basin and representing one-fourth of total groundwater production had been found to have concentrations of these chemicals in excess of state action limits. Since then, the number of active producing wells in the basin has dropped, from an average of 333 in the first six years under the judgment to 237 in 1988–89. Nevertheless, there has been no shortage of drinking water in the basin. Increased production from wells in noncontaminated areas of the basin, plus the availability of treated imported water, has allowed residents to continue to rely on water at the tap.

In 1984, four large areas of groundwater contamination in the Main San Gabriel Basin were designated Environmental Protection Agency (EPA) Superfund sites, making cleanup activities eligible for funding under the federal Superfund program. EPA officials have called the San Gabriel site "one of the worst pollution problems in the West," pointing out that the cleanup operation "is much larger in magnitude and more complex than the typical Superfund site." They have acknowledged that full implementation of basin cleanup could take as long as fifty years and up to $1 billion.

Discussions among the Main San Gabriel Watermaster, the California Department of Health Services, and EPA arrived at a planned approach to basin remediation. The remediation program would be directed by the Department of Health Services, financed with Superfund monies, and assisted by the Main San Gabriel Basin Watermaster as the water users' representative, with the Upper San Gabriel Valley Municipal Water District as the principal provider of staff support. A technical committee and a management committee were established to coordinate the remediation effort.

The organization of the cleanup operation has stirred some controversy about the roles of the USGVMWD and the Main San Gabriel Basin Watermaster. Valley residents have expressed frustration with the slow progress of the remediation effort.[6] Some of that frustration has been directed toward USGVMWD, since its name is associated with nearly all of the information the public receives. The USGVMWD formally agreed to assist EPA with community relations and public information. It has handled much of the task of informing residents about the contamination problems and the remediation program. In 1990, the Sierra Club's Angeles Chapter successfully backed candidates for seats on the USGVMWD Board of Directors, as well as on the boards of SGVMWD and the Three Valleys Municipal Water District (which overlies the far eastern section of the basin and used to be the Pomona Valley Municipal Water District). No seat on the USGVMWD board had been contested since 1972; after the 1990 election, a local environmentalist vowed, "From now on, every water board seat in the San Gabriel Valley is going to be contested."[7]

Supervision of the cleanup has given rise to further controversy. The EPA appears to have shifted its focus from the long-term cleanup effort to short-term efforts to treat the worst areas and intercept contamination plumes before they pass through Whittier Narrows and hit Central Basin, and to identifying the polluters so they can be forced to pay the long-term cleanup operation's costs.[8] State and local officials and valley residents have wanted to press ahead with full basin cleanup, however. A key question has become what entity should have principal responsibility for the cleanup operation.

A report released by the Regional Water Quality Control Board in spring 1990 recommended that the cleanup program be supervised locally by the Main San Gabriel Basin Watermaster. The MWD, local water producers, the overlying municipal water districts, and the watermaster agreed with that recommendation. However, two prominent local public figures, U.S. Representative Esteban Torres (D-La Puente) and California State Senator Art Torres (D-Los Angeles) have opposed expanding the watermaster's powers, and along with the Sierra Club and a local group (the East Valleys Organization), have called for the creation of a new "superagency" to organize and perform the cleanup. Senator Torres sponsored legislation in December 1990 to create such an agency, and his bill passed the California Senate in April 1991.

In August 1990, the Main San Gabriel Basin Watermaster returned to Superior Court seeking an amendment of the judgment to expand its authority to oversee the cleanup and to control pumping patterns within the basin in order to arrest the migration of contamination plumes. The watermaster's motion was supported by the MWD, the Regional Water Quality Control Board, and the three overlying municipal water districts. Those opposing the motion—the Sierra Club, the East Valleys Organization, and the office of Los Angeles County District Attorney Ira Reiner— alleged a conflict of interest among the water producers represented on the Main San Gabriel Basin Watermaster, and a lack of public accountability on the watermaster's behalf. Maxine Leichter, speaking for the

Sierra Club's Angeles Chapter, said, "The Watermaster cannot protect both the private interests of water companies and the public's interests." A brief by the county district attorney's office emphasized that the cleanup operation vitally affects all valley residents and water consumers, but the watermaster is accountable for its actions only to the court and the roughly 100 water producers in the basin.[9] There is no provision for participation by the general public in watermaster selection or decision making.

Watermaster representatives emphasized their desire to proceed with the long-delayed basin cleanup. They further contended that the water-master's coverage of the whole basin and all pumpers in it placed it in the best position to direct the cleanup effort. They rejected the conflict-of-interest argument, which implies that cities and water service companies have an interest in selling contaminated water to their residents and customers. In December 1990, Superior Court Judge Florence T. Pickard granted increased authority to the watermaster, provided that it hold public hearings before taking decisions on cleanup operations.

During the discussions about the cleanup, a new element was added to the governance system for the basin. In August 1990, the watermaster, the USGVMWD, the SGVMWD, and the Three Valleys Municipal Water District formed a joint-powers agency, the Main San Gabriel Basin Water Quality Authority, to develop financing for the cleanup operation.

Analysis

Despite the remaining uncertainty about the contamination problems and their implications for the basin governance structure and management program, it is possible to review the processes of institutional development in the Main San Gabriel Basin through 1990. After the impetus for developing collective decision-making arrangements came from Central Basin water users, Main San Gabriel Basin users engaged in considerable institutional innovation in devising basin governance and management arrangements.

Eliciting Information

The Baldwin Park Key Well and its incorporation into the judgment represents an institutional arrangement by which basin users developed a single signal of basin water conditions. The next organized steps in developing institutional arrangements to elicit information occurred in the late 1950s with the formation of the Upper San Gabriel Valley Water Association. Members submitted production reports to the association that later provided the preliminary production histories used to determine pumpers' shares in the basin. The association disseminated reports about the basin by other agencies, such as the Los Angeles County Flood Control District and the state Department of Water Resources.

The Upper San Gabriel Valley Municipal Water District also developed information about basin water conditions and water use. The 1961 Koebig and Koebig study encouraged water users to acquire supplemental water supplies, but also suggested that overdraft was a temporary phenomenon caused by the drought. Beginning in 1965, the USGVMWD commissioned consulting engineer Stetson to prepare annual reports on basin conditions and water use. He also developed the preliminary production histories while working on the recommended basin management plan.

Since the 1973 judgment, information about groundwater production and basin conditions has been generated by the Main San Gabriel Basin Watermaster, which has retained Stetson as consulting engineer. USGVMWD staff compile data from water users and the engineer and prepare the watermaster's annual report, which provides a regular source of information about basin conditions, the operation of the management program, decisions taken by the watermaster, and changes in basin governance or management.

Institutional Design

Main San Gabriel Basin users designed and implemented several institutional arrangements to solve their problems, beginning with the formation of the USGVWA and the USGVMWD in response to the pressures from the Lower Area. The association provided the first organization for governance of the groundwater basin, and the district developed and implemented the basin's artificial replenishment program. During the San Gabriel River adjudication, water users developed the usable water plan, created the San Gabriel River Watermaster, and modified the powers of the USGVMWD to temporarily meet the Upper Area's obligations to the Lower Area.

Thereafter, effort turned toward developing a basinwide governance structure and management program for the basin. During the adjudication of water rights within Main San Gabriel Basin, water users essentially wrote and ratified the basin's constitution, which was approved by the court in the form of the 1973 judgment. In the process, water users developed and implemented new institutional solutions to groundwater basin governance and management problems.

Several Main San Gabriel Basin institutional innovations have since been adopted in other basins:

- The multimember river system watermaster and usable water approach developed by the Central Basin and Main San Gabriel Basin negotiators are now used in the neighboring Santa Ana River watershed (see Chapter 11).

- The idea of a multimember, representative watermaster chosen by water users to govern the basin was adopted in the Raymond Basin in 1984, and by water users in the Chino Basin (see Chapter 12).
- The concept of a variable operating safe yield first implemented in the Main San Gabriel Basin is used in the San Fernando Valley and Chino basins. Also, water producers in the Raymond Basin now cooperate in a voluntary program of adjusting pumping patterns.
- Variations on the idea of the cyclic storage of water are in use in the San Fernando Valley and Chino basins.

Integration with Other Governance Systems

The San Gabriel River adjudication included arrangements for integrating the Main San Gabriel Basin with several other governance structures. Most of these arrangements were described in Chapter 7.

The Main San Gabriel Basin governance and management involves complex relationships among various water resource entities. Water delivery and financial relationships have been worked out among the three overlying municipal water districts in order to provide imported water throughout the basin for direct use and artificial replenishment. Artificial replenishment, as well as the conservation and spreading of local runoff, is performed by the county Department of Public Works in connection with the Main San Gabriel Basin Watermaster and the USGVMWD and SGVMWD. The Main San Gabriel Basin Watermaster includes representatives from the USGVMWD and SGVMWD, both of which provide replacement water to, and have cyclic storage agreements with, the watermaster. Primarily through the USGVMWD, basin governance and management are also connected with MWD. To address contamination problems, basin users have divided and coordinated functions among the Main San Gabriel Basin Watermaster, the three municipal water districts, the Regional Water Quality Control Board, the county health and public works departments, the state health department and water resources board, and EPA. The Main San Gabriel Basin Water Quality Authority is the most recent formal interorganizational arrangement to have evolved, with its role yet to be determined.

Operation and Performance of the Management Program

Compliance with the management program in the Main San Gabriel Basin has been high. No party has been sanctioned for overproducing or for failing to pay water production assessments. Through the first eighteen years of operation under the Main San Gabriel Basin judgment, groundwater production from the basin has remained close to the operating safe yield (Table 8.3).

TABLE 8.3

Main San Gabriel Basin Operations under the Judgment (acre-feet)

Year	Operating safe yield	Production rights[a]	Recorded production	Replacement water requirements
1973	NA	NA	241,098	NA
1974	226,800	238,133	235,460	14,519
1975	210,000	237,913	225,222	8,421
1976	200,000	231,392	242,246	24,745
1977	150,000	174,193	212,995	48,651
1978	150,000	170,473	198,257	36,818
1979	170,000	189,440	218,406	34,405
1980	220,000	237,226	226,280	9,894
1981	230,000	262,445	233,963	6,190
1982	210,000	255,281	223,245	10,592
1983	200,000	253,050	212,206	3,293
1984	230,000	287,395	238,586	2,152
1985	210,000	272,050	244,682	12,476
1986	190,000	240,320	248,802	33,111
1987	200,000	235,924	256,147	42,316
1988	190,000	222,985	251,949	51,990
1989	180,000	214,811	256,667	60,205

NA = Not applicable.
a. Production rights regularly exceed operating safe yield owing to the addition of carryover rights.
SOURCE: Main San Gabriel Basin Watermaster Annual Reports.

The program has been effective in keeping the basin within the target range indicated by Baldwin Park Key Well levels of 200 to 250 feet above sea level. As directed in the judgment, the watermaster has varied the operating safe yield in response to water supply and water storage conditions. When water supply conditions have been favorable and the Key Well level has reached or exceeded 250 feet, the watermaster has occasionally set the operating safe yield in excess of 200,000 acre-feet. Amounts this high exempt virtually all pumping from replacement water assessments; the judgment bars the spreading of replacement water in such years in any case. When the Key Well indicates that basin storage is low, the operating safe yield is lowered, and more groundwater production becomes subject to the replacement water assessment. Since the assessment is quite high (see Table 8.2), this tends to reduce pumping and at the same time provides funds for replenishment purchases.

Despite the great difficulties posed by water contamination, the management program has improved the efficiency of resource use by directing groundwater toward more highly valued uses and taking advantage of the basin's valuable storage space. As in the other basins of the San Gabriel River watershed, water rights transfers in the Main San Gabriel Basin help move groundwater production from those who value it less to those who value it more. To facilitate water rights transfers, the watermaster keeps a list of parties interested in selling or leasing their water production rights and another list of persons interested in acquiring such rights. Since the first few years after the judgment, water rights sales have averaged fewer than three per year. The market for water rights leases has been more active. There have been at least twenty-nine leases each year, and the average has been forty-two per year.

The judgment's provision for cyclic storage allow the basin's valuable storage space to be used. The watermaster's cyclic storage agreement with USGVMWD is indirectly an agreement with MWD to store imported water supplies in the Main San Gabriel Basin. The agreement has been altered by the parties to facilitate the conjunctive use of imported water supplies and basin storage by untangling a catch in the rules governing water spreading in the basin. Because spreading is prohibited when the level in the Baldwin Park Key Well exceeds 250 feet, spreading was usually blocked in precisely those years that surplus imported water was most likely to be available for cyclic storage.[10] The cyclic storage agreement with USGVMWD was changed to allow MWD to spread and store water even when the Key Well level exceeds 250 feet, provided the spreading occurs in the eastern part of the basin where water table increases are unlikely to cause problems for other users (see Table 8.4).

The Main San Gabriel Basin's management program is funded entirely by assessments against pumping, and it allocates basin management costs among water users in proportion to the benefit they derive from the basin. Watermaster expenses are not shared by the state or paid in part from local property taxes.

Given its greater speed and smaller costs, the Main San Gabriel Basin adjudication and management program do not appear to have significantly shut out small water producers or concentrated groundwater production in the hands of a small number of large pumpers. Groundwater production in the Main San Gabriel Basin was highly concentrated before the adjudications, and the rate of further concentration has not changed since the judgment. The thirty largest pumpers in the basin accounted for 88 percent of production before the adjudication, 91 percent at the time of the judgment, and 95 percent at present.

Water users clearly were concerned with adaptability when constituting the basin governance structure and management program. In reserving the continuing jurisdiction of the court, the judgment expresses this guiding principle: "In order that Watermaster may be free to utilize both existing and new developing technological, social and economic

TABLE 8.4
Main San Gabriel Basin Cyclic Storage (acre-feet)

Year	Accumulated cyclic storage: USGVMWD/MWD	Accumulated cyclic storage: SGVMWD	Accumulated cyclic storage: basin total
1975	0	45	45
1976	12,621	7,017	19,638
1977	12,674	9,739	22,413
1978	0	7,452	7,452
1979	0	9,004	9,004
1980	0	6,070	6,070
1981	0	4,709	4,709
1982	0	5,358	5,358
1983	3,189	6,735	9,925
1984	4,862	5,064	9,927
1985	4,862	4,234	9,096
1986	52,268	348	52,616
1987	70,613	7,648	78,262
1988	71,776	8,309	80,085
1989	71,886	4,465	76,351

SOURCE: Main San Gabriel Basin Watermaster Annual Reports.

concepts for the fullest benefit of all those dependent upon the Basin, it is essential that the Physical Solution hereunder provide for maximum flexibility and adaptability" (Judgment, p. 23).

Because the judgment is the basin's constitution, however, the governance structure or authority cannot be changed in any substantial way without amending the judgment. Court approval of amendments is not automatic. In 1989, the watermaster proposed an amendment to the judgment to authorize the use of reclaimed water as replacement water. As noted in Chapters 6 and 7, reclaimed water is used for replenishment in the West and Central basins and is much less expensive than imported water from MWD. In August 1989, Judge Pickard denied the proposed amendment, on the ground that sufficient quantities of imported supplemental water were available for basin replenishment.

Through its rules concerning pumping and imported water use, the Main San Gabriel Basin management program can adjust to basin conditions. Water users have demonstrated the ability to respond to other changes in conditions that were not anticipated at the time of the judgment. An example of that adaptability is the Alhambra Cooperative Water Exchange Agreement, which took considerable inventiveness to develop and could not have been implemented without a high degree of coordination among the city of Alhambra, the USGVMWD, MWD, and the Main San Gabriel Basin Watermaster. The agreement addresses a problem that had been brewing in the western part of the basin for years. A pumping trough developed after years of increased pumping and lower transmissivity rates around Alhambra. By 1973, water levels beneath Alhambra had dropped to 140 feet above sea level.

Alhambra is one of the SGVMWD cities and is located in a part of the basin where the SGVMWD has no turnout for the delivery of supplemental water. The USGVMWD, however, has a turnout from the MWD feeder in the area. The Alhambra Cooperative Water Exchange Agreement allows the city of Alhambra to reduce pumping and receive supplemental water from MWD indirectly through the USGVMWD. Alhambra pays the USGVMWD the full price for 37.4 percent of the treated MWD water it receives. For the other 62.6 percent, the city pays USGVMWD the difference between the MWD treated water and replenishment water prices, and the watermaster pays USGVMWD the MWD replenishment water price. The watermaster's payment reflects the benefit to the basin from Alhambra's pumping reduction. The agreement has stopped water levels beneath the city from falling further and has improved the dependability of its water supply.

Epilogue: The San Gabriel "Formula"

The governance structure and management programs developed by water users in the San Gabriel River watershed are composed of extraordinarily complex institutional and interorganizational arrangements. In each of the four groundwater basins, and in the allocation of San Gabriel River flows between the Upper and Lower areas, institutional development entailed considerable improvisation and adaptation to address the particular problems in each case (such as seawater intrusion in West and Central basins or the water supply position of cities such as Alhambra and Sierra Madre in the Raymond and Main San Gabriel basins). Furthermore, in each basin, and in the interbasin allocation of the river flows, adjustments and modifications have been made to respond to contingencies and emergencies.

To some water users, attorneys, judges, and engineers dealing with other overdrawn and endangered southern California basins, however, the institutional arrangements crafted in the San Gabriel River watershed seemed to offer what they needed most—a solution. In the San Gabriel cases, action appeared to follow a general pattern: acquisition of a supplemental supply of water, followed by an adjudication and limitation of groundwater rights according to mutual prescription, the designation of a watermaster, and the implementation of a management program balancing natural and artificial replenishment of the basin with withdrawals. The Raymond and West basin experiences had been long and difficult, to be sure, but Central Basin seemed to show that the same solution could be reached by a streamlined process, and the Main San Gabriel Basin appeared to confirm this belief.

Some southern California attorneys and judges in particular felt they had found a basin management "formula." During the 1960s and 1970s, they attempted to apply that formula in the Los Angeles and Mojave River watersheds. The results in each case were spectacular, in the sense that a fireworks display is spectacular.

NOTES

1. By 1985, agricultural acreage in the San Gabriel Valley was less than 2,000 acres (Stetson, 1986b: 12).

2. Civil Case 924128, Superior Court of the State of California in and for the County of Los Angeles, assigned to Judge John Shea.

3. One decision taken by the negotiators lightened the burden of assembling the stipulated agreement in the Main San Gabriel Basin case. They decided to omit the smaller, tributary Puente Basin that adjoins the Main San Gabriel Basin on the east from the adjudication. Instead, an agreement was incorporated into the Main San Gabriel Basin judgment, modeled after the San Gabriel River settlement, that allowed the Puente Basin water users to manage their own water supply, as long as they guaranteed not to interfere with the natural surface flows of San Jose Creek or with the subsurface inflow from Puente Basin to the Main San Gabriel Basin. The Puente Basin Water Agency committed to provide make-up payments to the Main San Gabriel Basin Watermaster for any deficiencies. A two-member representative Puente Narrows Watermaster monitors the agreement. Subsequently, the Puente Basin has itself undergone a water rights adjudication.

4. In selecting their representatives, water rights owners under the judgment are allocated one vote for each 100 acre-feet of production right, "creating in effect a quasi-political instrumentality controlled by water producers" (Lipson, 1978: 10).

5. High nitrate concentrations in drinking water have been found to cause a lethal condition in infants called methemoglobinemia, which prevents an infant's blood from carrying oxygen to its tissues and organs.

6. See, for example, Irene Chang, "Rewards Are Offered for Identities of Firms Linked to Water Pollution, *Los Angeles Times*, July 17, 1989, sec. 2, p. 6:

> Disappointed by the Environmental Protection Agency's delay in cleaning up contaminated ground water in the San Gabriel Valley, about 1,100 members of a church-based community organization voted Sunday to offer rewards to individuals who identify companies responsible for the pollution.
> But an EPA official, who spoke at the East Valleys Organizations' annual assembly at St. John the Baptist Church auditorium in Baldwin

Park, said it would be difficult to positively identify the sources of the pollution that has affected 20% of the 200-square-mile San Gabriel Valley water basin and seeped into 245 of the area's 400 wells.

Under the federal Superfund law, which provides money to remove toxics, the EPA must try to recover expenses from companies that caused the damage.

"While I support the concept of having citizens on the alert for companies that spill [toxic] materials, it's going to be very, very hard and very complex because for 50 years or longer industry and others have deliberately put contaminants in the ground water," said Jeffrey Zelikson, director of hazardous waste management in EPA's western region. . . .

EVO is a coalition of 12 San Gabriel Valley and Pomona Valley churches, and claims a membership of 35,000 families.

In June 1990, the EVO announced that it had raised $100,000 for its reward fund, and also released its first "clean water report card." The state Water Quality Board received a "D," apparently for its approval of the Azusa landfill expansion. The EPA received an "incomplete." Local municipalities and public officials received grades that appeared to be closely related to how much money they had contributed to EVO's reward fund. See Sheryl Stolberg, "Group Releases Water Report Card," *Los Angeles Times*, June 11, 1990, p. B-1.

7. Julio Moran, "Signals of a Right Turn Prove False in Santa Monica," *Los Angeles Times*, November 8, 1990, p. B-4.

8. Berkley Hudson, "Short-Term Plan for Cleaning Up Water Released," *Los Angeles Times*. April 18, 1990, p. B-1; "Drought Prompts Study of Basin Cleanup." *Los Angeles Times*, June 11, 1990, p. B-1.

9. Berkley Hudson, "Courtroom Battle Set in Historic Water Fight," *Los Angeles Times*, August 9, 1990, p. B-1.

10. In 1977, the California Department of Water Resources, exploring ways of improving the delivery of State Project water, approached the watermaster's consulting engineer, Thomas Stetson, about the possibility of a cyclic storage agreement that would allow the department to store surplus northern California water in the Main San Gabriel Basin. The judgment and the watermaster rules and regulations provide that stored water may be recaptured only for use in the basin, however. These restrictions blocked an agreement with the state, which wanted to be able to "bank" water in the basin for later extraction and delivery elsewhere.

9

The San Fernando Valley
Institutional Adaptation under Constraint

If someone were to say "San Fernando killed mutual prescription," he would have an arguable point.

John F. Mann, Jr., 1975

As explained in Chapter 4, the city of Los Angeles has successfully asserted and defended a pueblo water right to the use of the Los Angeles River since the 1800s. This makes Los Angeles not just another riparian or appropriator, but gives it an exclusive and paramount right to use all the water it needs from the river, up to and including the entire flow. In the early 1900s, the claim was extended to San Fernando Valley groundwater, which supplies the base flow of the Los Angeles River.

The groundwater basin underlying the San Fernando Valley also figured prominently in the early 1900s in the construction of the Los Angeles Aqueduct. The aqueduct was designed with substantial excess capacity in order to accommodate future growth and to make the project worth building and financing. For several years, the aqueduct would provide more water than the city needed, raising the question of what to do with the surplus in the meantime. There also were questions about where the aqueduct should terminate once it reached the San Gabriel Mountains.

At the request of William Mulholland, the Los Angeles Board of Water Commissioners turned these questions over to a panel of three prominent civil engineers—John Quinton, William Code, and Homer Hamlin—asking them to recommend a location for the aqueduct's terminus and find a place to accommodate the temporary surplus. Their choices were

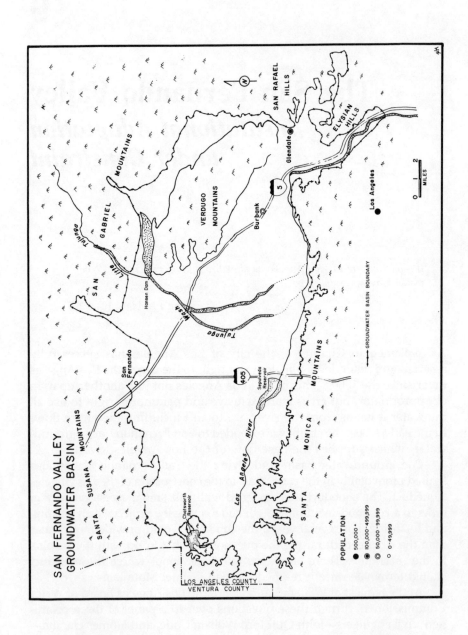

SAN FERNANDO VALLEY
GROUNDWATER BASIN

POPULATION
● 500,000 +
◉ 100,000 - 499,999
◎ 50,000 - 99,999
○ 0 - 49,999

constrained by the need to minimize the costs of water distribution, and the fact that the city's bonding power had been exhausted, so the aqueduct itself could not be brought all the way to the interior of the city. After comparing potential terminus locations, the panel published a report in 1911 recommending the San Fernando Valley. There would be adequate funds to reach the valley, and the elevation of the terminus would allow water to be conveyed to most of the city by gravity flow. Surplus water from the aqueduct could be used in the valley for irrigated agriculture, with irrigation return flows percolating underground and moving toward the Narrows to enhance the flow of the Los Angeles River. Also, surplus water stored underground in the valley would provide an emergency supply if the aqueduct flow were interrupted.

The area to be served by the surplus aqueduct water would be annexed and brought within the city and its municipal water system. Virtually the entire valley was unincorporated, save for Glendale. Burbank and San Fernando incorporated in 1911, the year the engineers' report was published. When deliveries of aqueduct water began in 1913, the remainder of the valley was annexed to Los Angeles. The annexation and the incorporations of Glendale, Burbank, and San Fernando set the stage for protracted battles decades later over San Fernando Valley water supplies.

Los Angeles's Early Conjunctive Use Program in the San Fernando Valley

Decision making within the Los Angeles Department of Water and Power (LADWP) constituted the nearest thing to governance of the San Fernando Valley basin for years. The other three cities in the valley pumped groundwater but did not participate in any form of collective decision making about groundwater rights or usage. LADWP began a program of conjunctive uses of its imported water supplies from the Los Angeles Aqueduct and the groundwater basin underlying the San Fernando Valley. The city withdrew water from the valley basin and the Los Angeles River and replaced what it withdrew, and more, from the aqueduct. Return flows from the irrigation of valley lands increased both the amount of groundwater in storage and the rising flow of the Los Angeles River at the Narrows (Mann and Blevins, 1986: 2). The LADWP began pumping groundwater in the Owens Valley in 1918 and began diverting water from the Mono Basin watershed in 1923, to increase the flow through the Los Angeles Aqueduct.

Activities of the Los Angeles County Flood Control District (LACFCD) and the U.S. Army Corps of Engineers in the San Fernando Valley during the 1920s facilitated the city's conjunctive use operation. The corps constructed the Hansen, Sepulveda, and Lopez flood control dams, and the flood control district constructed the Big Tujunga and the Pacoima dams. Each of these dams, operated by LACFCD, was accompanied by a reservoir and spreading grounds for capturing storm flows and recharging the groundwater supply. These dams, reservoirs, and spreading grounds supplemented the LADWP's Headworks Spreading Grounds. The Tujunga, Hansen, and Headworks (and later the Pacoima) spreading grounds were used for artificial recharge of the groundwater supply with aqueduct water imported by Los Angeles.

Roughly 150,000 acre-feet of water was spread at the locations through the 1930s. The city's pueblo water right did not attach to these imported and spread waters; the pueblo right applies only to "native waters" of the Los Angeles River watershed. The state had authorized municipalities to spread and store water for later use, however, and this practice was explicitly upheld with respect to public agencies importing waters from distant watersheds by the California Supreme Court's 1939 decision in *Stevens v. Oakdale Irrigation District.*

Battle between the Cities—Round One: The *Glendale* and *Burbank* Cases

Since Los Angeles was storing surplus aqueduct water in the San Fernando Valley basin, it was able to reduce pumping from its wells in the eastern part of the valley. The short-term groundwater surplus in the valley and the reduction of pumping by Los Angeles allowed Burbank and Glendale to accommodate their own rapid municipal growth with increased pumping from the eastern part of the valley. They spent millions of dollars on well fields and water distribution systems, including wells equipped with high-capacity turbine pumps. During the 1920s, the Los Angeles pumping reductions were more than offset by Burbank's and Glendale's increases, producing a net increase in pumping in the part of the valley that groundwater passes through before rising to the surface at the Los Angeles Narrows. The increased pumping and a series of dry years in the 1920s took their toll. In 1931, despite the artificial replenishment program and the fact that the Los Angeles Aqueduct was operating at nearly full capacity, the rising water flow of the Los Angeles River stopped.

Armed with numerous precedents establishing its paramount right to waters of the Los Angeles River watershed, and confident of its right to store and recapture its imports, Los Angeles sued Burbank in 1933, and Glendale in 1936. The cases were consolidated and assigned to Superior Court Judge Frank Collier, who was simultaneously presiding over the Raymond Basin adjudication. Glendale and Burbank were represented by attorney Kenneth Wright, who also represented a majority of the water users in the Raymond Basin case and later helped initiate the West and Central Basin adjudications.

Los Angeles requested declaratory judgments that its pueblo right to all native waters of the Los Angeles River watershed needed for its inhabitants was superior to the appropriative rights of Glendale and Burbank, and that Los Angeles had a prior and paramount right to groundwater in the valley that appeared as a result of its imports, return flows, and artificial replenishment. Los Angeles also requested an injunction restraining Glendale and Burbank from any further extractions of native waters, imported water recharged to the basin, or return flows of aqueduct water.

The *Burbank* and *Glendale* cases, as they were known, were tried before Judge Collier in 1939. Burbank and Glendale's arguments focused on the hardships the cities would experience, and the waste of water that would occur, if Los Angeles prevailed. Burbank and Glendale were original members of MWD, but imported Colorado River water was not yet available, so the cities would have no water supply at all if ordered to stop pumping. They also argued that if they stopped pumping, the combination of native water and Los Angeles Aqueduct imports would create a water surplus in the valley. Rising water would fill the concrete-lined Los Angeles River channel and flow straight out to the ocean. This would be manifestly against the state's declared policy against water waste.

Burbank and Glendale also argued that they had acquired prescriptive rights to at least some of the water in the valley. The flow of the Los Angeles River may have dried up in 1931, they contended, but their use of at least some of the water claimed by Los Angeles had been taking place for several years, and they should be entitled to continue to use that water. At a minimum, even if Los Angeles had a superior right to the native waters of the watershed, its right should extend only to the normal flows thereof. If nothing else, the cities argued, they were entitled to the extraordinary flows of the river, such as the flood flows captured and spread within the valley by the LACFCD.

Judge Collier held for Los Angeles on all three of its declaratory judgment requests, with one distinction. He accepted the defendants' distinction between ordinary flows and flood flows. Because the Los Angeles pueblo water right was defined in terms of need, it did not extend to "surplus waters," which were available for other appropriators. Judge Collier reasoned that flood waters are, by definition, "surplus waters." Therefore, Glendale and Burbank had a right to the use of flood waters that were captured and restored to the groundwater supply.

The declaratory judgments were appealed to the California Supreme Court, which unanimously upheld all the rulings in favor of Los Angeles and reversed the decision about flood flows that had favored Glendale and Burbank. The Supreme Court held that if Los Angeles could capture flood flows in the Los Angeles River watershed and put them to use, then its pueblo water right extended to those captured flows, as well. The pueblo water right extends to the peak as well as to the lesser flows of the stream (23 Cal.2d 68 at 74).

No injunction was issued in the Burbank and Glendale cases. The valley's water supply situation had changed again. Not only had the drought ended in 1936, disastrous flooding had occurred throughout southern California in 1938. By the time the trial was held in 1939, the San Fernando Valley was inundated with water, and rising water flows filled the Los Angeles River channel and headed for the sea. In 1940, Los Angeles River flows hit an all-time record high of 138,990 acre-feet, 100 times the amount in 1930. Unable to establish that the city's interests were currently being harmed by Glendale and Burbank, Los Angeles dropped its request for an injunction to halt their pumping, satisfying itself with the declarations (Mann, 1976: 268). Without the injunction, neither Glendale nor Burbank (nor any other pumper in the watershed) was restrained from continuing pumping. The stage was set for another confrontation when drought conditions returned in the 1940s.

Race to the Pumphouse: 1940–1955

Groundwater extractions in the San Fernando Valley escalated sharply after the *Glendale* and *Burbank* cases were resolved in 1943 without an injunction. From 1942 to 1950, groundwater extractions in the San Fernando Valley increased from just under 90,000 acre-feet per year to 140,000 acre-feet per year. In the meantime, Colorado River water became available in the San Fernando Valley, but went largely unused. Despite rapid urbanization and population growth, MWD deliveries to the valley totaled 320 acre-feet in 1941, 580 acre-feet in 1945, and 5,800 acre-feet in 1950. Even in the early 1950s, Glendale and Burbank hardly touched the Colorado River supplies. MWD deliveries to the two cities increased from 500 acre-feet in 1949–50 to 2,200 acre-feet in 1954–55 (California SWRB, 1956: 24). Glendale, Burbank, and others continued to increase pumping.

During this period, Los Angeles initially increased imports from its own aqueduct, which were less expensive and of higher quality than MWD Colorado River water. In 1940, Los Angeles had extended its aqueduct further into the Mono Basin watershed. Los Angeles Aqueduct deliveries reached 270,000 acre-feet per year in the mid-1940s and neared 300,000 acre-feet per year in 1950. Only then did it turn significantly to MWD for additional supplies. Los Angeles imports of Colorado River water rose from 5,300 acre-feet in 1949–50 to 29,000 acre-feet in 1954–55 (California SWRB, 1956: 24). By 1955, Los Angeles was importing more than 300,000 acre-feet of water annually from its aqueduct and MWD.

When the long drought cycle began in 1945, valley water conditions deteriorated rapidly. Water levels in wells in the eastern part of the valley dropped as much as 110 feet between 1945 and 1955. Groundwater in storage in the San Fernando Valley Basin, the largest groundwater basin in the Upper Los Angeles River Area (ULARA), fell 300,000 acre-feet from 1944–45 through 1949–50. Above-normal rainfall in 1952 brought a brief hope that the drought had ended. But when the drought resumed in 1953, the water level dropped again. On September 30, 1955, Los Angeles went back to court.

Battle between the Cities—Round Two: *Los Angeles v. San Fernando*

The new action, *City of Los Angeles v. City of San Fernando et al.*, covered all four groundwater basins within the Upper Los Angeles River Area and named as defendants the cities of San Fernando, Glendale, and Burbank, plus more than 200 other parties, mostly private producers. After initial assignment to another judge, the case was transferred to Superior Court Judge Virgil Airola of Calaveras County (who was later assigned the San Gabriel River adjudication described in Chapter 7). Upon motion of the defendants, and over the objections of Los Angeles, Judge Airola issued an order of reference on June 11, 1958, directing the State Water Rights Board to investigate and report on the physical facts affecting a determination of water rights in the ULARA.

Los Angeles opposed the reference, not only because it hoped to avoid the expense and delay, but because it opposed any "determination of water rights" in the ULARA. From its perspective, ULARA water rights had been determined in numerous previous cases, and they belonged to Los Angeles. Los Angeles moved that the *Glendale* and *Burbank* cases be reopened so that it could renew its request for an injunction. This motion was denied, the objections to the reference were overruled, and the referee's investigation began.

The investigation proceeded for four years, resulting in a two-volume report approved by Judge Airola on July 27, 1962. The referee report documented the rise in pumping, the fall in water levels, and the loss of groundwater in storage throughout the ULARA from the late 1920s through the late 1950s. After additional hearings, the judge ordered further reports on the Verdugo, Sylmar, and Eagle Rock subareas, which were presented to the court in October 1964. These reports were received by a new judge. Judge Airola retired from the bench in September 1964, and his replacement on this case (and the San Gabriel River case) was Judge Edmund Moor of Alpine County.

Judge Moor also presided over the Central Basin adjudication, which was nearing completion. Central Basin had been the third mutual-prescription adjudication in southern California. The Raymond and West basin adjudications had been appealed and upheld. Now Judge Moor had been assigned the fourth groundwater basin adjudication in Los Angeles County. In this one, Los Angeles asserted a paramount right to all groundwater in the ULARA, while the defendants argued the need for a mutual-prescription determination of rights owing to the existence of an overdraft. As the case progressed, Judge Moor was clearly more receptive to the mutual-prescription approach.

After extensive pretrial proceedings, and numerous stipulations reducing the number of defendants, the trial of the *San Fernando* case began on March 1, 1966.[1] It continued until June 15, 1967, and in the interim took up 181 court days, entailed more than 700 exhibits, and produced a trial transcript of 38,889 pages, the largest trial record in the 118-year history of the Los Angeles County Superior Court to that time (Mann, 1976: 270). The principal contested issues at trial were (1) the pueblo water right of Los Angeles; (2) the rights to return flows of imported waters; (3) the independence or interdependence of the sub-areas; and (4) the time that the overdraft began and thus whether a "prescriptive period" had run.

The issue of the pueblo water right lay at the heart of the trial. The defendants had to contest the right to have a chance of retaining pumping rights in the watershed. If they lost on this point, they would have to replace all use of local water supplies with more expensive imported water. For this reason, Los Angeles repeatedly asserted that this was not a case about water, it was a case about money. Los Angeles cited the series of cases in which the city's superior right to the waters of the Los Angeles River watershed had been upheld, but Judge Moor declined to consider the matter settled. He allowed the defendants to contest the existence of the pueblo water right. This part of the trial alone took up six months, as testimony was gathered from experts in Spanish, Mexican, and California history and law.

In his memorandum of decision on October 30, 1967, Judge Moor completely rejected the claim that the city of Los Angeles possessed a pueblo water right. He concluded that the pueblo water right concept had been "adopted by the courts in time of need to protect the very existence of the City of Los Angeles." Since Los Angeles now had a population of two million and imported water supplies from both the Owens Valley–Mono Basin area and the Colorado River, the pueblo right was no longer necessary. In his view, the history of the pueblo and water rights indicated that either (1) the pueblo right did not exist, and the court could equitably apportion the water supply among the competing claimants, or (2) the pueblo right did exist, but required equitable apportionment of the waters by the sovereign in times of scarcity, and in this case the sovereign was "represented by the courts of the State of California."[2] Either way, it was the court's job to make an equitable apportionment of ULARA waters. With the question of the pueblo water right discarded, that apportionment depended on issues such as the status of imported waters and return flows, the relationship among the subareas, and the beginning of the overdraft and the possible acquisition of prescriptive rights.

If the court were to equitably apportion ULARA waters, it mattered first which waters were subject to such an apportionment. Clearly, the naturally occurring waters derived from local precipitation and runoff would be among the waters to be apportioned, but what of the large quantities of waters that were imported into the watershed and found their way underground, where they moved through the ULARA along with the native waters? Citing the decisions in the *Glendale* and *Burbank* cases, Los Angeles contended that it had a prior and paramount right to recapture the return flows of waters it had imported into the ULARA. Judge Moor refused to admit the city's evidence on its intent to recapture these waters, including the 1911 engineers' report recommending San Fernando Valley as the Los Angeles Aqueduct terminus. He filed instead a finding of fact that there was no intent on the part of Los Angeles to recapture its imported waters—the opposite of the finding in the *Glendale* and *Burbank* cases (Mann, 1975: 4). He concluded that once water from any source reached the underground supply, it could no longer be differentiated and separate rights could not be assigned to its use. He chose instead to apportion the "available safe yield" of the ULARA, without distinguishing return flows of imported water from the native water.

The next question that had to be settled was whether the San Fernando, Sylmar, and Verdugo subareas were independent or interdependent. Because Los Angeles asserted a superior right to all water in, and tributary to, the Los Angeles River, its obvious strategy was to claim that all surface and groundwater in the ULARA was tributary to the Los Angeles River and subject to the city's superior right. The defendants had just the opposite interests. Glendale and the Crescenta Valley County Water District pumped water from the Verdugo subarea. San Fernando's wells were all in the Sylmar subarea. If the subareas were treated separately, these defendants might gain some advantages in acquiring rights in those subareas. On the basis of evidence of hydrologic discontinuities between Sylmar and San Fernando, and between Verdugo and San Fernando, Judge Moor concluded that the subareas were in fact separate basins and that he would have to apportion the available safe yield in each of them.

What remained to be determined was the basis for that apportionment. With the pueblo water right and import return flow claims discarded, consideration turned to the mutual-prescription approach urged by the defendants. Mutual prescription clearly was to the defendants' advantage, inasmuch as they had increased their pumping while Los Angeles had increased its imports. The prescriptive rights formula used in the adjudications with which Judge Moor was familiar generally worked to the benefit of parties whose pumping rose after the overdraft began and through the prescriptive period.

There was no question as to when the action had been filed. There was no question as to the parties' extractions during the five-year period before the filing, since those had been investigated by the referee. But there was "a great battle" at the trial "over the date when the overdraft began" (Mann, 1976: 270). If the court found that overdraft had begun more than five years before the filing of the action, then a prescriptive period would have run and a mutual-prescription apportionment was possible in light of *Pasadena v. Alhambra* and its progeny. If overdraft had begun less than five years before the filing of the complaint, there could not be mutual prescription. Following the approach of previous adjudications, the defendants argued that overdraft began when groundwater extractions exceeded replenishment from all sources. According to the data in the referee report, this occurred in 1941–42. To avoid mutual prescription, Los Angeles had to counter that contention.

At the trial, Los Angeles presented its "new theory of overdraft," a theory associated with its expert witness, Dr. John Mann, Jr. Los Angeles argued that the previously accepted definition of overdraft was too simple, because it failed to take into account two factors that were crucial to the optimal management of a groundwater basin. The first factor was the existence of a "temporary surplus" in the basin—that is, the possibility that a basin might be "too full." If a basin such as the San Fernando Valley basin were too full, water would escape the basin and be wasted. Under these conditions, restraining extractions to the level of average annual replenishment would simply maintain the surplus and the resulting loss of water that might otherwise be beneficially used. Under surplus conditions, extracting more than nature replenished actually constituted good groundwater basin management, according to the new theory of overdraft (Mann, 1976: 272). The second factor had to do with maintaining "regulatory storage capacity" in the basin. Under conditions of optimal groundwater management, a basin's total water in storage should be held at a little less than maximum, in order to leave some capacity for the capture of excess water that might occur (given the erratic precipitation pattern of the area) and would otherwise be wasted.

Under the new theory, overdraft commenced in a groundwater basin once extractions exceeded replenishment *and* any temporary surplus in the basin had been removed *and* the "regulatory storage capacity" had been restored. Only beyond that point would continued extractions in excess of replenishment become harmful to the basin and its users. Los Angeles conceded that extractions had exceeded replenishment beginning at some point in the 1940s. But at that point, Los Angeles contended, the groundwater supplies of the ULARA were in surplus. The heavy rainfall (and even floods) of the late 1930s and early 1940s had produced record amounts of water escaping the basin at the Narrows and flowing down the Los Angeles River channel to the ocean. Even Judge Moor acknowledged that groundwater in storage had increased 260,000 acre-feet from 1929 to 1941. According to Los Angeles, overdraft had not really begun until 1953–54, when the temporary surplus had been removed from the basin and the recommended regulatory storage capacity of 350,000 acre-feet (based on San Fernando's estimated total storage capacity of 3.2 million acre-feet) had been restored. If overdraft began in 1953–54, no prescriptive period had elapsed by the time the suit was filed in September 1955.

Judge Moor rejected the new theory of overdraft and accepted the defendants' contention that overdraft had begun in 1941–42. He therefore made a mutual-prescription apportionment of the ULARA waters in each of the three subareas in dispute. He determined the total prescriptive rights of the parties in each of the subareas: 117,992 acre-feet in San Fernando; 5,377 acre-feet in Sylmar; 4,315 acre-feet in Verdugo. Using the referee's determinations of the available safe yield of each subarea, Judge Moor adjusted each party's prescriptive right to a restricted pumping right, so all restricted pumping rights in a subarea equaled its available safe yield. The referee had determined the available safe yield to be 90,680 acre-feet per year in the San Fernando Subarea (of which the native safe yield was 43,660 acre-feet in the absence of artificial replenishment and return flows), 6,210 acre-feet per year (3,850 native) in Sylmar, and 7,150 acre-feet per year (3,950 native) in Verdugo.

At this point, Judge Moor's conclusions combined to produce a tremendous logical collision. The total prescriptive rights were *less than* the available safe yield in the Sylmar and Verdugo subareas. By treating the basins separately, refusing to separate native from imported waters, and concluding that the prescriptive period had run, the judge had awarded the parties prescriptive rights to less than the yield of two of the three subareas. Undeterred, he assigned the parties in Sylmar and Verdugo restricted pumping rights that were *higher* than their prescriptive rights. For the first time in California water law, parties had acquired prescriptive rights to water they had not used yet.

Judgment was entered on March 15, 1968, twelve and one-half years after the filing of the complaint. The judgment reached 214 parties and awarded rights to 28 (the others having disclaimed, defaulted, or stipulated previously), of whom only 24 remained active pumpers. Judge Moor appointed the Southern District office of the state Department of Water

Resources to serve as watermaster, and it began monitoring extractions and basin conditions and issuing annual reports just as it did for the Raymond, West, and Central basins. A six-member Watermaster Advisory Committee representing the four cities, the Crescenta Valley County Water District, and the private producers was established, and the court retained continuing jurisdiction of the case. In a separate judgment, Judge Moor ordered Los Angeles to pay all of the approximately $500,000 in referee's costs.

The trial court judgment proved effective in curtailing pumping in the San Fernando subarea, and in halting the decline in water levels there. Compliance with the terms of the trial court judgment was fairly high.[3] With its pumping restricted to 66,075 acre-feet per year, Los Angeles raised its imports from 323,252 acre-feet in 1967–68 to 485,959 acre-feet in 1970–71. In 1970, the city completed and placed in operation a second barrel of the Los Angeles Aqueduct, expanding the aqueduct's capacity to 565,000 acre-feet per year, with the additional water coming from more surface-water diversions in the Mono Basin and more pumping in Owens Valley.

Los Angeles remained unsatisfied. In the *San Fernando* judgment, the city had lost its pueblo water right, lost its right to import return waters, been assigned the costs of the reference, and been forced to rely more on imported water at considerable additional expense. Los Angeles appealed.

Battle between the Cities, Round Three: The *San Fernando* Case On Appeal

Appellate briefs—eleven volumes in all—were compiled and presented to the District Court of Appeal over the next three and a half years. After hearing oral arguments on November 9, 1972, the three appellate judges issued a unanimous decision on November 22, reversing every aspect of Judge Moor's decision. They held that all native waters in all subareas of the ULARA were tributary to the Los Angeles River, and under the prior decision in the *Glendale* and *Burbank* cases, Los Angeles had a prior and paramount pueblo water right to the native waters of the entire area. They issued the injunction long requested by the city against continued pumping of native waters by Glendale and Burbank. They held that each party importing water had a right to capture its return flows, and to capture water it had spread. And they reassigned the court costs and referee's costs to the defendants. The defendants' petition for a rehearing was denied.

The defendants appealed to the California Supreme Court. By this time, the number of parties was down to fifteen—the cities of Los Angeles, Glendale, Burbank, and San Fernando, the Crescenta Valley County Water District, and ten private parties. New briefs were prepared and filed during 1973 and 1974. The California Supreme Court heard oral arguments on January 14, 1975, and issued its unanimous decision on May 12, in an opinion written by Chief Justice Donald Wright.

In accord with its previous decisions and affirming the Court of Appeal, the California Supreme Court upheld the pueblo water right of Los Angeles, although it expressed reservations about the concept. The Supreme Court considered and reviewed the evidence presented at the original trial concerning the historical basis of the pueblo right. The justices upheld the right on the fairly narrow ground that it was a rule of property, and that *stare decisis*—the rule of precedent—"applies with special force to rules of property on which those engaged in business transactions have relied in gauging the probable returns on their acquisitions and investments" (14 C.3d 199 at 240). Under *stare decisis*, previous decisions should be overturned only if shown to be "palpably erroneous or unreasonable." The historical data considered by the trial court did not provide such a showing. Nevertheless, the Supreme Court acknowledged, "The historical conditions which led to the creation of the pueblo water right have long since disappeared. This court has upheld, and now upholds, the existence of that right principally because of the pueblo successor's reliance upon that right in planning and developing a municipal water supply" (14 C.3d 199 at 250). The justices would not, however, extend the pueblo right beyond previous decisions, that is, beyond the San Fernando subarea. Unlike the Court of Appeal, the Supreme Court would treat Sylmar and Verdugo as independent basins.

The Supreme Court affirmed the Court of Appeal on the issue of rights to return flows of imported waters, declaring that each importer of water to a subarea should have a right to its return flows. Like the pueblo right, these rights to import return flows are superior to overlying or appropriative claims and cannot be lost by prescription. The percentage of imported waters to be credited as return flow rights was left for determination on remand of the case. Thus, in the San Fernando subarea, Los Angeles would have an exclusive and paramount right to pump some percentage of the water it imported plus its exclusive and paramount pueblo right to the native safe yield of 43,660 acre-feet per year. Burbank, Glendale, San Fernando, and the Crescenta Valley County Water District would have exclusive and paramount rights to some percentage of the waters they imported into that or other subareas. The private parties would have no import return water rights.

The justices then addressed the question of what constituted an "overdrafted" basin. They accepted the new theory of overdraft presented by Los Angeles. The opinion turned next to the problem of mutual prescription, the propriety of Judge Moor's mutual prescription and restricted pumping rights solutions, and the issue of what *Pasadena v.*

Alhambra really meant. Could the *Glendale* and *Burbank* cases be squared with *Pasadena v. Alhambra,* or would one or the other have to be discarded?

Chief Justice Wright's opinion was crafted to "save" *Pasadena* by distinguishing it thoroughly from the *San Fernando* case, allowing the justices to reach a different result here without overturning the earlier decision. Upon declaring itself in favor of the new theory of overdraft, for example, the justices observed that the trial judge in *Pasadena* had "expressly noted that 'the ground water storage capacity is adequate to store the excess during wet years for the following dry years'" (14 C.3d 199 at 280). Thus, Raymond Basin was in overdraft even under the new theory, since there was no temporary surplus there when parties' rights were assigned.

The justices addressed mutual prescription by acknowledging its usefulness as a concept, but pointing out that it was not the only possible solution to an overdraft problem. Parties in an overdrafted basin need a fair apportionment of rights coupled with administration under a watermaster and the retention of continuing jurisdiction by a court. Mutual prescription was only one of several possible methods of apportionment that might accomplish this result. The justices seemed bothered by the almost reflexive character of Judge Moor's decision. Chief Justice Wright called the application of the prescriptive rights formula in the *San Fernando* case "mechanical," and stated that it "does not necessarily result in the most equitable apportionment of water according to need. A true equitable apportionment would take into account many more factors" (14 C.3d 199 at 265). He continued, "This does not mean that the *Pasadena* decision fell short of reaching a fair result on the facts there presented" (14 C.3d 199 at 266). But the *San Fernando* case arose in a different factual context. In the *Glendale* and *Burbank* cases, the California Supreme Court had declared that Los Angeles had a prior and paramount pueblo water right to all the water it needed from the native yield of the San Fernando subarea and from its imports. Judge Moor could not use the mutual-prescription approach now to award Glendale and Burbank prescriptive rights to that same water (14 C.3d 199 at 268).

Another important issue distinguished *Pasadena* and its progeny from *San Fernando*: the meaning of Civil Code Section 1007. As observed in Chapters 5 and 6, Section 1007 provided that no water right could be acquired by prescription against any public agency, including any city. In *San Fernando,* Los Angeles raised the Section 1007 issue squarely, objecting that Judge Moor's decision awarded prescriptive water rights against the city. The defendants countered that mutual-prescription judgments had been entered in the Raymond, West, and Central basin adjudications, and the Raymond and West basin judgments had been appealed and upheld. Furthermore, Los Angeles itself had been one of the pumpers whose extractions had been curtailed in the West and Central basin adjudications.

Closer examination, however, revealed that Los Angeles had never agreed to the prescriptive rights formulation in the West or Central basin adjudications, and thus remained free to raise the issue in the *San Fernando* case. According to the city's key expert witness:

> Los Angeles has carefully preserved its position on 1007, knowing that its most important local source of water (San Fernando Valley) would some day be involved in another water rights litigation. While agreeing to curtail pumping, Los Angeles did not sign the stipulated judgment in the West Basin case. In the Central Basin case, while again agreeing to a numerical reduction in pumping, Los Angeles negotiated a separate stipulation denying the waiving of any rights under 1007. (Mann, 1975: 6)

The Supreme Court noted that the Section 1007 issue had never been raised in *Pasadena*, and the disposition of the Hawthorne appeal in the West Basin case offered no guidance. So there was no precedent on Section 1007, leaving the Supreme Court free to interpret it for the first time. The court stated that Section 1007 meant exactly what it said: no prescriptive rights to groundwater could be acquired against any public entity.

All that remained before the Supreme Court, then, was the allocation of rights to the native waters of the Sylmar and Verdugo subareas. The justices rejected Judge Moor's allocation of prescriptive rights and restricted pumping rights in basins that were not yet overdrafted. Oddly enough, the Supreme Court nevertheless had to let the assignments of rights in the Verdugo subarea stand, because there was no issue properly before the court about it. None of the defendants had objected to the allocation of rights in Verdugo, and Los Angeles had not pumped any water from Verdugo and so had acquired no rights there. So, the only party that objected was not harmed, and the parties that might be perceived as harmed had not objected.

The Supreme Court did decide that Judge Moor had erred in finding the Sylmar subarea to be in overdraft. Sylmar had actually been in surplus in the year 1954-55, so there had not been an overdraft in all five years prior to the filing of the *San Fernando* case. Under such circumstances, the task was to determine the respective overlying and appropriative rights of the parties extracting from Sylmar: the cities of Los Angeles and San Fernando, and two private defendants who pumped groundwater but had no imports. The Supreme Court left this determination to be made by the trial court on remand. The Supreme Court encouraged the trial court to consider the possibility of a physical solution in the Sylmar subarea, because most of San Fernando's imports would return to the groundwater of the San Fernando subarea but the city's groundwater pumping facilities were in Sylmar, while Los Angeles had imports and pumping facilities in both places.

The trial court was further encouraged to investigate the possibility of a physical solution in the San Fernando subarea, where Glendale and Burbank had relied so heavily on groundwater extractions and could perhaps pump a bit more than their right in exchange for compensating Los Angeles for additional imports. Furthermore, although Los Angeles was entitled to an injunction against private parties throughout the San Fernando subarea, the trial court was urged to at least consider the arguments of some of those private defendants that some of their uses are nonconsumptive and therefore do not result in any injury to Los Angeles.

The case was remanded to Los Angeles County Superior Court for further proceedings to construct a judgment consistent with the Supreme Court's opinion. The morning after the Supreme Court's decision, the *Los Angeles Times* (May 13, 1975, p. 1) described the practical impact of the case on local interests:

> Partly because of an award made by Spain's King Charles III when the pueblo of Los Angeles was founded in 1781, the city of Los Angeles Monday won a twenty-year battle with Glendale and Burbank. . . . Monday's ruling will force Glendale and Burbank to stop pumping from the San Fernando Valley section of the upper Los Angeles River area. They will have to replace that water with a higher-priced supply from the Metropolitan Water District. Glendale, for example, is now importing about 40% of its water from the MWD. . . . A city official said the court ruling will require Glendale to boost imports to 80%. The MWD price is almost three times the cost of water pumped from the San Fernando Valley underground basin.

It had turned out to be, as Los Angeles had contended, less a case about water than about money, about who would pay for which water. The Los Angeles share of the waters of the ULARA would grow from about two-thirds under the 1968 trial court judgment to about four-fifths under the Supreme Court's guidelines. Los Angeles could use more of the cheaper water and the defendants would have to use more of the expensive water.

The 1979 *San Fernando* Judgment—
A Complex Division of ULARA Waters

On remand, the *San Fernando* case was assigned to Judge Harry Hupp, who met with the parties and issued a series of orders in early 1977 allowing continued extractions and continued watermaster service. Drafting and reviewing new findings of fact, conclusions of law, and a new judgment occupied the rest of 1977 and all of 1978. On January 26, 1979, Judge Hupp signed the final judgment, more than twenty-three years after Los Angeles filed the original complaint.

The 1979 judgment provides for a complicated division of the waters of the Upper Los Angeles River Area. Rights and extractions of the parties in the four subareas are determined, quantified, and monitored by type of water right. To oversee this operation, the judgment provides for a three-part governance arrangement. First, the watermaster shall be "a qualified hydrologist, acceptable to all active public agency parties" (that is, the four cities and Crescenta Valley County Water District) and "shall serve at the pleasure of the Court, but may be removed or replaced on motion of any party after hearing and showing of good cause" (Judgment, 1979: 23). Advising and consulting with the watermaster is an administrative committee, with one representative from each of the parties with extraction rights. The committee is to act unanimously. The Superior Court retains continuing jurisdiction, overseeing the watermaster, providing for modifications of the judgment as needed, and resolving matters on which the Administrative Committee cannot reach consensus.

Melvin Blevins, a hydrologist with the Los Angeles Department of Water and Power, was chosen as ULARA watermaster, replacing the Southern District office of the Department of Water Resources. The distinction is important: Los Angeles is not the ULARA watermaster, Melvin Blevins personally is the watermaster. Mr. Blevins, who was present through the entire adjudication, was acceptable to all of the cities and the county water district, and he continues to serve as watermaster. He and his staff occupy part of the space of the LADWP's offices in downtown Los Angeles. Since the LADWP already gathered most of the data on the ULARA and since the city (with rights to approximately 80 percent of the water) pays most of the watermaster costs, this has been perceived to be an economical arrangement.

The watermaster, his staff, and the Administrative Committee develop policies and procedures for basin operation and oversee and account for parties' extractions. In doing so, they keep track of pueblo, overlying, appropriative, and prescriptive rights of the parties to native groundwater, import return water, stored waters, and water withdrawn under various physical solutions.

In the San Fernando subarea, Los Angeles has a pueblo water right to the entire native safe yield of 43,660 acre-feet per year, is enjoined from pumping more native water than that, and has an injunction against any other party from pumping native waters. The city may pump underlying pueblo waters (that is, the basin's stock rather than its annual yield or flow) when needed, as long as it replaces the mined water within a reasonable time. Los Angeles, Glendale, Burbank, and San Fernando all have rights to their import return flows in the San Fernando subarea. Return flow percentages have been calculated in various parts of the subarea to determine each of the cities' import return water rights: Los Angeles receives credit for and may pump up to 20.8 percent of the waters it imports into the San Fernando subarea for delivery to customers; Glendale, 20.0 percent; Burbank, 20.0 percent; and San Fernando, 26.3 percent. Import return waters not pumped within the same year are carried over and maintained as a cumulative credit for pumping in future years.

The cities in the San Fernando subarea receive stored water credit for imported waters spread for recharge into the groundwater reservoir. Rights to stored water are credited at 100 percent. In addition to their extractions of stored water or import return waters in the San Fernando Subarea, Glendale, Burbank, and San Fernando may, in any year, pump up to an additional 10 percent of the amount of their previous year's import return water credit, subject to an obligation to replace those additional extractions the next year. There also is a physical solution to ease the difficulties parties might have in complying with the formal allocation of rights in the San Fernando subarea. Under a strict application of the injunction against any pumping of native water by any party other than Los Angeles, the value of Glendale and Burbank's extensive investments in pumping and distribution facilities would go down, and they would be forced to construct new ones elsewhere. Therefore, Glendale and Burbank are permitted to pump up to 5,500 and 4,200 acre-feet per year, respectively, from the subarea in exchange for compensating Los Angeles for acquiring additional imports to make up the difference. Three private defendants are also permitted to pump up to a combined total of 245 acre-feet per year if they compensate Los Angeles for additional imports, two other private defendants are permitted to pump up to a combined total of 475 acre-feet if they compensate Glendale for additional imports, and two more private defendants are permitted to pump up to an additional 325 acre-feet per year if they compensate Burbank.

In the Verdugo subarea, the original assignment of rights made by Judge Moor in 1968 was left undisturbed by the Supreme Court. Glendale and Crescenta Valley County Water District had reduced their pumping there because of poor water quality, so Judge Hupp found on remand that Verdugo was no longer in a state of overdraft. Glendale and Crescenta Valley's combined appropriative and prescriptive rights, however, amounted to Verdugo's native safe yield (3,856 acre-feet for Glendale, 3,294 acre-feet for Crescenta Valley, totaling 7,150 acre-feet), so they are limited to pumping those amounts. Both parties also import and deliver MWD water within the subarea, and their return flow percentage is 36.7 percent.

Los Angeles imports and delivers water in the Verdugo subarea, but has no groundwater pumping facilities there. The judgment provides that Los Angeles may exercise a right to pump import return flows there in the future, upon application to the watermaster.

The Sylmar subarea was determined not to be in overdraft, nor to have been in overdraft for any consecutive five-year period. Accordingly, two private defendants were awarded overlying rights to their small portion of Sylmar's native safe yield of 6,210 acre-feet per year. The balance of the native safe yield was divided between San Fernando and Los Angeles as appropriative rights of equal priority. San Fernando's appropriative right was determined to be 3,580 acre-feet per year and the appropriative right of Los Angeles was determined to be 1,560 acre-feet per year. The trial judgment provided that extractions from Sylmar could be limited by injunction upon notification of the parties and the court at some future point that the subarea was in overdraft condition. This was done in 1984. Los Angeles and San Fernando also import water into the Sylmar subarea, and have rights to pump import return flows at 35.7 percent of imported water delivered.

The court also provided for a physical solution in Sylmar. Only about 9 percent of the city of San Fernando overlies the Sylmar subarea, but the city's pumping facilities are located there. Most of the city's import return flows sink into the San Fernando subarea, where 91 percent of the city's territory is located. Therefore, San Fernando is permitted under the judgment to pump its import return water rights for both subareas from Sylmar, while Los Angeles, which has pumping facilities in both subareas, pumps an offsetting lesser amount from Sylmar and more from the San Fernando subarea.

New Challenges and Problems for the ULARA

The 1979 judgment constituted a new governance structure and basin management program for the ULARA. As in the Main San Gabriel Basin, ULARA water users barely began operating under their new governance and management arrangements before serious new challenges arose. Less than a year after implementation of the 1979 judgment began, analyses of San Fernando Valley groundwater by LADWP and the California Department of Health Services found large areas contaminated by volatile organic chemicals. Nearly half of the ninety wells tested in the San Fernando subarea showed traces of trichloroethylene (TCE), and about 15 percent of the wells showed tetrachloroethylene (PCE) and other industrial chemicals. The areas most affected were also among those most heavily pumped in the past.

These were not the first water-quality problems experienced in the ULARA, but they were the most extensive and dangerous. LADWP and the cities of Glendale, Burbank, and San Fernando, in cooperation with the Southern California Association of Governments, applied to the State Water Resources Control Board for funding under the U.S. Environmental Protection Agency's Section 208 grant program to develop a basinwide groundwater-quality management plan. Funds were received, and work began on the plan in July 1981. Completed in 1983, the plan recommended actions for controlling and preventing further contamination: phasing out private sewage disposal systems, regulating underground storage tanks and pipelines as well as landfills, sealing and packing well casings to prevent movement of contaminants between aquifers, and augmented enforcement. These recommendations have been implemented. The plan also recommended that contaminated groundwater be treated to reduce concentrations of TCE and PCE. An interagency coordinating committee was formed to oversee the implementation of the plan, with participants from twenty state and local agencies.

Cleanup of the contaminated waters remains to be fully implemented. As in the Main San Gabriel Basin, four sites within the San Fernando subarea have been designated as EPA Superfund sites. At the North Hollywood–Burbank site, LADWP and the EPA agreed on plans for an aeration facility for groundwater treatment. Lockheed Aircraft, found by the EPA to be "potentially responsible" for the TCE and PCE contamination that eliminated the city of Burbank's groundwater source, has agreed to pay $86 million of the $92 million cost of building and operating the treatment plant. The balance of the cost will be shared by the city of Burbank and Weber Aircraft, another "potentially responsible" party.[4]

Losses of Aqueduct Water

After Los Angeles completed the second barrel of its aqueduct in 1970, LADWP began pumping groundwater from the Owens Valley in large quantities. From 1931 through 1969, its groundwater extractions from Owens Valley averaged 7,000 acre-feet per year. In the first few years after the second aqueduct was completed, 1971–74, LADWP pumping averaged 112,000 acre-feet per year.

Inyo County officials filed suit in 1972, charging that the groundwater production to supply the second aqueduct was causing widespread environmental damage. In 1985, after several clashes in court over environmental impact reports submitted by LADWP purporting to show no damage to Owens Valley, representatives from Inyo County and LADWP began to negotiate about Los Angeles pumping from Owens Valley. Agreements reached in 1989 would allow LADWP to continue pumping from the valley (prompting angry protests by Inyo County residents, including recall efforts directed toward Inyo County officials), but also provided for the reduction or cessation of pumping if water conditions could not sustain it without causing further environmental damage. LADWP also agreed to jointly prepare an environmental impact report with Inyo County.

In April 1990, the LADWP agreed that conditions would not allow it to pump water from Owens Valley for export to Los Angeles for at least a year, and some DWP wells were shut down altogether. Pumping at other DWP wells was restricted to amounts needed to maintain Owens Valley rangeland owned by Los Angeles, and to keep local fish hatcheries in operation. In September 1990, the jointly prepared environmental impact report was released in draft form. In it, the LADWP acknowledged that serious environmental harm has been inflicted on Owens Valley since the second pipeline was placed in operation: wetlands and springs have dried up, trees and brush on more than 1,000 acres have died, another 1,100 acres of former cropland have failed, and air-quality problems are threatening human health as a result of the fine silt and dust blowing off valley lands no longer covered by vegetation. The draft environmental impact report was available for public review and comment through December 1990.

Los Angeles Aqueduct controversies also involve Mono Lake, a beautiful area in the eastern Sierras northeast of Yosemite National Park. It is a salt lake with water two and one-half times saltier than ocean water. Since 1941, Los Angeles has diverted water from four of the five surface streams that flow into the lake, on the rationale that freshwater flowing into the salt lake becomes unusable. This rationale was accepted by the State Water Resources Control Board in 1974 when it granted licenses to the city to continue its Mono Lake diversions.

Since 1941, the lake level has dropped approximately 40 feet. This has, in the view of many, marred the lake's natural beauty and ecosystem. Populations of brine shrimp and brine flies living in the lake's intensely salty waters are the desired food of at least seventy-nine identified waterfowl species, for whom the lake is a favorite spot. During migration, a third of the world's population of Wilson's phalaropes rest and feed there. Thousands of California gulls—perhaps two-thirds of the state's gull population—nest and breed at Mono Lake, feeding on the brine shrimp and brine flies.

Diversions of the freshwater streams feeding Mono Lake have increased its already high salinity. Beyond a point, even the brine shrimp and brine flies cannot live there, and a decline in their populations would adversely affect the food supply for the migrating species and for the gulls that nest and breed there. In addition, lake levels have dropped so low at times that local predators, such as coyotes, have been able to walk to Negit Island in the middle of the lake, where most of the gulls breed, and feed upon gull eggs and hatchlings that normally are protected by the water.

The National Audubon Society and a local group called the Mono Lake Committee have sued Los Angeles in order to stop the decline in lake levels. In 1989, Los Angeles was ordered to stop diverting water from the Mono Basin, at least through the spring of 1990, to permit a reassessment of Mono Lake's natural replenishment and the effect of the city's diversions. The El Dorado County Superior Court set a target lake level of 6,377 feet above sea level, on the basis of testimony identifying that level as essential to maintaining the Mono Lake ecosystem. In the spring of 1990, the lake level stood 1½ feet below that mark, and the ban on diversions was extended to the spring of 1991. As an auxiliary measure in the meantime, the U.S. Forest Service installed an 1,100-yard electric fence in March 1990 to keep predators away from Negit Island.

The drought has kept the lake level from rising to the target level; however, the gull population of Mono Lake increased to record numbers during the 1990–91 water year, and LADWP officials contended that the city should be allowed to resume its diversions from the watershed. In April 1991, the El Dorado County Superior Court judge denied Los Angeles a request to resume the diversions, holding fast to the 6,377-foot target. In May 1991, acknowledging the likelihood that at least some Mono Basin diversions would be lost permanently, the LADWP Board announced its support for a State Lands Commission proposal to transfer some San Joaquin Valley farmers' water rights to Los Angeles to offset the lost diversions.[5]

There are many other intriguing elements to the Owens Valley and Mono Basin stories, but the limitations on water export are of principal significance for the ULARA.[6] The cutoff of groundwater pumping in Owens Valley alone drops Los Angeles water supplies at least temporarily by 75,000–100,000 acre-feet per year—enough to supply 150,000 to 200,000 households. The cessation of water diversions from Mono Basin eliminates another 100,000 acre-feet temporarily. In the long run, LADWP anticipates that even if the California Water Resources Control Board agrees in 1994 to renew the city's license to divert water from Mono Basin, it will probably cut the regular allotment Los Angeles receives from the basin in half, to about 50,000 acre-feet.

LADWP has been making up some of its loss of Los Angeles Aqueduct supplies by purchasing more water from MWD. The city's draw on MWD supplies rose fourfold from 1989 to 1990. LADWP also increased pumping from the ULARA. Assessing the effects of more pumping, Rick Caruso, then president of the DWP Board of Commissioners, said in April 1990, "It leaves us in very rough shape for next year."[7]

Analysis

The development of a basin governance structure and a management program in the ULARA clearly was a long, difficult, and expensive process, complicated by the attempt to apply the San Gabriel "formula" in a neighboring watershed with historical and legal circumstances that were different in important ways. The 1987–1991 drought, the losses of imported water, and concern about contaminated groundwater have combined to place new pressures on the governance and management system developed in the *San Fernando* adjudication. So far, ULARA's governance structure has provided a means of adapting to changed conditions and developing coordinated responses to these challenges.

Eliciting Information

In numerous court actions beginning in the late 1800s, Los Angeles attempted to define and defend its right to the water of the Los Angeles River. Those actions, up to and including the *Glendale* and *Burbank* cases in the 1930s and 1940s, generated considerable information about the water supply of, and conditions in, the Upper Area of the Los Angeles River watershed. LADWP, the county flood control district, and the U.S. Army Corps of Engineers further researched and reported on the ULARA as the aqueduct terminus was completed and flood control and spreading facilities were built and placed in operation. With the addition of the referee report, by the time of the trial in the *San Fernando* case there were no disputes among the parties over basin boundaries and water supply conditions. As the most frequently litigated groundwater supply in the Los Angeles metropolitan area, the ULARA was also one of the best understood by the 1960s.

The relatively small number of large pumpers in the ULARA (owing especially to the annexation by Los Angeles of most of the San Fernando Valley in 1913) reduced the problems of eliciting information about groundwater production. Los Angeles, Glendale, Burbank, and San Fernando have accounted for 90 percent or more of pumping in the ULARA for years, and by the time of the 1979 judgment in the *San Fernando* case, less than two dozen active pumpers remained. Both the 1968 and 1979 judgments have required pumpers to report information about their water production, imports, and exports to the ULARA Watermaster, which produces and circulates annual reports containing this and other information among the pumpers and other interested parties.

Institutional Design

Debate over what set of rules should govern the use of ULARA groundwater supplies was long and hard-fought. The *San Fernando* defendants wanted the San Gabriel formula of mutual prescription and guaranteed prescriptive rights applied, whereas Los Angeles wanted to maintain its right to all the native water of the watershed plus its imports. There was no effort to design and implement a new set of institutional arrangements for governing the use of ULARA water supplies; each side went into court armed with what it believed to be convincing precedents about how rights to the water supplies should be apportioned. Only after 1975, when the California Supreme Court sent the case back to the trial level without giving Los Angeles or the defendants everything they wanted, were serious efforts undertaken to design rules and governance arrangements for basin operation.

In the course of fighting over the definition of overdraft, however, the city of Los Angeles did advance its new theory of overdraft, with its associated concept of regulatory storage capacity. These concepts have been important elements of basin management programs developed since 1968, providing part of the rationale for conjunctive-use programs and the idea of operating safe yield. The California Supreme Court's acceptance of the new theory of overdraft in 1975 has reinforced water users' willingness to incorporate flexible notions of safe yield into basin management designs.

ULARA water users also added the idea of pumping rights to import return flows and adopted the notion of stored water credits (also used in Raymond Basin and, with modifications, in the Main San Gabriel and Chino basins). In the 1979 judgment, ULARA water users agreed to a basin management program that recognizes and tracks water production by type of water user and by type of right, a structure closely followed in the Chino Basin (see Chapter 12), the only major basin adjudication since the California Supreme Court's 1975 *San Fernando* decision.

Integration with Other Governance Structures

The ULARA adjudication resulted in one of the most independent basin governance structures in southern California. Under the continuing jurisdiction of the court, ULARA water users choose their own watermaster and administrative committee, write their own basin management policies, and provide their own information about basin water conditions and use. The administrative committee structure guarantees representation and requires agreement from each importer of water to the basin, as well as all pumpers, in order to change basin management policies.

This does not mean that ULARA governance and management are not connected with other systems in important ways. The ULARA Watermaster is also an employee of the LADWP. The LADWP and Los Angeles County Flood Control District (now the Department of Public Works) have worked closely together in building, maintaining, and operating the flood control and spreading facilities essential to groundwater recharge in the ULARA. Los Angeles, Burbank, Glendale, San Fernando, and the Crescenta Valley County Water District are all MWD members with representation on the MWD Board and access to MWD water. ULARA water users have worked with the State Water Resources Control Board and the California Department of Health Services, as well as EPA, to deal with groundwater-quality problems.

Operation and Performance of the Management Program

The management program established under the 1979 judgment has been operating for more than a decade. Under that program, the ULARA provides groundwater for the cities of San Fernando, Glendale, Burbank, and Los Angeles, each of which also imports substantial amounts of its water supply. The Crescenta Valley County Water District blends Verdugo extractions with MWD imports, and some private parties continue to pump ULARA water. There remain only eighteen active pumpers in the ULARA. There have not been any actively pumping nonparties in the ULARA for at least ten years.

The basin management program has operated with apparent effectiveness and without conflict, with respect to restrictions on withdrawal quantities, storage and withdrawal of imported and native waters, and physical solutions to accommodate the special needs and circumstances of some of the parties. Water levels recovered from their record lows since 1968, especially in the eastern part of the ULARA where the worst overdrafting occurred. Pumping has remained between 80,000 and 120,000 acre-feet in all but a few years (Table 9.1). Total groundwater extractions have been more variable since the 1975 decision than they were under the trial court judgment, but this is to be expected under conjunctive-use, as opposed to fixed safe-yield, operation. With rights to store and recapture waters at later dates, and to carry over credits from one year to the next, parties vary the amounts of their groundwater extractions in response to changes in surface water conditions and availability of imported water.[8]

The cities have actively taken advantage of opportunities to store water in the ULARA for later withdrawals. They have "banked" water, which has been extremely valuable in meeting water demands during drought. In large measure, they have done so by importing water and storing it underground. MWD and Los Angeles Aqueduct imports to the ULARA increased from the time of the 1968 judgment through the late 1980s, when imported water became less available because of the drought (Table 9.2).

TABLE 9.1
ULARA Groundwater Extractions by Subarea, 1969–1990 (acre-feet)

Year	San Fernando	Sylmar	Verdugo	ULARA total
1969	91,785	5,568	6,717	104,070
1970	96,290	6,412	6,916	109,618
1971	85,936	4,143	6,477	96,556
1972	91,376	6,140	6,665	104,181
1973	88,770	5,876	6,260	100,906
1974	92,867	5,944	6,397	105,208
1975	100,373	6,138	5,455	111,966
1976	108,457	6,557	4,962	119,975
1977	129,439	6,223	4,173	140,019
1978	70,543	6,068	3,747	81,398
1979	64,645	7,164	3,511	75,483
1980	63,337	6,102	3,307	72,925
1981	97,789	7,497	4,262	109,730
1982	87,675	6,776	5,608	100,237
1983	71,312	6,181	5,187	82,855
1984	119,560	7,013	5,560	132,299
1985	105,782	6,232	5,834	118,151
1986	90,833	6,242	5,493	102,752
1987	96,604	6,139	4,874	107,788
1988	109,624	5,937	4,364	120,100
1989	132,581	5,459	4,349	142,559
1990	86,898	5,390	4,232	96,689

SOURCE: ULARA Watermaster Reports.

The costs of basin governance and management, which consist primarily of ULARA Watermaster costs, have remained low since 1968. These costs have been paid by the parties in proportion to their water production from the ULARA, so costs are related to benefits received. Basin management costs have risen since the early 1980s in the ULARA as elsewhere, reflecting expenditures for monitoring and protecting water quality.

Epilogue: *Los Angeles v. San Fernando* and the Advantages and Disadvantages of "Judge-Made" Law

The California law of water rights, especially groundwater rights, is largely "judge-made" law. This can be desirable: through the use of equity

TABLE 9.2
Water Imported into ULARA, 1969–1990 (acre-feet)

Year	San Fernando subarea			Total ULARA		
	LA-Owens	MWD	Combined	LA-Owens	MWD	Combined
1969	335,235	28,500	363,735	342,665	33,878	376,543
1970	377,320	27,623	404,943	385,294	33,070	418,364
1971	478,535	24,866	503,401	485,969	30,552	516,511
1972	452,867	28,929	481,796	460,396	34,665	495,061
1973	447,034	28,344	475,378	453,916	33,307	487,223
1974	435,011	22,080	457,091	441,843	27,033	468,876
1975	433,683	22,940	456,623	440,774	27,847	468,621
1976	443,778	54,446	498,224	451,814	59,252	511,066
1977	296,101	49,468	345,569	302,881	54,468	357,529
1978	399,797	48,142	447,939	406,615	53,957	460,572
1979	464,701	51,089	515,790	472,255	56,843	529,098
1980	470,224	57,508	527,732	477,754	63,499	541,253
1981	458,178	56,170	514,348	465,944	62,263	528,207
1982	461,579	59,017	520,596	469,453	65,233	534,686
1983	444,017	59,761	503,778	451,712	65,582	517,294
1984	489,717	65,758	555,475	498,738	72,764	571,502
1985	584,835	64,809	649,644	595,807	71,673	667,480
1986	584,660	64,664	649,324	594,500	72,081	666,581
1987	589,945	68,888	658,633	601,017	72,684	673,701
1988	562,644	76,972	639,616	574,664	85,114	659,778
1989	554,502	81,517	636,019	565,524	89,578	655,102
1990	142,707	470,202	612,909	145,507	489,937	635,444

Source: ULARA Watermaster Reports.

jurisprudence, specific decrees can be formulated to govern water supply situations while taking unique local circumstances into account. Dangerous overdrafting has been controlled in a number of California basins under such a case-by-case approach. Solutions worked out for particular cases may be more flexible than state statutes imposed on potentially very different situations.

Judge-made law also comes at a price. Ordinarily, courts cannot decide issues that the parties to a case do not raise. A potentially important question may go unresolved for decades—or worse may appear to have been resolved because of the outcome of a case when it was never even addressed. This happened with Civil Code Section 1007, which was not addressed in *Pasadena v. Alhambra* or the appeals from the West Basin judgment, opening the door to the California Supreme Court's decision many years later in *Los Angeles v. San Fernando.*

After that decision, public agencies and public utilities may be expected to be aware of their Section 1007 immunity and to take advantage of it. They still can waive their Section 1007 immunity, but they are unlikely to ignore it. For this reason, John Mann wrote that one could argue that *San Fernando* "killed" mutual prescription (Mann, 1975: 7). The Supreme Court's decision certainly altered the deliberations among the parties in the Chino Basin concerning how to allocate the scarce and overdrafted supply there. Still, as Chino Basin illustrates, "Although mutual prescription may die, mutual agreement can not" (Mann, 1975: 8). Parties to a basin adjudication remain free to work out a stipulation and present it to a court for approval.

The flexibility of judge-made law may at times be compromised by another of its qualities, adherence to precedent. Courts may continue to follow rules of their own devising long after the circumstances that gave rise to them have disappeared. The pueblo water right of Los Angeles is an example. Given the number of prior decisions on this right, plus the assiduous defense of, and reliance on, that right for a century, there may have been no other practical way for the Supreme Court to decide. Nonetheless, as the court's ambivalent language indicates, deciding an important water rights issue in an area as radically transformed as the Los Angeles metropolitan area on the basis of the ghostly presence of a Spanish king and what he may have meant to do 200 years ago leaves one to wonder whether devotion to precedent is an unmitigated virtue.

The definition of "overdraft" also invoked questions of precedent. When the highest court in a state accepts a definition of "overdraft," lower court judges are inclined to follow and apply that definition, with little incentive to recognize that the state of knowledge about that issue has changed since the earlier definition was accepted. In the *San Fernando* case, Judge Moor stayed with the definition of "overdraft" as extractions in excess of average annual replenishment regardless of basin conditions, even though the concept of conjunctive use was well received by then and in practice in several basins.

Mutual prescription helped to resolve problems in the San Gabriel River watershed, and the California Supreme Court decided the *San Fernando* case so as to preserve the results reached in Pasadena and its progeny. But, as the Supreme Court declared, a solution may be *an* equitable apportionment without necessarily being *the* equitable apportionment to be followed in every case. One may hope that the real outcome of the *San Fernando* decision is not that mutual prescription is dead, but that "in the future, each basin will be evaluated according to legal and physical conditions that exist in that area, and not automatically follow a formula that may not be the best way to allocate pumping rights" (Blevins, 1975: 206).

Judges are not the only ones who can be "mechanistic," and inappropriately attempt to apply a "formula" to different sets of circumstances. Water agency personnel, and the attorneys who bring basin adjudications before the courts, can make similar errors of strategy or judgment. As the *San Fernando* case went to trial and proceeded through its appeals, water users in the Mojave River watershed displayed some fireworks of their own.

NOTES

1. More than 100 court days were consumed in pretrial—86 under Judge Airola and another 18 under Judge Moor. Depositions of major witnesses took weeks, and the three years of "interrogatories and answers to interrogatories must have consumed several man-years of labor" (Mann, 1976: 269). Expert witnesses of significant notoriety were engaged by both sides: Dr. John Mann, Jr., for Los Angeles, Max Bookman for the defendants.

Many defendants entered disclaimers or defaults, or were dismissed. The only two parties extracting water from the Eagle Rock subarea—Sparkletts Drinking Water Corporation and Deep Rock Water Company—entered into separate stipulations with Los Angeles, effectively eliminating the Eagle Rock subarea from the litigation. The stipulations permitted the two companies to continue extracting water from Eagle Rock, on the condition that they compensate Los Angeles for its importation of additional waters.

2. Judge Moor's reasoning involved five steps. First, although the concept of a pueblo water right had been recognized by the California Supreme Court in *Lux v. Haggin* (1886), it was only dictum in that case and thus had no value as a precedent. Second, the expert testimony on Spanish and Mexican law indicated that no particular preference was given to one type of settlement over another with respect to water rights, and there were provisions for sharing available water supplies by proration in times of shortage. Third, there was no evidence that a generic pueblo water right attached automatically through Spanish or Mexican law to pueblos established in "the Indies," in the absence of a special grant of such a right. Fourth, there was no explicit evidence to indicate the existence of a specific grant of such a right to the pueblo of Los Angeles. Fifth, none of the land grants made by Spain or Mexico to other individuals within the San Fernando Valley contained any reservation of water rights in favor of the pueblo of Los Angeles.

3. During the first four years of operation under the judgment, the watermaster identified only two parties that continued to overextract their water rights. One party had been awarded zero rights under the judgment but had continued

to pump groundwater until the 1971–72 water year, when it indicated to the water-master that it would begin to lease rights thereafter. The other party also had zero water rights and had continued to pump groundwater and had not taken action to lease rights from other parties, but its total cumulative extractions over the first four years of operation under the judgment had only been 13.46 acre-feet, so its noncompliance had not threatened the stability of the groundwater supply under the judgment. This latter party subsequently stopped pumping, though it never made up its cumulative deficit.

4. Greg Braxton, "Lockheed to Pay Most of Water Cleanup Costs," *Los Angeles Times*, March 27, 1991, p. B-3.

5. The farmers are on valley lands badly deteriorated by agricultural drainage pollution. The State Lands Commission proposal would compensate the farmers for taking the land out of production, and project water that would have been used to irrigate those lands could be reallocated to Los Angeles.

6. See Kahrl (1981) for some of the stories concerning Owens Valley. For consequences of LADWP land ownership and water withdrawals on Owens Valley development during the 1980s, see Kevin Roderick, "Little Towns That the Boom Just Bypassed," *Los Angeles Times*, October 1, 1990, p. A-3.

7. Frederick Muir and Kevin Roderick, "L.A. Agrees to Shut Owens Valley Pumps," *Los Angeles Times*, April 4, 1990, p. B-1.

8. Operation of the basin under Judge Hupp's temporary order during and after the 1976–77 drought is illustrative. In June 1977, to meet an emergency situation caused by the drought and MWD's halt of State Water Project deliveries, Judge Hupp signed an order authorizing temporary mining of San Fernando Basin. The cities pumped about 45,000 acre-feet of additional groundwater from the San Fernando subarea, on the condition that those amounts would be restored to the basin later upon resumed availability of imported supplies. Parties pumped a total of 140,000 acre-feet from the ULARA in 1976–77. In the wetter years of 1977–78, 1978–79, and 1979–80, parties stored water in the ULARA and pumped between 73,000 and 81,000 acre-feet.

The Mojave River Basins
High Desert Drama and Institutional Failure

. . . the single most frustrating experience of my life.

—Carl Coleman

. . . the single most frustrating experience of my life.

—Arthur Littleworth

Sure it was frustrating; you'd better believe it was. . . .

—H. James Gilliam

Responses to water supply problems along the Mojave River were not crafted over time through the development of a consensus among water users, based on shared information about water conditions and sensitivity to local differences in physical circumstances. Instead, during the 1960s, while water users still disagreed about whether an overdraft problem even existed, the San Gabriel River watershed "formula" was imported to the Mojave River watershed. A special district—the Mojave Water Agency (MWA)—was formed to acquire access to a supplemental water supply, and an adjudication of pumping rights was begun. The Mojave River area was proceeding according to plan.

There were a few flaws in the plan. The Mojave Water Agency bore no relation to the hydrologic boundaries of local water supplies. Depending on how one counts, the Mojave Water Agency encompasses all or

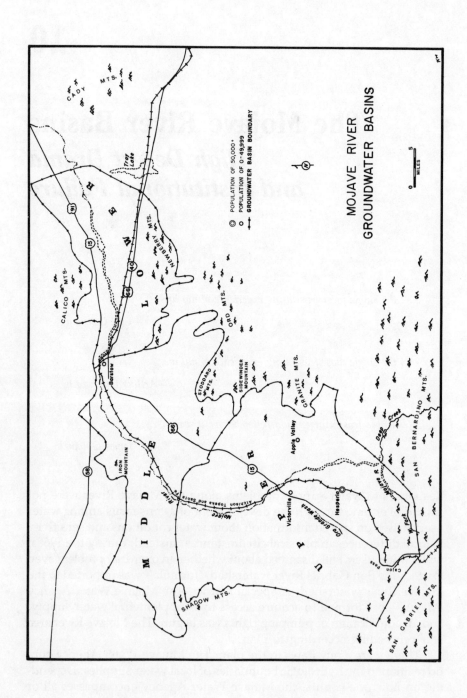

MOJAVE RIVER
GROUNDWATER BASINS

◎ POPULATION OF 50,000+
○ POPULATION OF 0-49,999
↟ GROUNDWATER BASIN BOUNDARY

part of twelve to fifteen groundwater basins. The adjudication of pumping rights was prosecuted by the MWA but involved only some of the basins along the Mojave River. The adjudication was supported by a small number of large upstream water users but not by many smaller and downstream water users.

Today, the overdraft along the Mojave River is greater than ever, and pumping continues to increase. The adjudication begun in the 1960s was dropped in 1976. The MWA's entitlement of supplemental water has been left unused because there has been no means to pay for it, and even the delivery of the MWA's full entitlement of supplemental water every year would not offset the current rate of overdraft. The attempt to impose a formula in the Mojave River watershed did not merely fail; it backfired.

Those who are inclined to think that undertaking inclusive processes for crafting well-designed responses to imperfectly understood problems is unnecessarily burdensome and time-consuming should consider the experiences of water users in the Mojave River watershed. There, people who were absolutely convinced that they had the answer for overdrafted basins, that they knew what they were doing, and that what they were doing was right, created the stormiest political fight along the Mojave River in the past thirty years.

"Making Hay While the Sun Shines"

Rapid agricultural development and population growth did not take place in the High Desert area until World War II. The area's population doubled during the 1940s and more than doubled in the 1950s. By 1960, the population of the Upper, Middle, and Lower basins along the Mojave River (plus the adjacent Lucerne Valley and Yucca Valley areas) was nearly 60,000. This increase was accompanied by an expansion of irrigated agriculture to about 20,000 acres. The greatest rate of increase was downstream, in the Lower Mojave River Basin.

By far, the irrigators' crop of choice was alfalfa, which thrived in the desert environment. It could be grown and harvested at low cost with little labor and was easily irrigated from relatively shallow wells (Stickel, 1980: 156). Ranchers reported alfalfa yields of 5 to 9 tons per acre. The desert's long growing season allowed up to five or six cuttings per year. Alfalfa is also the most water-consumptive crop one can grow. Even rice, often grown in standing water, does not consume as much water per acre. Growing alfalfa hay in the Mojave Desert means growing the most water-consumptive crop in one of the most water-deficient regions in the United States.

According to recent Mojave Water Agency (1986a) estimates, the average annual supply of water available along the Mojave River is approximately 74,800 acre-feet. If native vegetation along the river consumes about 28,000–30,000 acre-feet per year (a common estimate), approximately 45,000 to 47,000 acre-feet remain available for use and recharge in the Mojave River area. The 1956 level of irrigated acreage in the Mojave River Valley was estimated to consume about 56,000 acre-feet of water annually (Troxell, 1957: 118). By the end of the 1950s, water supplies in several parts of the Mojave River watershed were being overdrafted (see Table 10.1). Water levels fell and pumping lifts and costs rose. The situation grew worse as development continued in the region and the 1945–1965 drought persisted.

The Mojave Water Agency and the California Aqueduct

The State Water Project planned in the 1950s to convey northern water to the south called for the East Branch of the California Aqueduct to cross the Upper Mojave River Basin. Local water users formed the Mojave Water Agency Committee to establish a local agency to contract with the state for access to this supplemental water. Attorney William J. Johnstone of Victorville drafted the appropriate legislation, and San Bernardino County's state senator, Stanford C. Shaw, introduced it in the legislature. Senate Bill 1068, the Mojave Water Agency Law, was passed and signed into law during the 1959 session. After a public hearing in November at which all but one of the thirty-five residents testifying supported the agency's formation and activation, and a special election in July 1960 at which agency formation carried handily, the Mojave Water Agency was established.[1]

The newly created MWA encompassed 2,750,000 acres or 4,300 square miles, an area almost the size of Connecticut. It included the Mojave River Valley from The Forks to Camp Cady, an area to the north from Harper Basin to beyond Red Mountain, and an area to the south that included Lucerne, Fry, and Johnson valleys. In 1965, voters annexed the Yucca Valley/Joshua Tree and Landers areas east of the Lucerne, Fry, and Johnson valleys to the MWA, bringing its total area to about 4,800 square miles, and its total population to about 75,000.

In June 1963, the agency and the state signed a contract allocating MWA up to 44,000 acre-feet per year of State Project water. A modification in 1964 added another 6,800 acre-feet per year, bringing the MWA's share to 50,800 acre-feet per year by the year 1990.

MWA's share of State Water Project costs are considered operating costs to be met by an assessment on land only, of 45 cents per $100 valuation.[2] If in any year this raises insufficient revenue to pay the contract costs, an additional tax on land only may be levied to redress the shortfall. The MWA may raise revenues for actual purchases of State Project

TABLE 10.1

Annual Groundwater Extractions, 1950–1981 (acre-feet)

Year	Upper Basin[a]	Middle Basin[b]	Lower Basin[b]	Lucerne Valley[c]	Warren Valley[d]	MWA total estimate[e]
1950	n.a.	n.a.	n.a.	4,000	n.a.	n.a.
1951	n.a.	n.a.	n.a.	4,000	40	144,376
1952	n.a.	n.a.	n.a.	6,000	60	151,719
1953	n.a.	n.a.	n.a.	8,000	70	164,271
1954	n.a.	n.a.	n.a.	13,000	100	163,453
1955	n.a.	n.a.	n.a.	12,000	100	166,884
1956	n.a.	n.a.	n.a.	13,000	650	149,582
1957	n.a.	n.a.	n.a.	12,000	650	148,548
1958	100,000	47,000	n.a.	12,000	650	152,950
1959	108,700	50,600	9,700	6,000	670	171,265
1960	110,700	56,200	10,200	5,000	690	178,325
1961	110,200	55,600	10,600	9,000	760	183,912
1962	103,600	54,600	11,000	9,000	850	177,773
1963	102,800	51,300	12,600	9,000	950	178,423
1964	109,300	54,400	17,000	9,000	1,090	190,868
1965	110,000	49,200	16,000	9,000	1,180	185,083
1966	107,400	47,700	15,200	9,000	1,340	177,671
1967	107,200	52,200	15,500	8,000	1,350	177,041
1968	113,500	55,100	17,400	9,000	1,510	181,629
1969	109,200	45,500	21,000	11,000	1,530	175,473
1970	90,400	53,600	20,800	11,000	n.a.	171,992
1971	84,200	55,400	22,000	10,000	n.a.	168,423
1972	81,200	55,800	20,200	9,000	n.a.	n.a.
1973	92,000	52,600	19,100	8,000	n.a.	n.a.
1974	93,400	55,600	19,600	8,000	n.a.	n.a.
1975	94,900	58,600	20,800	10,000	n.a.	n.a.
1976	96,400	61,600	20,500	10,000	n.a.	n.a.
1977	96,200	64,500	20,900	n.a.	n.a.	n.a.
1978	98,900	67,000	23,500	n.a.	n.a.	n.a.
1979	101,600	69,300	26,100	n.a.	n.a.	n.a.
1980	104,200	71,800	28,600	n.a.	n.a.	n.a.
1981	106,600	74,000	28,800	n.a.	n.a.	n.a.

n.a. = Not available.
a. John S. Murk Engineers, Inc. (1985b).
b. C M Engineering Associates et al. (1983).
c. Schaefer (1979).
d. Lewis (1972).
e. Stetson (1974).

water through water sales or an assessment against pumping of ground-water. MWA's administrative expenses may be met by a tax on all taxable real property within the agency of up to 10 cents per $100 valuation.[3]

The Mojave Water Agency Law provided for the MWA to be governed by an eleven-member board of directors, serving four-year terms and subject to recall. The MWA's territory would be divided into seven divisions, each represented by an elected director. Another director would be elected at large from the entire agency, and the other three would be appointed by concerned local governments within the agency.[4] The law authorized the MWA to enter into contracts with the state, to acquire and dispose of property, issue and redeem bonds, undertake water resource studies, replenish underground water supplies, store and distribute water for use within the agency, acquire water rights by appropriation, develop and sell hydroelectric power, and "to begin, defend, or participate in any action or proceeding before any state or federal court involving or affecting the ownership, use or supply of water, water rights, or water service which is or may be used within the agency."

A 1963 amendment authorized the MWA to initiate in state or federal court "an adjudication of substantially all of the rights of whatever nature to extract water from any of the ground water basins underlying or affecting the water supply," and to "recognize such judicial determination" by levying pump taxes on each water producer's supplies in excess of his allocated share of the safe yield. This amendment authorized what some MWA board members and others had decided they wanted to do: adjudicate the water rights of the Mojave River basins, with the MWA acting as plaintiff much as the Central and West Basin Water Replenishment District had in Central Basin, and use a net pump tax to finance the purchase of supplemental water.

The amendment reflected one view of the agency's mission—that the MWA should be the region's governing water management institution. On this view, the agency was created to make collective decisions and perform management functions for which the smaller special districts within the region were ill-equipped. The MWA was obliged not only to contract with the state for a supplemental supply of water, but to devise and implement a plan for purchasing and distributing that supplemental water, and for alleviating problems caused by limited local supplies.

Others disagreed with this conception of the MWA's mission. The view espoused by State Senator Shaw (who left the State Senate and moved from Ontario into the MWA near Newberry Springs) and others was that the MWA and its State Project water entitlement were like an insurance policy. There doubtless would come a time when the imported water of the California Aqueduct would be desired strongly enough to pay for, but it was not yet. In the meantime, since a State Project contractor had to exist for the area to have any entitlement, MWA residents would pay their annual share of State Project costs, much as one pays an insurance premium year after year for the sake of being able to present a claim when needed. It was perfectly acceptable for the MWA to do nothing but exist, collect the money to pay the capital costs of the State Project, and wait until local water supplies were sufficiently strained that water users would pay for the purchase and distribution of State Project water.[5]

The MWA's first Board of Directors clearly embraced the view of the MWA as the area's water management institution. As they saw it, "the principal reason for organizing the Mojave Water Agency" was that the "natural supply of water to the Mojave River basins is limited. More water is being used than nature is putting back" (MWA, 1964: 14). The area was "faced with the *unquestionable fact* that there has been and there is at present a *serious overdraft* of the local water supply" (MWA, 1964: 3, emphasis added). State Project water would be more costly than the MWA's property tax base would yet support, and certainly more costly than the continued practice of pumping local groundwater. The report continued:

> Hence the basic problem arises as to who is entitled to the local supply, and who should pay for the more expensive imported water. To make this determination it is appropriate to determine what interest each existing and future pumper has, as a matter of law, in the available local supply. The *traditional method* of making this determination is to file an action in the local superior court to determine the rights of each of the users, and at the same time to determine whether any parties who are not now using the local supply will in the future be entitled to use any portion of it. (MWA, 1964: 14, emphasis added)

Adjudication without Consensus

As mentioned in Chapter 5, southern California attorney James H. Krieger wrote a paper in 1955 criticizing the Raymond Basin adjudication on several grounds. Mr. Krieger and the Riverside firm of Best, Best, and Krieger subsequently became involved in the appeal of the West Basin adjudication, in the San Gabriel River adjudication, and in the adjudication of water rights in Central Basin. By the early 1960s, Krieger was chairman of the Southern California Water Conference and had become one of the best-known water rights attorneys in the United States.

On March 17, 1964, the MWA Board of Directors hired Krieger as special legal counsel. This move "officially set into motion the program of water rights determination" (MWA, 1964: 3), less than four years after the MWA's formation, and eight years before the earliest anticipated arrival of supplemental water. Krieger made an initial presentation to the board on May 18, 1964, and the board, "upon hearing this presentation, felt that the water users should be advised of the upcoming plan of action" (MWA, 1964: 13). The 1964 annual report noted that the MWA

> has engaged in a series of meetings with the big pumpers on the River, including industry, public utilities, the military and farmers. The Agency has begun to explore with these groups the elements of a solution which recognizes the substantial rights of all interested parties, and at the same time aims at the welfare of the entire community as its ultimate objective. (MWA, 1964: 13)

The board set the agency's manager, Carl Coleman, and his staff to work on the task of identifying pumpers. The 1955 Recordation Act helped in identifying the larger pumpers along the river, as well as the pattern of pumping. Citing Krieger's presentation, the annual report suggested that the expense, time, and complexity of a lawsuit might be avoided if the principals along the Mojave would agree to "calculations made by the Agency's staff": "This has been the history of other areas. Even though 100 percent cooperation may be difficult to obtain, as much as 75 percent agreement could well prepare the way for workable arrangements pending the arrival of northern water" (MWA, 1964: 15).

Also during 1964, on Krieger's recommendation, the board engaged the services of Dr. John F. Mann, Jr., as MWA's consulting geologist-hydrologist. Dr. Mann also served as a consulting geologist in the San Gabriel River adjudication and as principal expert witness for Los Angeles in the *San Fernando* case. Krieger, Mann, and MWA Manager Coleman constituted the MWA's "special staff" for working on the water-rights determination program, which was beginning to run into a few problems.

For one thing, not everyone agreed that their local water supply came from a "groundwater basin." Was the Mojave River area a series of ground-water basins arrayed along a stream, or an "underground stream" whose flow affected the surrounding water table? The legal implications of the distinction were enormous. If the water supply was an underground stream, the law of surface water rights applied, and most users along the river would be considered appropriators without permits, and thus without firm rights to any quantity of Mojave River water. The MWA board responded that doubts about the entire theory underlying the intended adjudication should not stand in the way of a "desirable" result for the existing pumpers:

> While there may be conflicting theories concerning the Mojave River system, that is, whether it is a series of underground basins connected by a stream, or whether it is a continuous surface and underground stream system, and while different priorities of rights can follow from such different physical theories, it appears desirable to treat the local supply of water as the collective property of those who have been using it for the last five years. This would include riparians, overlying users and

appropriators, without attempting to favor one type of right or use over any other. By this coequal treatment, all who have built an economy on the local water supply would be able to continue with their enterprises, and no particular type of use would be given precedence over another. (MWA, 1964: 16)

Of course, to overlying landowners along the river and the few appropriators who had taken the trouble to obtain permits, it mattered more than a little whether all uses were going to be treated the same. In the end, the agency finessed the issue: Dr. Mann demarcated the Mojave River's "area of influence," and the adjudication was defined as the attempt to determine rights to water within that area.[6]

Another problem was that the serious overdraft that the MWA board declared in 1964 to be an "unquestionable fact" was not quite so unquestionable, after all. That same year, the state Department of Water Resources published a bulletin on groundwater availability and quality within the Lahontan region, which includes the Mojave River area. It acknowledged that pumping along the river had been heavy during the drought. Nevertheless, the department's descriptions of each of the Mojave River basins—Upper, Middle, and Lower—concluded with the statement: "Overdraft does not appear to exist at present" (California DWR, 1964c: 290–310).

For anyone attempting to persuade a group of water users to agree to a determination and restriction of their pumping rights, and to be taxed to pay for more expensive imported water, there is a cavernous difference between an "unquestionable fact" of "serious overdraft" and a situation where "overdraft does not appear to exist." Two fundamental issues—whether this was groundwater, and whether it was being overdrafted—were still in question in 1964. Proceeding toward an adjudication under those circumstances called for more risk preference than attorneys normally display.

There also were problems of appearances concerning the MWA Board and its program. First, if the adjudication was supposed to be a means of generating the funds to purchase supplemental water, questions arose about the relationship between the Mojave River area water users and water users elsewhere in the agency. It seemed that either the Mojave River water users would pay net pump taxes to provide supplemental water to the whole agency, or that the supplemental water supply for the whole agency would be delivered only to the Mojave River area. Either prospect was unsuitable to some segment of the MWA's populace.

Second, the board had hired a large law firm from the other side of the mountains, Riverside's Best, Best, and Krieger, and a Los Angeles area geologist. Third, the agency office was located in Victorville, the officers of the Board of Directors were all from the Upper Basin, and (because of the process for selecting directors) only three of the eleven directors were from the Middle and Lower basins. Fourth, the agency's actions contributed to a perception that large pumpers were receiving especially solicitous attention from the board and staff. For instance, when the MWA board "felt that the water users should be advised of the upcoming plan of action," the large pumpers "were invited by letters and all other interested parties were invited by public notice . . . to hear and participate in the Agency's first public presentation" (MWA, 1964: 13). This pattern was maintained. Meetings were held with large users; "presentations" were given to everyone else. Large users were invited personally; everyone else was invited by "public notice" in the newspapers.

Indeed, the 1964 annual report presented the water-rights determination program in terms that suggested it could be put together without a consensus of water users, as long as the big users coordinated their efforts. After pointing out that "100 percent cooperation" among pumpers may not be necessary if "as much as 75 percent agreement" could be obtained, the report described what "75 percent agreement" meant:

> Only 28 entities owning 168 wells reported pumping more than 1,000 acre-feet each. The total extractions of these 28 amounted to 92,353 acre-feet, and represents 74.2 percent of the entire reported production.
>
> Another statistic is quite revealing. In 1961 fifty-three entities reported pumping in excess of 500 acre-feet from 229 wells. Their total production was 100,341 acre-feet, or 88.7 percent of the entire reported production. (MWA, 1964: 15)

Some small pumpers took this to mean: you may as well get on board, because this train is leaving the station, with or without you. According to local reports, such feelings were aggravated by attorney Krieger's personal style, which struck some desert residents as high-handed.[7]

Perceptions grew that "outsiders," "upstreamers," and "big pumpers" were behind the adjudication and were deciding the allocation of the desert's water supply. The perceptions fed each other: most large pumpers were located upstream, the meetings were held in the upstream area, the largest pumpers were always represented at the meetings, and they could put together enough of the pumping rights to leave any dissidents out. The stage was set for the classic political battle of "little guys" versus "big guys" to be overlaid with the classic water battle of downstreamers versus upstreamers.

Going to Court

Instead of slowing down and building a consensus behind the water-rights determination program, the MWA board and special staff pressed ahead during 1965. At a special board meeting on January 20, 1965, the special staff recommended a management plan be developed for the area's water supply on the basis of an adjudication of pumping rights. Krieger suggested a water production verification program be initiated to verify the Recordation Act filings, starting with the records of pumpers reporting production of 500 acre-feet per year or more. The board agreed, and appointed Manager Coleman to the verification task.[8] Krieger also suggested that "interested parties, acting through their attorneys and engineers" should attempt to reach a general agreement before the agency proceeded with filing a complaint. Presumably, this included small pumpers with their own attorneys and engineers, as well.

The "interested parties" met on February 23, 1965, and were designated the Special Committee on Water Development, with Krieger as chairman. They decided to meet monthly to work out an ultimate course of action, and recommended that the MWA board postpone filing a complaint until early 1966. The board reported to agency residents that it would "rely heavily on its staff and the Special Committee to assist in making the many decisions necessary for proper management and utilization of your water" (MWA, 1965: 3).

Krieger then appointed from among the Special Committee a smaller Working Committee on Water Development to meet monthly with the special staff to work on "specific problems." The Working Committee consisted of the special staff, the MWA board, and representatives of the pumpers. Among the pumpers represented were those known locally as the Big Five—Southern California Water Company, Southern California Edison Company, Kemper-Campbell Company, the Silver Lakes Ranch, and the K-Line Ranch. Members of the Working Committee accounted for more than half of the groundwater pumping in the area.

By March 1966, the Working Committee had arrived at a policy resolution to be adopted by the MWA board, and the text of a complaint to be filed in the San Bernardino County Superior Court. On March 8, the MWA directors and thirteen Working Committee members appeared at a public meeting attended by 116 persons to explain Mojave Water Agency Policy Resolution 99-66, which set forth the agency's policy regarding water management and authorized the filing of a complaint for the adjudication of water rights. On March 15, the board adopted Resolution 99-66. On March 18, Krieger filed the complaint in the case of *Mojave Water Agency v. Clarence L. Abbey et al.*[9]

Negotiating the *Abbey* Case, 1966–1974

The *Abbey* case provided enough activity to keep several attorneys busy. Summonses and other forms of notice were issued, defendants were added, defendants defaulted, more were added, more defaulted, motions were filed, orders issued. A second complaint, naming dozens of additional defendants, was filed in 1970 and consolidated with the *Abbey* case.

A list of the motions and orders from 1966 through 1974 fills eleven single-spaced typed pages.

Behind this procedural activity, important negotiations about parties' rights took place. Using data from the verification program, the Working Committee drafted a proposed stipulation in 1970, assigning and limiting pumping rights, providing for a net pump tax, and designating the MWA as watermaster. Stipulating defendants waived any separate findings, conclusions, or judgment, as well as rights of appeal, although a defendant who signed the stipulation could withdraw from it before it took effect. It would take effect immediately when signed by parties with an aggregate of 150,000 acre-feet of production rights.

The Race for Signatures

By the time the stipulation was ready to be circulated for signatures, proponents of the adjudication were racing against time. Opposition to the adjudication was building and finding some sympathetic ears on the MWA board. Eventually, active opposition found its way onto the MWA board and into the courtroom and challenged the survival of the adjudication.

The MWA board was reorganized after the 1965 annexations of the Yucca Valley/Joshua Tree and Landers areas. Board membership became more dispersed, with one director each from Lucerne Valley, Apple Valley, Hinkley, Daggett, Yermo, and Joshua Tree. By 1968, there were three directors from Barstow. With more members from downstream in the Mojave River Valley or from MWA areas outside the Mojave River, adjudication opponents were in a better position to question the board's adjudication policy.

Three events that occurred in 1969 worked against the adjudication. Tremendous floods in January and February raised water levels in desert wells by as much as 40 feet and erased years of decline in thirty days. The area's water situation suddenly appeared less urgent. Precipitation averaged at or above normal from 1969 through 1976.

Also in 1969, the MWA board discussed with Southern California Edison (one of the Big Five) the possibility of Edison obtaining an allotment of State Project water from MWA for a proposed coal-burning generating plant. Edison planned to build the plant in the Johnson Valley area to produce electricity for Orange County, where demand was increasing rapidly. A majority of the board favored the idea because Edison was willing to fund a pipeline to convey State Project water as far southeast as Johnson Valley, and the MWA could use that pipeline to convey State Project water to other users along the route. The public, however, scorned the idea of both the plant and water deal, arguing that this was part of a scheme to benefit one of the big water users, and that using scarce desert water for a coal-fired power plant would pollute the desert's air to serve Orange County.

Also in 1969, former state senator Stanford C. Shaw was appointed a director on the MWA board. Shaw was knowledgeable about the agency and held a different view of its purpose from the view that prevailed on the board at the time. A self-described "gadfly" and no stranger to politics, Shaw was accustomed to "stirring things up." He opposed the Edison deal as sacrificing the desert's water and air to produce electricity for Orange County, and he criticized the adjudication for giving away inflated water rights to large upstream interests at the expense of the overlying landowners elsewhere in the system. He himself was a landowner with a one-quarter interest in a few thousand acres of downstream land with no pumping history. There also was some personal animosity between Shaw and attorney Krieger, and Krieger's successor on the case, Arthur Littleworth. Shaw would not hesitate to attempt to build an opposition majority on the board. By his own account, he went on the MWA board with three objectives in mind: to stop the power plant; to get Best, Best, and Krieger off the case as the agency's counsel; and to stop the adjudication.

In 1970, the Mojave River County Water District requested permission to enter the *Abbey* case as an intervener on behalf of its residents, primarily farmers along the river between Victorville and Barstow, plus the Oro Grande cement manufacturing plant. The district had asked Martin Whelan, Jr., a prominent water-rights attorney from the Los Angeles–Orange County area, to review the proposed stipulation. Whelan perceived serious problems in it, not the least of which lay with the underlying theory. In Whelan's view, the Mojave River system was not an underground basin filled with percolating water, but an underground stream, and upstream appropriators who did not have appropriation permits were trying to lock up the water rights through a mutual-prescription arrangement that did not fit the facts. Whelan's deposition of MWA's consulting geologist and expert witness, Dr. John Mann, did not change his belief that the basic theory of the case was faulty.

Whelan also noted the omission of several important water producers from the case, not the least of which was the United States. Although George Air Force Base at Adelanto and the Marine Corps Supply Center at Nebo were both significant pumpers within the area of influence, the United States had not been made a party to the suit. There were, of course, practical reasons for not doing so, primarily that the immediate reaction of the United States upon being named a party in this or any civil action would be to remove the case from state to federal district court.

Also, upon checking into the water rights that had been awarded to some of the major pumpers, Whelan concluded, as Shaw had done, that proponents of the stipulation had engaged in some significant giveaways. Pressed to round up the support of users with 150,000 acre-feet of production rights as fast as possible, proponents offered favorable treatment of parties' claims in exchange for their agreement to the stipulation. In particular, parties represented by attorney Ed Taylor—the Victorville County Water District, and some Apple Valley interests—were holding out for ever larger concessions.

Whelan initially used these problems to try to get a better arrangement for his clients in negotiating with the MWA board and the Working Committee. But matters began to unravel. The Mojave River County Water District Board of Directors instructed Whelan that if there were any more negotiations of concessions to other parties in the *Abbey* case, they intended to fight the adjudication in court. When additional concessions were negotiated (or at least were rumored), Whelan was told to prepare to contest the *Abbey* case.

By the end of 1970, there was opposition to the adjudication on the MWA board and in the courtroom. In addition to the Mojave River County Water District, a group of smaller downstream pumpers had organized the Desert Well Owners Association to fight the adjudication. They also sought and were granted leave to intervene in the *Abbey* case.

The Edison power plant issue reemerged in 1971. The MWA board majority was so concerned with finding the financial wherewithal for a pipeline to convey State Project water to the agency's service area that it ventured into this political thicket again and actually entered into a contract to supply State Project water to Edison. The contract called for Edison to build a pipeline and for MWA to supply the water, which was to amount to 15,000 acre-feet per year during the first fifteen years of operation and 9,000 acre-feet per year for the last nine years of its planned operation. At the same time, the contract contained an option for Edison to purchase up to an additional 13,000 acre-feet in any given year, allowing for a maximum purchase of 28,000 acre-feet in any year during the first fifteen years (MWA, 1979: 9). If this option were exercised by Edison, it would tie up the majority of MWA's State Project water allocation.

The calendar and the mathematics of the stipulation were working against the proponents. The most optimistic estimates of the natural water supply to the Mojave River area of influence placed it in the neighborhood of 75,000 acre-feet per year, perhaps 100,000 acre-feet with return flows. Proponents of the stipulation were trying to collect signatures from parties representing some 150,000 acre-feet of annual water production, but had left out important producers such as the United States, and now the MWA board had committed 15,000 to 28,000 acre-feet of its 50,800 acre-feet annual State Project water allocation to the Edison project. It became increasingly clear that water rights were being awarded in excess of the total available water supply, even under the most optimistic of assumptions.

The Adjudication Flounders

The stipulation was extremely close to the needed number of signers. Yet the closer the proponents came, the better the negotiating position for holdouts. In 1972, stipulation proponents attempted to openly buy out some members of the Desert Well Owners Association. The down-streamers in an area designated Subarea 20 could have no determination or limitation of their pumping rights if they would (1) acknowledge that the upstream arrangements were just and consistent with California water policy, (2) recognize the MWA as watermaster and provide data to the watermaster as requested, (3) forfeit the acquisition of any present or future water rights against any upstream producer, and (4) forfeit any present or future claim to the acquisition of rights to water pumped from groundwater in storage in Subarea 20.[10]

Upstream, Ed Taylor and the Victorville County Water District were being especially difficult in the negotiations, demanding that their pro-duction rights be calculated on an entirely new basis. Krieger's successor on the case, Arthur Littleworth, at one point told the MWA board to forget about the district and its constantly increasing demands. Like Whelan and his clients, Littleworth had lost patience with Taylor, his clients, and their tactics. Besides, he thought the stipulation could be completed without them. Still, the MWA board instructed Littleworth to go back and try again. In 1973, as other parties were preparing for trial, Taylor and the Victorville County Water District moved for dismissal of the adjudication, and Whelan and the Mojave River County Water District threatened to present a motion to compel the joinder of the United States, which would have kicked the adjudication out of the California courts.

Opposition in the courtroom was matched by growing opposition on the MWA board. After being off the board during 1972, Shaw returned in 1973, to find a growing number of adjudication opponents, including William Orchard, Howard Harsh, and Beverly Lowry. With Shaw's return, the MWA board was divided 7 to 4 on the adjudication. As 1973 came to a close, the *Abbey* case was nearing trial, and the stipulation was approaching its needed level of agreement, but the dissidents were gaining ground.

The Mojave River in 1974:
Where Watergate Was a Page-Two Story

Opening arguments in the *Abbey* case were presented in March 1974 by attorney Littleworth for the plaintiff, Mojave Water Agency, and by attorney Whelan for the defendant, Mojave River County Water District. A contin-uance was requested and granted until May, while Whelan prepared his motion to require the joinder of the United States and other parties. That motion was filed on May 15.

It became increasingly difficult to separate political activity surrounding the MWA board from the courtroom activity surrounding the case, as the players in one arena began to react to what was happening in the other. Mustering their forces, the Desert Well Owners Association raised a recall petition against long-time Director LeRoy Scott of Adelanto, an adjudication proponent. Scott chose to resign his seat on July 29, the day before his recall election. The Desert Well Owners Association also rounded up enough signatures to demand a recall election on another adjudication proponent on the MWA board, Division Five's Johnathan Carter. Carter's recall election was set for November. If Scott and Carter were replaced with adjudication opponents, opponents would have a majority on the board. The four opponents already on the board announced that if that happened, they would vote to drop the suit.

Adjudication proponents responded with a new maneuver in the courtroom. On July 12, Southern California Water Company (SoCal), a proponent of the adjudication and one of the Big Five pumpers, filed a notice of a motion for relief from the stipulation for judgment. The company was withdrawing from the stipulation, even though the withdrawal of its signature would kill the agreement. In a memorandum to all 1,000-plus parties, SoCal's attorney, Donald Stark, explained the company's position:

> During the past year, serious attacks on the proposed judgment have been undertaken by Mojave River County Water District and others. Minority members of the Mojave Water Agency Board have indicated a desire to abandon the case. Having invested a decade of work in the proposed stipulated judgment, Southern California Water Company has determined to withdraw from its stipulation and to file an answer and cross-complaint in order to actively participate in all trial proceedings hereafter.

By withdrawing from the stipulation and filing a cross-complaint, SoCal would become a co-plaintiff with the Mojave Water Agency. Even if the agency attempted to drop the adjudication, SoCal could keep it alive. Of course, without the stipulation, the company would have to try to make the *Abbey* case work in the courtroom—a considerably more challenging task, but preferable, in SoCal's view, to abandoning the entire adjudication.

At the MWA board's July 16 meeting, Director Shaw moved that the board instruct attorney Littleworth to oppose SoCal's cross-complaint. Shaw pointed to the recent changes on the board, the impending vote on the recall of Director Scott, the recall election on Director Carter which the board had just set for November 5, and referred to SoCal's move as "an attempt to threaten the democratic process." Littleworth replied that he could not act on the basis of some "hypothetically reconstituted board which may oppose the present adjudication."[11] The board defeated Shaw's motion to oppose the cross-complaint, 6 to 3.

In the July 30 special election, Scott's seat was filled by the candidate backed by the Desert Well Owners Association, Glenn R. "Dick" Hartman, an adjudication opponent. In Victorville on July 31, the page one headline was "Hartman Wins MWA Landslide," and in Barstow, it was "Hartman Wins MWA Seat." This was on July 31, 1974, the day after the House Judiciary Committee voted the first article of impeachment against President Richard Nixon and while the committee was considering voting a second article.

On September 23, Judge Henry Busch issued orders directing the joinder of additional parties other than the United States and allowing the Southern California Water Company to withdraw from the stipulation and file a cross-complaint. The company's answer and cross-complaint were filed the next day, six weeks before the recall election in MWA Division Five. MWA could not unilaterally drop the adjudication it had begun seven and a half years earlier, regardless of the election outcome. The judge scheduled a status hearing on the suit for January 6, so that the MWA board could advise the court of how it wished to proceed after the recall election.

On November 5, Division Five voters recalled Director Carter, and Jess King—the antiadjudication, anti-Edison candidate endorsed by the Desert Well Owners Association—won the vacated seat. At the November 26 MWA board meeting, the new majority deposed At-Large Director William Porter of Victorville from the position of board president and replaced him with Stan Shaw. On the evening of December 17, 1974, MWA Director William Orchard sat back in his chair at the meeting of the board and said, "It took five years to do that."[12] The board had just passed, 6 to 5, Orchard's motion to instruct MWA counsel to drop the Mojave River adjudication.

A week later, a group of large ranch owners in the Upper Basin formed the Water Association to Establish Rights (WATER). Their stated purpose was "to see that the present adjudication and stipulated judgement are carried forward on schedule."[13] They felt that their historical use of the waters in the basin had entitled them to a protection of their rights to the safe yield of the Mojave River system. As a special consultant, they hired Carl Coleman, the former MWA general manager.

As 1974 ended, the board found itself trying to drop the adjudication but possibly unable to do so because of the cross-complaint, while adjudication proponents were organizing to keep the suit going. On January 6, 1975, Arthur Littleworth walked into the Superior Court of San Bernardino County at the appointed hour of 10:00 A.M. There he was met by Ed Taylor, whom he had encountered many times as the attorney for the Victorville County Water District and other holdouts from the stipulation. Taylor showed Littleworth a copy of a substitution of attorneys for the Mojave Water Agency. The substitution had already been filed with the court. The new attorney for the Mojave Water Agency was Ed Taylor.

Judge Busch walked in to begin the status hearing on the adjudication. He requested that counsel note their appearances for the record. Mr. Littleworth identified himself as "counsel for the Agency, at least up until this moment." Judge Busch told Mr. Littleworth that, indeed, the substitution of attorneys had been filed with the court, and it appeared to be duly executed by the agency. Mr. Littleworth replied, "I presume, then, that Mr. Taylor will take care of sending out notice of that to everyone." Mr. Taylor said he would, and went on to inform the judge that the Mojave Water Agency opposed the adjudication and wished to see it dismissed.

With the announcement of the California Supreme Court's decision in the *Los Angeles v. San Fernando* case in May 1975, SoCal's chances of making a mutual-prescription decision work in the *Abbey* case plummeted. On March 15, 1976, Judge Henry Busch accepted the company's motion to drop its cross-complaint. On May 3, 1976, after ten years and an estimated one million dollars in costs to the parties, Judge Busch granted MWA attorney Ed Taylor's motion to dismiss the adjudication.

Unfinished Business, 1976–1991

The dismissal left at least two important questions unanswered. How would State Project water be purchased and delivered within the MWA? And how would the increasingly severe overdrafts be addressed? Neither question has yet been answered satisfactorily.

Getting Water Out of the Aqueduct

The MWA's entitlement to State Project water is nearly three decades old, and MWA residents have been paying their share of the project's capital costs since 1964. The project water entitlement remains unused, because there are no means of purchasing the water. Since the dismissal of the adjudication, there have been other proposals for getting project water out of the California Aqueduct, but none has been adopted.

Facing the opposition of the majority of the MWA board, Edison dropped its pipeline project in 1979. Another pipeline plan was initiated in the mid-1980s by residents of the critically water-short Yucca Valley/Joshua Tree area. This area, in the southeastern corner (Division 2) of the MWA, measures its remaining local water supplies not in decades, but in years. In June 1985, the MWA board approved a joint powers agreement with a consortium of water companies and districts in Division 2, authorizing the MWA to plan and build a 71-mile pipeline from the Hesperia turnout of the California Aqueduct to Yucca Valley. A feasibility study was completed in 1987, recommending the formation of an "improvement district" within the MWA to support the pipeline with a property tax increment. After an August 12, 1988, public hearing in Joshua Tree, the MWA board voted to establish Improvement District "M" for the Morongo Basin Pipeline Project, and to place a $70 million bond issue on the November ballot within the affected area.[14]

Two weeks later, on August 30, the MWA Board of Directors voted to pull the bond initiative from the November ballot.[15] Organized opposition to the project had appeared in the form of a local citizens' group calling itself Fairness in Bonding, which objected on the ground that many residents of the proposed improvement district were retired persons with fixed incomes who could not afford the substantial property tax increases.

Another effort to get water out of the aqueduct fell to local opposition in 1988. In November 1987, the MWA board announced plans to make their first sale of water from the California Aqueduct to the Las Flores Development Group in Summit Valley.[16] A contract was signed with the Las Flores group in September 1988.[17] The city of Barstow, concerned about deals being made with upstream developers, protested to the agency in October 1988 and filed suit in November to enjoin execution of the contract.[18]

The MWA has on two occasions purchased surplus State Project water and demonstrated the Mojave River's ability to convey that water to the Middle and Lower basins. In 1978, the state Department of Water Resources held a "water sale," because of substantial surplus flows in the California Aqueduct. The MWA participated, in order to recharge the groundwater basins along the river and to examine how well the river channel would work to convey the water. The MWA purchased 22,000 acre-feet of water from the state, using a one-time surcharge on the property tax supporting agency operating expenses. The river channel had already been wetted by natural flows, which was essential to keep the surplus water from disappearing into the Upper Basin instead of flowing downstream. The surplus project water discharged into the river channel flowed downstream for several days, recharging basins all along the river. Water levels in wells recovered by as much as 30–40 feet. In another water sale in 1983, the MWA purchased another 24,489 acre-feet, and again the sale produced favorable results.

These occasional surpluses cannot be planned, however, and the essential problem of how to deliver and allocate the supplemental water supply from the aqueduct throughout the MWA remains unsolved. A recurring suggestion for financing regular purchases of aqueduct water has been that a gross pump tax be imposed on all groundwater withdrawals, as in the Orange County Water District and the Central and West Basin Water Replenishment District.

Opposition to the gross pump tax came from several quarters. The larger upstream ranchers represented by the WATER group said it would create undue financial hardship for local agriculture.[19] Others argued that the tax would amount to a subsidy of downstreamers by upstreamers. Downstreamers countered that with upstream pumping all the water would be withdrawn upstream and never get downstream. Residents in areas such as Lucerne Valley and Yucca Valley opposed an agency gross pump tax if the supplemental water would go only into the Mojave River system. In 1984, after a series of public hearings at which opposition to a gross pump tax was expressed, MWA officials declared that the agency had "no desire" to employ pump taxes to purchase and deliver aqueduct water.[20]

Redressing the Supply-Demand Imbalance

The 1980s ushered in a period of accelerated growth in the Mojave River area, during which its population climbed to 250,000. The area included three of the fastest-growing communities in southern California—Hesperia, Victorville, and Apple Valley. The population of Hesperia, for example, jumped 268 percent in these years, bringing it up to 49,818 by 1990.

Since most of the land being developed and urbanized in the Mojave River watershed had not previously been used for agriculture, this population growth pushed up total water production and consumption. Currently, consumptive use in the Upper Basin alone exceeds the average annual supply of water to the Mojave River watershed. Because the watershed's natural supply is consumed in the Upper Basin, the available supply downstream vanishes, and the overdraft there increases. In the Lower Mojave River Basin, the overdraft was close to 40,000 acre-feet per year by 1981, and 87,000 acre-feet per year by 1984 (MWA, 1986a: 11). On the basis of these trends and other data, MWA officials in 1988 estimated that the overdraft agency-wide was nearing 200,000 acre-feet per year. If that is true, even the agency's full State Project entitlement of 50,800 acre-feet per year soon will not be enough to settle the dust.

Without a determination and limitation of pumping rights, a pump tax (gross or net), or regular imports of supplemental water, MWA board and staff members have been trying to address the demand-supply imbalances within the agency by other means. In particular, they have been trying to conserve Mojave River supplies, curtail the growth of water demand through land-use restrictions, and draw more attention to the severity of overdraft problems within the agency (for details of these efforts, see Blomquist, 1989).

The MWA's public information and public involvement initiatives have yet to bear full fruit. The agency contracted for individual studies of the historical and present conditions of the Lower, Middle, and Upper Mojave River basins, which were completed in 1982, 1983, and 1985, respectively. Reports on management alternatives, complete with rankings of the alternatives for all three basins were completed in 1984, 1985, and 1986, respectively. The MWA offered these alternatives to basin advisory committees, composed of local residents representing different population groups within each basin. The committees deliberated on the alternatives and presented their collective opinions to the MWA in 1985 and 1986. Adjudication alternatives were ranked low, and in one case were openly and explicitly rejected. Instead the committees preferred the alternatives "no project," and "abandon current practices."

The Current Picture

More than thirty years ago, local residents and community leaders convened at a public hearing in Victorville and endorsed the formation and activation of the Mojave Water Agency. Whether a similar meeting today would produce a similar result is open to question. Local residents have seen the MWA begin an adjudication of water rights, pursue it for ten years, and then drop it. They have seen the agency sign a contract with the Edison company and then try to cancel it. They have seen the agency propose a gross pump tax and then back away from the idea. They have seen the agency plan to build a pipeline to Yucca Valley, place the bond issue on the ballot, and then remove it. They have seen the agency enter into a contract to sell State Project water, and wind up in court. And for more than twenty-five years, they have paid property taxes for the California Aqueduct while northern California water is delivered to other southern California communities. Some area residents have even formed a group called the Citizens for Accountable Water Management, pressing to "make the MWA go away."

In the meantime, history repeats itself. In January 1988, at a meeting of the Victorville City Council, Mayor Terry Caldwell suggested that adjudication should be the "cornerstone" of a city water policy.[21] At another meeting in February, the council recommended the adoption of an official water policy that would include the adjudication of rights in the "Mojave Corridor." In September 1988, the Mojave River Resources Technical Advisory Committee, formed to help the MWA assemble a comprehensive water management plan, heard from a special guest speaker who brought with him a copy of the Chino Basin judgment as an example of what could be accomplished in a cooperative adjudication. The speaker was Dick Anderson, an attorney with the Riverside, California firm of Best, Best, and Krieger.[22]

On June 1, 1990, the *Los Angeles Times* reported, "War broke out in the Mojave Desert on Thursday, and at stake is the single most precious commodity in this vast, arid land—water."[23] On May 30, the city of Barstow and the Southern California Water Company (which is the principal supplier of water to Barstow residents) filed a complaint in San Bernardino County Superior Court against 100 upstream defendants, to initiate an adjudication of its rights to Mojave River flows, similar to the San Gabriel River adjudication described in Chapter 7 and the Santa Ana River adjudication described in Chapter 11. The Barstow and SoCal complaint requested a declaration of Barstow's right to an average annual flow of 30,000 acre-feet at the Barstow gauging station, and an injunction against upstream water users to guarantee Barstow that amount. The Barstow city manager stated succinctly the city's view of the stakes involved: "The bottom line is, if there isn't any water in Barstow, then there isn't any Barstow."

In July 1991, the Mojave Water Agency, named as a defendant in the Barstow-SoCal complaint, filed a cross-complaint naming additional pumpers downstream. The MWA cross-complaint seeks a determination and limitation of pumping rights in order to eliminate the overdraft along the river. The MWA has entered upon the same type of adjudication it began twenty-five years ago.

Analysis

A number of important lessons can be gleaned from the experience of the Mojave Water Agency, perhaps the primary one being that it is essential for all parties concerned to have a clear and common understanding of the components of their water system.

Eliciting Information

To this day, water users along the Mojave River have not had a shared picture of their water supplies and water use. Despite several U.S. Geological Survey and California Department of Water Resources studies of the Mojave River area during this century, not to mention studies commissioned by the Mojave Water Agency, disagreement still remains about whether Mojave River water supplies should be treated as an underground stream, a single groundwater area, or multiple groundwater basins. Under these circumstances, it is unlikely that water users will be able to construct a governance structure or devise a strategy to treat the area's water problems. The adjudication program attempted between 1964 and 1976 faltered in part because of this disagreement over the nature and boundaries of the resource.

The latest adjudication illustrates that the situation remains much the same. The Barstow-SoCal complaint treats the basins along the river as distinct, and seeks to guarantee a minimal inflow to the Middle Basin from the Upper Basin. This approach, like the San Gabriel River and Santa Ana River adjudication, would leave the Upper Basin pumpers free to allocate their water supply among themselves as long as they meet their obligations to the next basin downstream. The MWA cross-complaint treats the entire length of the river within the agency's domain as one basin (or area of influence) and does not distinguish the effects of pumping in the Lower or Middle basins from the effects of pumping in the Upper Basin. Ultimately, water users along the Mojave will have to decide whether their local water supply comes from three distinct groundwater basins or one, or a court will decide for them.

Water users along the Mojave River have also not agreed on the presence or the extent of overdraft. As noted earlier, at the same time that adjudication proponents on the MWA board were voicing their alarm about the serious overdraft along the river, the state Department of Water Resources was announcing that none of the three basins along the river was in overdraft at all. Recent estimates of the overdraft along the river have ranged from 200,000 acre-feet per year to less than 30,000 acre-feet.

The experience of the Mojave Water Agency also has underscored the importance of such apparently simple institutional arrangements as monitoring and reporting on pumping and water conditions. Pumpers in each of the other basins discussed so far have received annual reports on water production and basin conditions for at least twenty years, and in some cases more than forty years. The Mojave Water Agency is now thirty years old but has produced annual reports only sporadically. Simple data such as total groundwater production, imports, exports, total water use, and water levels, which keep water users apprised of their situation and how it has changed, have not been available on a regular basis from the MWA or any other organization. This leaves users to argue unproductively over whether and how much their water situation has worsened.

Institutional Design

As the preceding chapters show, this is not the first time that southern California has been faced with the problems of multiple basins and questions concerning their independence or interdependence. Unlike the Los Angeles, San Gabriel, and Santa Ana River watershed users, however, those in the Mojave River area have not yet developed the polycentric systems that would allow them to make collective decisions both within and across related basins. The main reason they have not done so is that the design of the Mojave Water Agency does not match the tasks some people think it has been assigned.

There are as many as fifteen groundwater basins within the MWA's boundaries, and when the MWA attends to problems in one area, its efforts are often perceived as being at the expense of some other area. Because all subareas have representation in MWA decision making, it is exceedingly difficult to develop a management program in one without involving the others; furthermore, it is equally difficult to arrive at a consensus on how to manage the entire area when each subarea sees itself as the rival of every other. Year after year, time and money are expended but nothing gets done.

These institutional design flaws have been compounded, to be sure, by local factors. The river itself, with its rising water at some locations and occasional flooding, creates illusions that inhibit efforts to restrain use. At the Narrows around Victorville, people wade and play in the river, among trees and other vegetation. Overdraft, they ask? What overdraft? By contrast, in the neighboring Antelope Valley, where there is no such river, and where the Antelope Valley–East Kern Water Agency was created under virtually identical legislation as the MWA, voters passed a bond issue for a conveyance system in 1974 and have been receiving State Project water since 1976.[24] The river also gives rise to the evident "upstream-downstream" division between water users that has inhibited cooperation.

The MWA may have failed as a water manager, but the deck has been stacked against its success from the moment it was given that role for an area as large and diverse as the western half of the Mojave Desert. Had the MWA become the potential water wholesaler for the desert region and not its water manager, it might have stood a better chance of success. Some day, a project like the Morongo Basin pipeline may succeed in getting water out of the aqueduct. If it does, perceptions of the MWA's mission may change. Such a change may hold more promise for the agency's future success than any new legislation, agency reorganization, or engineering studies and advisory groups. It may not be necessary to "make the MWA go away," but any notions that the MWA can solve the water supply-and-demand problems of fifteen groundwater basins in an area the size of Connecticut do need to disappear.

NOTES

1. Mayor George Oakes of Barstow (accompanied by the city's legal counsel, Ed Taylor) did not oppose the agency's formation per se, but questioned the need for its immediate activation since Californians had not yet passed the State Water Project bond referendum.

2. As one of the thirty-one State Water Project contractors, the MWA would act as tax collector for the state, generating revenues to pay back a share of the State Water Project revenue bonds corresponding with the area's allocation of project water. The obligation to repay the bonds is not the MWA's obligation, but an obligation of the taxpayers of the area that has been allocated water—that is to say, abolishing the agency would not erase the repayment obligation.

3. One director would be appointed by the Mojave River Soil Conservation District, another by the San Bernardino County Board of Supervisors (as Board of Directors for the County Flood Control District), and another by the municipalities and water districts within the MWA.

4. The MWA also may tax real property to repay bonded indebtedness incurred by the agency, subject to voter approval.

5. This "insurance policy" notion was not unique to the MWA. In the Raymond Basin, the residents of the city of San Marino paid taxes to the Metropolitan Water District for years without taking water, just in order to be assured that a supplemental water supply would be there when needed. In some areas in central California and in MWA's neighbor, the Crestline–Lake Arrowhead Water Agency, special districts were supported by "standby charges" assessed against local residents, not for water actually delivered, but to pay for projects that ensured future access to additional water.

6. Curiously, it appears from the drawing included as plaintiff's Exhibit A that the "Area of Influence" ends before the river does.

7. This perception is gathered from local interviews conducted by the author and is consistent with the printed recollections of one local resident who attended a negotiation meeting. He recalled an incident involving "one white-haired man who came to a committee meeting to ask about his rights. His sons had abandoned the ranch following World War II and now wanted to return and resume pumping. Krieger's answer was polite but curt, to wit: 'Mister, if we didn't give you any water rights, then you haven't any.' " ("Water Grab Alleged in Adjudication Suit," a letter to the editor by Allen Noble of Hesperia, in the *Victor Valley Daily Press*, May 31, 1976, p. 10.)

8. Later the verification program was expanded and turned over to E. F. "Jerry" Dibble and his firm, Dibble Engineering.

9. Case 130759 in the Superior Court of the State of California in and for the County of San Bernardino.

10. Additional Stipulation filed 11/27/72 in *Mojave Water Agency v. Abbey and Allison et al.*, Case 130759, California Superior Court, San Bernardino County.

11. "MWA Sets Recall in November," *Victor Valley Daily Press*, July 17, 1974, p. 1.

12. "MWA Board Votes to Kill River Adjudication," *Victor Valley Daily Press*, December 18, 1974, p. 1.

13. John Crowe, "New Group to Do Battle on Adjudication," *Victor Valley Daily Press*, December 24, 1974, p. 1.

14. Judith Pfeffer, "Water Earmarked for Yucca Valley," *Victor Valley Daily Press*, August 13, 1988, p. A-1.

15. Judith Pfeffer, "MWA Removes Yucca Valley Pipeline's Financing Plan from November Ballot," *Victor Valley Daily Press*, August 31, 1988.

16. William Couey, "Aqueduct Water to Supply Las Flores Project," *Victor Valley Daily Press*, November 3, 1987, p. A-1.

17. Judith Pfeffer, "MWA Makes Its First Significant Aqueduct Water Sale," *Victor Valley Daily Press*, September 28, 1988, p. A-1.

18. Judith Pfeffer, "MWA's First Water Sale Lands in Court," *Victor Valley Daily Press*, November 30, 1988, p. A-1.

19. Ibid. See also John Crowe, "Gross Pump Tax Opposed," *Victor Valley Daily Press*, April 28, 1976, p. 1.

20. "No Pump Tax Plan, MWA Board Says," *Victor Valley Daily Press*, May 18, 1984, p. 1.

21. William Couey, "City's Reversal on Water Adjudication Surprising," *Victor Valley Daily Press*, January 22, 1988, p. A-1.

22. Judith Pfeffer, "MWA Advisors Seek to Avoid Water Battles," *Victor Valley Daily Press*, September 8, 1988, p. A-1.

23. Jenifer Warren, "Barstow Accuses Upstream Towns of Hogging Water," *Los Angeles Times*, June 1, 1990, p. A-3.

24. "The MWA: The Mojave Connection," *Victor Valley Daily Press*, April 6, 1986, p. A-1.

11

Orange County
Governing by District, Managing by Incentives

Water management in Orange County has been consistently directed toward protecting and enhancing the region's water supply. To this end, the Orange County groundwater basin has been used not only as a local water source, but also as a storage and distribution facility for water from upstream in the Santa Ana River watershed or from the Colorado River and northern California. Orange County water users also developed different institutional and organizational arrangements for governing the basin and managing water supplies. They refrained from an intrabasin adjudication of pumping rights and centered basin governance in the Orange County Water District. As a nonadjudicated basin governed through a single public jurisdiction, Orange County provides an important contrast with the adjudicated basins in Los Angeles County, especially with the basins of the San Gabriel River watershed.

Orange County Water Supply Problems

As in Los Angeles County, the Coastal Plain in Orange County at the turn of the century contained areas of artesian water flow and of swamp and was subject to occasional flooding. "Until the 1920s, the main water problems of public concern were land drainage, storm water control and sewage discharge" (Weschler, 1968: 6). Early agricultural development alleviated the drainage problem somewhat by reducing the area of artesian flow and lowering the water table. Lands that had been too swampy to farm were drained and brought into cultivation. By 1920, there were nearly 100,000 acres of irrigated agricultural land in Orange County,

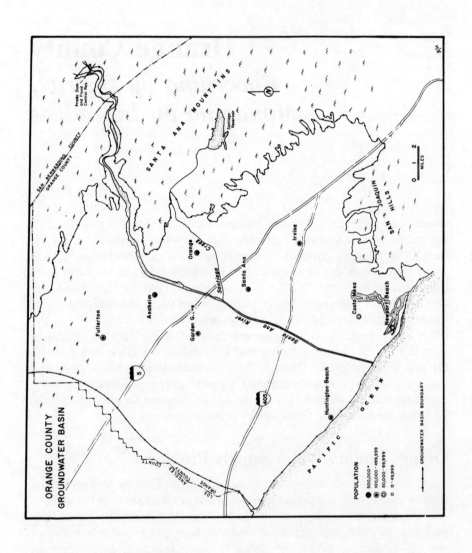

ORANGE COUNTY
GROUNDWATER BASIN

POPULATION

⬤ 500,000 +
◉ 100,000 - 499,999
◎ 50,000 - 99,999
○ 0 - 49,999

◀——▶ GROUNDWATER BASIN BOUNDARY

almost twice as much as in 1910. This figure was near the peak of 130,000 acres reached in 1928.

The rapid development of Orange County agriculture overran the supply of freshwater from the underlying groundwater basin. Groundwater extractions of 180,000 acre-feet in 1920 already exceeded the basin's estimated annual safe yield of 150,000 acre-feet. And as water withdrawals within the county increased, the inflow from upstream declined. With the beginning of a cycle of dry years in 1923, water levels dropped throughout the basin. The Orange County Board of Supervisors commissioned engineer J. B. Lippincott to prepare a report on local water supply conditions.

The Lippincott report, delivered in 1925, formally confirmed what several water users already knew: the Coastal Plain was a water-deficient area, the basin was being overdrawn, the water table was falling sharply, and the natural inflow to the basin from the Santa Ana River had been reduced to insufficient levels. The report also contained the alarming observation that seawater intrusion was occurring along the Pacific coast and warned that serious degradation of the groundwater supply would occur if remedial measures were not taken. Underground water levels along the coast had fallen to below sea level, and seawater had begun flowing into the basin. The Lippincott report also recommended some flood control measures to conserve occasional storm runoff and protect property.

In providing Orange County water users with this shared information about their local water supply situation, the report contributed to three important actions. In 1927, the Orange County Board of Supervisors received state legislative approval to form the Orange County Flood Control District, to control and impound storm flows, in order to protect property on the Coastal Plain and conserve water supplies. In 1928, the cities of Anaheim, Fullerton, and Santa Ana joined with others in the region to form the Metropolitan Water District of Southern California (MWD) and to attempt to gain access to supplemental water supplies from the Colorado River. In 1929, the Tri-Counties Water Conservation Association, of which Orange County was a member along with San Bernardino and Riverside counties (see Chapter 4), expanded its upstream water storage and spreading operations.

By 1930, groundwater extractions were in excess of 200,000 acre-feet per year. In 1934, the California Division of Water Resources documented the deterioration of local water supply conditions during the dry decade from 1923 through 1933. Water levels in the Santa Ana and Santiago area had fallen from 100 feet above sea level in 1923 to 23 feet above sea level in 1933. In the Irvine and Tustin areas, artesian flows had disappeared, replaced by water at depths of 20 to 50 feet. Throughout the Orange County basin, heavy pumping had produced cones of depression and had changed the direction of groundwater movement.

Orange County water users became discouraged with the water-spreading program of the Tri-Counties Water Conservation Association, which seemed to be benefiting only the upstream water users, whose increased water production left less water moving into Orange County. In 1930, the Orange County engineer recommended that the county oppose any further expansion of upstream water-spreading operations (Trager, 1988: 45–46). In November 1932, concern about the loss of natural replenishment from the Santa Ana River flows prompted a lawsuit against upstream water producers. The lawsuit was not undertaken by the county or other local government, but by the Irvine Company, "the dominant economic organization within the county" (Weschler, 1968: 13). The Irvine Company possessed approximately 92,000 acres of land in Orange County in 1932, which included some of the county's best farmland. These holdings were watered by a combination of surface water diversions and extractions of groundwater from the company's eighty wells.

The Irvine Company filed a suit in federal court in Los Angeles against upstream parties spreading water adjacent to the Santa Ana River, Mill Creek, and Lytle Creek. The company sought a declaration of its rights and an injunction restraining the defendants from diverting water in sufficient quantities to damage the company's rights. The original action, *Irvine Co. v. Fontana Union Water Company et al.*, grew to include twenty defendants.

The Orange County Water District and Supply-Side Water Management

If successful, the Irvine Company's suit stood to benefit many Coastal Plain water users by restoring natural inflow. As the scope of the litigation and the number of defendants grew, the prospective costs to be incurred by the Irvine Company escalated, as did the potential benefit to other downstream users if upstream diversions were curtailed. It seemed reasonable to create some means of apportioning some of the litigation costs among the several potential beneficiaries. Also, the upstream defendants had created a collective representative entity in the San Bernardino Valley Water Conservation District, which could claim to represent the interests of all the appropriators in the San Bernardino Valley. The Irvine attorneys perceived an advantage to be gained from being able to make a similar claim for Orange County water users.

The possibility of having an organization that could represent Coastal Plain water users and get them to contribute to the action against the upstream users had already been raised. The Water Committee of the Orange County Farm Bureau, one of the most active associations of water user interests in Orange County, recommended seeking legislative approval for the creation of a special water district encompassing the

Coastal Plain area. In April 1931, the Farm Bureau sent a letter to the county's state senator, N. T. Edwards, and to state Assemblyman Ted Craig, requesting their help with the authorization of such a district, to "look out for the question of replenishing the Basin, conservation of the waste, and questions of that nature" (OCWD, 1983: 16).

No bill was introduced that year, but in April 1933, Senator Edwards introduced the Orange County Water District Act, which was approved on June 4, 1933. The Orange County Water District (OCWD) established in 1933 covered approximately 156,000 acres of the Coastal Plain, and so contained most of the overlying owners of the groundwater basin. Significant by their exclusion were the cities of Anaheim, Fullerton, and Santa Ana, and parts of the Irvine Ranch overlying the basin. The enabling legislation authorized the OCWD "to represent the water users and landowners of the Coastal Plain in all litigation involving outsiders." The district entered the Irvine litigation as intervener on behalf of the Irvine Company and other Orange County water users and reimbursed the Irvine Company for a major part of the court costs it had incurred in prosecuting the action to that point (Scott, 1977: 224).

In addition to representing Orange County water users against "outsiders," the OCWD was charged to undertake management of the groundwater basin, conservation of the quantity and quality of the groundwater in the basin, reclamation of water for beneficial use, and conservation and control of storm and floodwaters flowing into the district. To accomplish these purposes, the district was granted powers to import, sell, and store water; conserve or replenish water within or outside the district; and protect the water supply and water rights of Orange County users through any action or proceeding.

Establishment of the district capped the first phase of institution building in Orange County, during which the Orange County Board of Supervisors, the Farm Bureau's Water Committee, and the Irvine Company were instrumental in calling attention to the area's water problems and initiating some responses to them, including the formation of the Orange County Flood Control District and the OCWD. The OCWD held the promise of providing a basin governance structure for representing water users and taking collective decisions and actions on their behalf, including the development of a basin management program based on augmentation and conservation of natural inflow.

The district was *not* given power to regulate or restrict water production by users within its boundaries, however. The Orange County Water District Act did not authorize the district or its Board of Directors to undertake a determination and limitation of water rights. Indeed, the law specifically prohibited the district from taking part in any action or proceeding against or between owners of land or water rights within its boundaries

(Krieger, 1961: 8). Partly as a result of this rule, and partly because of Orange County water users' attitudes toward water supply management, rights to the flows of the Santa Ana River within Orange County and to pumping from the Orange County basin have never been adjudicated.

The rule barring OCWD's participation in an intrabasin adjudication reflects an attitude of the Orange County water user community, an attitude the district's board and staff have internalized as a fundamental policy commitment. Their commitment, described as "inviolate" (Weschler, 1968: 28), is to provide a water supply that will be adequate to meet demands regardless of growth, development, drought, and the like. As part of a general "philosophy of plenty" in Orange County, the district's board and staff, like other water policy leaders in Orange County, "feel that providing a full and plentiful supply of water is a superior policy to rationing a limited supply" (Weschler, 1968: 28). Instead, the OCWD operates much as a replenishment district would. Even when it has acquired powers that could be used to restrict demand, they have been used primarily to improve supply. Without an adjudication of water rights, and with its "inviolate" policy commitment, Orange County has chosen to manage the basin from the supply side.

The District's Supply-Management Program, 1933–1948

The OCWD's principal concern from 1933 until 1942 was the Irvine litigation against the upstream water users. After several failed attempts to negotiate settlements, the parties agreed in 1936 to a study to be conducted by a three-person watermaster, one chosen by the downstream litigants, one by the upstream litigants, and one by the court. They supervised spreading experiments on the Santa Ana River, from late 1937 through 1939 (Scott, 1977: 225). In 1942, the U.S. District Court for the Southern District of California issued three judgments based on stipulations by the parties: for Mill Creek, Lytle Creek, and the Santa Ana River. Each judgment reduced the amounts of water the defendants could divert for spreading upstream, set specific amounts per water year, specified the spreading locations the defendants could use, and placed the administrative and monitoring responsibilities on the defendants.

Other occurrences during this period improved local conditions. Supplemental water became available to Anaheim, Fullerton, and Santa Ana with the completion of MWD's Colorado River aqueduct in 1941. Above-average rainfall from 1938 to 1944 increased natural inflow and percolation. The OCWD and the Orange County Flood Control District enhanced basin recharge capabilities by rechanneling and improving stream beds to increase percolation of surface water into the Orange County basin.

After a destructive flood in 1938, the Orange County Flood Control District and the U.S. Army Corps of Engineers undertook the construction of Prado Dam in the Santa Ana Canyon, where the Santa Ana River flows into Orange County. Since its completion in 1941, Prado Dam has been central to the OCWD's supply management program, allowing for conservation and controlled release of Santa Ana River flows into the Coastal Plain.

In 1944 Orange County groundwater levels reached a high mark that has served since as the measure of desirable water conditions. Water levels were high enough to create economically favorable pumping lifts and to block the seawater intrusion that had begun in the 1920s. As elsewhere in southern California, however, the 1944 peak turned out to be a precipice. When the twenty-year drought began in 1945, water levels began a fall that was not arrested until 1956. Basin conditions changed so markedly that it is now conceded that 1944's profile is no longer an attainable goal.

By 1948, 250,000 acre-feet per year were being pumped from the basin, a pace that produced an annual overdraft of approximately 100,000 acre-feet and would have completely eliminated the water stored in the basin's usable storage capacity in fifteen years. From 1945 to 1948, the average water level in the basin fell from 20 feet above sea level to 5 feet above sea level, and levels along the coast again fell below sea level. Seawater intrusion resumed, threatening water quality along the coast and spreading inland. Users began to abandon wells along the coast as the line between fresh and brackish groundwater moved inland 8,000 feet from 1945 to 1950 (Weschler, 1968: 15). By 1953, the average water level had fallen to 15 feet below sea level. State Senator John A. Murdy, Jr., testified that year before the Joint Legislative Committee on Water Problems:

> I remember that as late as 1928, after I became a farmer myself, . . . I rented a piece of land and on it was an artesian well that had so much water pressure that it was practically impossible for one man to cap that well. . . . At the present time I have in that well a deep well turbine pump with a bowl setting at 85 feet and 15 feet of suction in the bottom of the bowls, and this last year, 1952, during the summer when I was irrigating, that pump broke suction because of the lowering of the water table. (Quoted in Cooper, 1968: 139)

The District's Supply Management Program, 1949–1964

It was evident that a supply-oriented program based on natural replenishment alone could not ensure the desired water supply for Orange County and protect groundwater quality. Orange County would need artificial replenishment. Losing the local groundwater supply would be a disaster; it would have to be replaced with a surface delivery and storage system for imported water, which would be a massive financial undertaking. A replenishment program that supplemented groundwater supplies and used the basin to store and distribute imported water was a preferable alternative (Weschler, 1968: 29).

Artificial replenishment to restore underground water levels also seemed the only feasible means of halting seawater intrusion. Ross Shafer, of the Coastal Plain Water Supply Committee of the California Chamber of Commerce, told the Joint Legislative Committee on Water Problems in November 1948, "There isn't a ghost of a chance that we can keep the salt water from coming in unless we can tap the supplemental supply in this area and that is the supply under control by the Metropolitan Water District" (California JLCWP, 1949: 166). He continued: "We do have an inward movement of water and we are attempting to evaluate the situation and make an estimate of what we can do. The only thing that seems practical under our present knowledge is to keep a fresh-water head against it" (California JLCWP, 1949: 169).

The unresolved question was how to design and implement an artificial replenishment program. Artificial replenishment meant access to an external source of supply, and money. Satisfying these requirements necessitated some institutional design, and redesign.

Redesigning the District

The OCWD began purchasing replenishment water with a special allotment of Colorado River water from MWD during the 1948–49 water year. The water was directed into the reservoir behind Prado Dam, then released into the surface stream beds that the OCWD and the flood control district had improved for percolation. Because the OCWD was not an MWD member agency, the MWD would not make regular water sales directly to the Orange County Water District. Replenishment purchases continued to go through the MWD member agencies within the county, principally the Coastal Municipal Water District (formed in 1942) and the Municipal Water District of Orange County (formed in 1951). As the larger of these two districts, the Municipal Water District of Orange County became the principal source of MWD replenishment water to the OCWD.

The MWD wished to increase Colorado River water purchases to perfect its right to the water, so replenishment water availability was not a limitation on OCWD replenishment activities at this time. The principal limitation faced by the OCWD was lack of an adequate and regular funding base for purchasing large amounts of replenishment water from the MWD. The amounts purchased with property tax revenues in water years 1949–50 to 1952–53 averaged about 28,000 acre-feet per year, far too little to cover annual overdrafts of 100,000 acre-feet per year.

The OCWD was authorized to levy special assessments against property if approved in a special election, and to issue bonds, but the Board of Directors had not used either of these revenue powers. The authorities were reluctant to fund an artificial replenishment program through increased property taxes or a special assessment. A special assessment would require a special election, the assessment would have to be large in order to purchase enough replenishment water to stop the decline in water levels, and no claim could be made that it was "temporary," since replenishment water purchases would be needed for the foreseeable future.

There was also a growing uneasiness about the use of property taxes to fund replenishment activities. Property owners in most of the district were already annexed to MWD and paying property taxes to it for the acquisition and transportation of the Colorado River water. They then were paying property taxes to OCWD to purchase Colorado River water from the MWD; correctly or not, some felt they were paying for the same water twice. Also, property owners in areas overlying the basin but not annexed to MWD or not within the OCWD would benefit from the replenishment program without paying for it. Furthermore, the property tax subsidized pumpers, because nonpumping property owners paid for replenishment activities that primarily benefited pumpers (Weschler, 1968: 24–25).

The area's water management problems were discussed at a joint meeting in 1952 of the Water Problems Committee of the Orange County Farm Bureau, the Water Committee of the Associated Chambers of Commerce, and the Board of Directors of the Orange County Water District. The twelve-man Orange County Water Basin Conservation Committee (the Committee of 12) was formed to study the issues further and develop recommendations (Weschler, 1968: 16; Crooke and Toups, 1961: 5–6). The Committee of 12 maintained the area's basic commitment to increasing supply rather than restricting demand. They considered and rejected centralized control over water consumption and distribution by an agency empowered to enforce conservation, or adjudication and limitation of water rights using the court-reference procedure. They supported instead a proposal to fund replenishment by taxing pumping. This approach held the promise of raising the necessary funds, relating pumpers' taxation to their benefits received, and relieving nonpumpers from paying for replenishment except to the extent that they purchased water from pumpers. Furthermore, at least theoretically, a tax on pumping would build in conservation incentives without mandating conservation.

The OCWD was not authorized to tax pumping, so the Orange County Water District Act would have to be amended. The Committee of 12 assembled a package of amendments that amounted to a substantial redesign of the district. To be fair, a pump tax would have to be implemented basinwide, so the committee proposed enlarging the district's territory to include Anaheim, Fullerton, and Santa Ana, plus areas owned by the Anaheim Union Water Company and the Santa Ana Valley Irrigation Company near the canyon. A pump tax would make it necessary to measure and record water production from the thousands of wells within the district, so an amendment was proposed requiring every pumper therein to register wells with the OCWD and to record and submit production data to the district twice per year. The committee also proposed that an annual district engineer's report on basin conditions and groundwater production be submitted to the district and water users, to allow them to monitor the effects of the replenishment program and to provide a shared picture on a regular basis of basin conditions, including the extent of seawater intrusion and the level of the water table.

The committee's recommendations also included a limited property tax provision to help offset some of the overhead or administrative expenses involved in starting up the pump tax program. In addition, the ad valorem tax would be used to purchase up to 375,000 acre-feet of replenishment water, an amount equivalent to 1953 estimates of the accumulated overdraft of the basin. Since the accumulated overdraft had occurred during the three preceding decades, the committee felt it was appropriate to assess all property owners in the district to make up for past overdraft conditions, especially in light of the territorial expansion of the district, to include those who had previously been placing heavy demands on the basin without paying OCWD taxes. Even so, the general assessment was lowered from 15 cents to 8 cents per $100 of assessed valuation, and the provisions for a special assessment would be dropped from the district act.

These amendments to the Orange County Water District Act were passed by the state legislature in 1953. The amendments, including the pump tax provisions, were upheld in a validation suit in Orange County Superior Court, and the OCWD Board of Directors voted the first "replenishment assessment" (as the pump tax was known) on June 9, 1954.

Without a limitation on pumping, the pump tax represented the OCWD's only demand-side management tool. Because the pump tax adds to the pumper's production costs, reinternalizing some of the external costs of pumping, the tax could be used to reduce groundwater production. To do so, however, the tax must be set high enough to raise production costs above the benefits gained from additional pumping by those producing for their own consumption and must also be high enough to raise marginal cost above marginal benefit for consumers of water produced and retailed to them. If the demand for water is inelastic over the relevant range, the pump tax may have to be quite high, indeed, to bring about a significant reduction in pumping.[1] In practice, the Orange County Water District has not set the replenishment assessment at such a high level, for four reasons (Weschler, 1968: 22–23, 43–44):

1. The district is committed to providing a plentiful water supply rather than restricting consumption.
2. The amount of the pump tax is bounded above by the Orange County Water District Act, and increases above that upper bound require either amendment of the act or an extraordinary majority (8 of 10) of the OCWD Board of Directors.
3. Increases in the pump tax have been unpopular with pumpers, who are the OCWD's primary constituency.
4. The district is not allowed to discriminate among pumpers in the amount of replenishment assessment charged, so rates high enough to curtail pumping in certain troughs within the basin would have to be levied on all pumpers regardless of the water level in their locales.

The pump tax has not really been employed by the OCWD as a demand-management tool. The guiding considerations in setting the pump tax rate are supply needs rather than demand management. Each year, the Board of Directors has set the tax at whatever level would buy enough replenishment water to restore the average annual overdraft from the preceding five years plus one-tenth of the accumulated overdraft. "[T]he pump tax program of the OCWD does what most people in Orange County expect it to do: it provides a relatively steady supply of ground water" (Weschler, 1968: 59). Pump tax rates for the region are shown in Table 11.1.

Basin Protection II:
Orange County Water District v. Riverside

In 1951, shortly before the Committee of 12 set to work on revamping the OCWD's authority, the district used its existing powers to initiate another lawsuit against upstream water users. The district sued four major upstream appropriators of Santa Ana River flows—the cities of Riverside, San Bernardino, Colton, and Redlands—to restrict their water production and protect the natural inflow to Orange County. Their use of local water supplies had continued to grow, in part because they had failed to annex to MWD and obtain supplies of supplemental water. San Bernardino, for example, had failed for the second time to obtain voter approval to annex to MWD. The OCWD's complaint alleged that the defendant cities had for years taken water from the watershed and that either they had no right to the water or whatever right they had was subordinate to its right. The relief requested was a declaration of the water rights of each city (but not of the OCWD) and an injunction prohibiting each city from taking water in excess of its declared right.

TABLE 11.1

Orange County Water District Replenishment Assessment ("Pump Tax"), 1955–1990 (dollars per acre-foot)

Year	Replenishment assessment	Year	Replenishment assessment
1955	3.50	1973	10.00/13.00
1956	3.50	1974	10.00/17.00
1957	3.90	1975	10.00/17.00
1958	3.90	1976	12.00/22.00
1959	3.90	1977	12.00/25.00
1960	4.30	1978	12.00/26.00
1961	5.50	1979	12.00/30.00
1962	6.00	1980	17.00/30.00
1963	8.00/11.00 [a]	1981	17.00/30.00
1964	8.00/11.00	1982	15.00/21.00
1965	8.00/11.00	1983	14.00/21.00
1966	8.00/11.00	1984	23.00/32.00
1967	8.00/11.00	1985	23.00/32.00
1968	9.50/12.50	1986	16.00/32.00
1969	10.30/13.30	1987	16.00/32.00
1970	10.00/13.00	1988	16.00/32.00
1971	10.00/13.00	1989	21.00/42.00
1972	10.00/13.00	1990	23.00/45.00

a. First rate is per acre-foot of water for irrigation, second rate is per acre-foot of water for nonirrigation use.
SOURCE: Orange County Water District Annual Reports.

In 1957, the 114-day trial of *Orange County Water District v. City of Riverside et al.* was held before Judge Albert F. Ross, who had been specially assigned to the case. Judge Ross ruled against the OCWD's allegation that the cities had no right to any of the waters of the Santa Ana River watershed, holding instead that the defendants had acquired and perfected prescriptive rights to some of the water by adverse possession. At the same time, Judge Ross established the five-year period prior to the initiation of the lawsuit (that is, 1946 through 1951) as the relevant period of adverse use for the purpose of determining the prescriptive rights. The declared right of each city was limited to the amount of its taking in the first year of that period. Thus, each city in 1957 was enjoined from taking more water from the Santa Ana River watershed than it had taken in 1946. This meant a substantial reduction for each city and had the effect of forcing them to obtain supplemental water. The 1957 trial court judgment was appealed by the defendant cities twice. Each time, the District Court of Appeal upheld the judgment while ordering some modifications in the amounts of the declared rights of the defendant cities. After the second appeal ended in 1961 the same way as the first, the cities did not appeal again.

"Fill the Basin": *1954–1964*

Apart from the litigation against the four upstream cities, basin replenishment was the OCWD's principal program from 1948 through 1964. After the 1953 amendments, that program was pursued more aggressively and has been referred to as the "fill-the-basin" policy. Beginning in 1954, the district purchased as much MWD replenishment water as it could. The aim was to fill the basin as rapidly as possible to restore the 1944 water levels. The increase in purchases was rapid and large: in 1954, the five MWD member agencies in Orange County bought 48 percent of the water MWD delivered in southern California, although their combined entitlement was to 7 percent of the water (Weschler, 1968: 30).

The fill-the-basin program took a couple of years to bring the water levels back up and halt seawater intrusion. The year 1956 was the basin's historic low point and is regarded with the same significance from a negative standpoint as 1944 is from a positive standpoint. Water levels near the coast and along the Los Angeles County border in 1956 were as much as 40 feet below sea level, and saltwater had advanced 3½ miles inland. In the Irvine Ranch area, there was a pumping hole of 80 feet below sea level. It is estimated that the accumulated overdraft by 1956 was anywhere from 500,000 to 700,000 acre-feet, or between one-third and one-half of the usable storage capacity of the basin.

After 1956, water levels began to recover and rose through 1964, despite the continuing drought. Replenishment water purchases escalated to roughly 83,000 acre-feet in 1957, 144,000 acre-feet in 1960, and 235,000 acre-feet in 1963 (see Table 11.2). The funds devoted to replenishment purchases rose from $500,000 in 1954 to $830,000 in 1957 and $3,200,000 in 1964. The OCWD simply poured more water into the basin than pumpers pulled out. By 1960, Orange County water users were drawing 59 percent more water than the basin could safely provide. Moreover, they were drawing 75 percent of their supply from the basin, but its levels were rising, not falling. The fill-the-basin program peaked between 1961 and 1964, when an average of 190,000 acre-feet per year were purchased to be sunk underground.

The replenishment program was aided by a reduction in pumping. While total water obtained within the district rose 16 percent from 1954 to 1964, groundwater production declined 12 percent, and groundwater production as a percentage of total water production declined from 92 percent to about 68 percent (see Table 11.3). Three factors contributed to the decline in pumping during this period. First, more and more of

TABLE 11.2

Orange County Replenishment Water Purchases and Costs, 1950–1990

Year	Colorado River water (acre-feet)	State Project water (acre-feet)	In-lieu program water (acre-feet)	Total cost (dollars)
1950	22,726	0	0	181,805
1951	22,183	0	0	221,831
1952	39,177	0	0	391,774
1953	27,956	0	0	279,561
1954	50,000	0	0	500,000
1955	67,789	0	0	621,626
1956	20,916	0	0	209,159
1957	82,955	0	0	829,548
1958	77,145	0	0	925,738
1959	81,710	0	0	980,520
1960	144,471	0	0	1,733,657
1961	165,118	0	0	2,044,158
1962	174,916	0	0	2,294,895
1963	234,789	0	0	3,247,136
1964	185,439	0	0	2,712,971
1965	132,367	0	0	2,018,592
1966	116,820	0	0	1,869,115
1967	114,422	0	0	1,945,169
1968	92,452	0	0	1,664,127
1969	53,373	0	0	1,014,091
1970	85,664	0	0	1,713,282
1971	56,386	0	0	1,240,483
1972	35,325	0	0	847,805
1973	53,764	4,142	0	1,584,169
1974	49,412	42,795	0	3,161,047
1975	52,633	46,151	0	3,266,993
1976	14,914	73,802	0	3,578,648
1977	15,470	16,753	0	1,270,703
1978	35,714	93	48,290	2,206,894
1979	43,824	11,718	23,792	3,457,925
1980	21,765	21,765	25,180	2,325,729
1981	16,510	16,510	36,373	1,994,445
1982	16,440	16,440	0	2,002,488
1983	7,410	7,410	0	1,170,780
1984	7,907	7,907	0	4,089,755
1985	16,367	16,367	0	6,016,069
1986	30,235	0	0	4,943,184
1987	25,940	0	0	4,505,420
1988	28,897	5,769	18,856	5,615,445

TABLE 11.2 (continued)

Year	Colorado River water (acre-feet)	State Project water (acre-feet)	In-lieu program water (acre-feet)	Total cost (dollars)
1989	13,213	6,792	15,022	5,425,148
1990	27,395	3,306	38,961	6,342,506

SOURCE: Orange County Water District Annual Reports.

the area in Orange County was annexed to MWD (by 1960, 99 percent of the assessed valuation of Orange County was in MWD), with the result that users throughout the basin were able to use supplemental water if they chose to do so. Second, the OCWD encouraged water users with access to imported water to use it for at least half of their supply during the fill-the-basin effort (Weschler, 1968: 43–44). This was a jawboning effort by the district, without sanctions or inducements. Third, the Orange County Coastal Plain urbanized rapidly during this period, so thousands of acres of land were converted from irrigated agriculture to residential and commercial use. Pumping for irrigation use fell considerably from 1954 to 1964 and was cut almost in half in the three years from 1961 to 1964. The decline in the demand for irrigation water exceeded the increase in demand for urban uses while the basin replenishment effort was at its peak.

Fill-the-basin was a successfully implemented program. In 1964, average water levels in the basin were 24 feet above sea level, up from 20 feet below sea level in 1956 and equal to the average water level in the landmark year of 1944. The district had developed the financial and physical capacity to handle 200,000 acre-feet of replenishment water per year. Despite these remarkable accomplishments, the OCWD abandoned the fill-the-basin program after 1964.

The 1964 water levels for the basin as a whole equaled those of 1944, but, in ways not anticipated at the outset of the fill-the-basin program, the basin had changed. Pumping patterns, the accumulated overdraft, and subterranean geologic changes had altered the distribution of water in the aquifers. In addition, the spreading facilities and replenishment were necessarily concentrated in the forebay area in the upper part of the basin. As a result, although the average water level in 1964 equaled that of 1944, the 1964 levels were far above the 1944 levels in the inland parts of the basin and far below the 1944 levels along the Pacific coast and the Los Angeles County border. Without the ability either to limit

TABLE 11.3

Orange County Groundwater Production and Total Water Obtained, 1953–1990 (acre-feet)

Year	Groundwater production	Total water obtained	Groundwater percentage
1953	213,800	230,386	92.8
1954	210,000	229,113	91.7
1955	148,224	173,281	85.5
1956	153,677	181,822	84.5
1957	186,025	233,290	79.7
1958	160,247	203,724	78.7
1959	208,572	260,587	80.0
1960	207,448	278,605	74.4
1961	226,025	309,188	73.1
1962	177,172	255,190	69.2
1963	186,093	273,285	68.0
1964	188,603	290,039	65.0
1965	179,798	283,278	63.5
1966	182,172	272,813	66.8
1967	169,375	264,295	64.1
1968	193,656	303,860	63.7
1969	178,798	288,413	62.0
1970	194,379	331,660	58.6
1971	203,923	337,763	60.4
1972	229,048	372,737	61.5
1973	214,983	332,960	64.6
1974	218,863	353,723	61.9
1975	225,597	356,256	63.3
1976	245,456	399,728	61.4
1977	243,511	392,919	62.0
1978	188,407	347,290	54.3
1979	213,290	376,797	56.6
1980	221,453	402,129	55.1
1981	228,943	445,308	51.4
1982	244,184	416,463	58.6
1983	249,548	392,480	63.6
1984	223,207	450,130	49.6
1985	252,070	414,000	60.9
1986	270,932	459,569	59.0
1987	276,354	459,949	60.1
1988	265,226	489,609	54.2
1989	275,077	507,380	54.2
1990	261,190	516,873	50.5

SOURCE: Orange County Water District Annual Reports.

pumping or to discriminate in pump tax charges, the district was raising a "tilted" water table. Toward the coast, seawater intrusion continued despite the aggressive replenishment program; by the end of the fill-the-basin period, more than 500,000 acres of the district were underlain by seawater, and fifty wells had been abandoned (Crooke and Toups, 1961: 11).

By 1965, total water use in the district was approaching 300,000 acre-feet per year. From 1961 through 1965, Santa Ana River inflow averaged roughly 30,000 acre-feet per year, and water imported from MWD for direct use had increased to approximately 90,000 acre-feet per year. Thus, Orange County water users had an incoming water supply of about 120,000 acre-feet to meet a demand of nearly 300,000 acre-feet. The remainder was being pumped from the basin, to be replaced by artificial replenishment. The replenishment program therefore required annual purchases of up to 200,000 acre-feet. At the same time, MWD's long-term Colorado River supply was in danger of being cut in half after the U.S. Supreme Court's 1963 decision in *Arizona v. California.*

Although successfully implemented, the fill-the-basin program had failed to achieve two of its main objectives: seawater intrusion continued, and the accumulated overdraft, although reduced to 140,000 acre-feet, had not been eliminated. Reviewing the operations of the previous ten years, the OCWD engineer wrote in the annual report on the 1965–1966 water year: "It now appears certain that spreading in the forebay cannot entirely eliminate sea water intrusion. . . . It is also apparent that under future water supply and demand conditions, it would be unwise to rely solely on ground water replenishment in the forebay area to prevent sea water intrusion."

The District's Supply Management Program, 1965–1991

OCWD purchases of MWD replenishment water dropped from about 185,000 acre-feet in 1964 to slightly more than 50,000 acre-feet in 1970, as the district moved away from its fill-the-basin policy toward conjunctive management of the basin. The conjunctive management program represents an attempt to alter use patterns in order to minimize reliance on the basin as a source of supply for daily needs and preserve it for water supplies during emergency and peaking periods.

The Santa Ana River Adjudication

Once again, reduced inflows from the Santa Ana River prompted litigation against upstream water users. In the neighboring San Gabriel River watershed in Los Angeles County, downstream water users had sued upstream water users in 1959 over the decline in natural inflow. Principles of settlement worked out in that case in 1961 (see Chapter 7) obliged the upstream water users to guarantee a specific amount of water to the downstream users every year. On October 18, 1963, the OCWD filed a complaint that began the case of *Orange County Water District v. City of Chino et al.*[2] This time, the district did not name as defendants a few upstream water companies or a handful of upstream cities, but 1,200 defendants and 20,000 John Does; subsequent amendments raised the number of named defendants to more than 2,500. The complaint requested an adjudication of the water rights of every user in the Upper Area. The defendants filed thirteen cross-complaints, naming as cross-defendants essentially all of the water rights users and water rights owners in the Lower Area, and bringing the total number of named parties to more than 4,000.

Serious negotiations ensued, intensifying after judgment was entered in the San Gabriel River adjudication in 1965 guaranteeing the Lower Area in that watershed a minimum annual inflow from the Upper Area. In 1968, the OCWD's complaint was dismissed against all defendants except the three major upstream municipal water districts—the Chino Basin Municipal Water District, the Western Municipal Water District of Riverside County, and the San Bernardino Valley Municipal Water District. The cross-complaints were also dropped. The four water districts negotiated a stipulated judgment similar to the one on the San Gabriel River. The Santa Ana River judgment was entered and filed on April 16, 1969, and became effective on October 1, 1970.

Under the judgment, Orange County was entitled to receive, as a long-term average, 42,000 acre-feet of usable "base flow" per year at Prado Dam, plus all storm flows reaching Prado Flood Control Reservoir. In addition, the OCWD was given a protected right to store water behind Prado Dam for controlled releases. The three upstream municipal water districts were made responsible for guaranteeing the long-term annual average flow to Orange County. In recognition of the fact that the Upper Area in the Santa Ana River watershed is itself divided into an eastern (Bunker Hill–San Timoteo) area and a western (Chino-Riverside) area, the responsibilities for guaranteeing the base flow were divided between San Bernardino Valley Municipal Water District (SBVMWD), on the one hand, and Chino Basin Municipal Water District (CBMWD) and Western Municipal Water District of Riverside County (WMWD), on the other. Within the Upper Area, Riverside Narrows was used as the dividing point. SBVMWD was made responsible for ensuring that an average annual base flow of 15,250 acre-feet reached Riverside Narrows. CBMWD and WMWD were made responsible for ensuring that an average annual base flow of 42,000 acre-feet reached Prado Dam. Like the San Gabriel River judgment, the Santa Ana River judgment included some flexibility in meeting these long-term average obligations, with a system of cumulative credits and cumulative debits and provisions for a long-term accounting every ten years.

In contrast to the San Gabriel River approach, however, the Santa Ana River judgment took water quality into account in its formula for calculating the base flow received, both at Riverside Narrows and at Prado Dam. Samples of the water passing each of these points were to be used to adjust the amount of base flow downward when the total dissolved solids (TDS) of the water were too high, to penalize the upstream areas for delivering poorer-quality water downstream. When the TDS of the water was especially low, the calculation of base flow received would be adjusted upward, to reward the upstream areas for providing better-quality water to the downstream area. The judgment also formally established the Santa Ana Watershed Project Authority (SAWPA), a joint-powers agency of the four districts whose mission was to attend to water supply and water-quality issues throughout the watershed.

The base flow at Prado Dam and at Riverside Narrows has recovered since the entry of judgment. The base flow at Prado Dam reached a low of 26,190 acre-feet in the 1960–61 water year. In the first ten years under the judgment, the base flow at Prado averaged in excess of 50,000 acre-feet per year.

Like the San Gabriel River judgment, the Santa Ana River judgment is administered by a multimember, representative watermaster, with continuing jurisdiction retained by the court. The Santa Ana River Watermaster consists of five persons appointed by the court, two nominated by the OCWD, and one each by the three upstream districts. To avoid 3 to 2 splits between the Upper Area and the Lower Area, the judgment also stipulates that all findings and determinations of the Watermaster are to be unanimous, with the court retaining the authority to settle issues on which unanimity cannot be achieved.

The judgment necessitates considerable coordination with the U.S. Army Corps of Engineers, which operates Prado Dam as both a flood-control and a water conservation facility, and with the U.S. Geological Survey (USGS), which operates several gauging stations along the Santa Ana River and its tributaries. Gradual releases of water stored after storms enhance the conservation and use of the water in Orange County. The corps also provides data from Prado Dam required by the Santa Ana River Watermaster in monitoring the judgment. The USGS provides stream flow measurements from its gauging stations and water-quality data to the Santa Ana River Watermaster, as part of a cooperative monitoring program funded by the USGS and the parties to the Santa Ana River judgment. The watermaster receives additional data on water quality needed to adjust the base flow measurements from the California Department of Water Resources, the Riverside and Corona City Sanitation

Departments, and the Chino Basin Municipal Water District. This inter-jurisdictional coordination has kept the annual costs of administering the Santa Ana River judgment to less than one dollar per acre-foot of required base flow at Prado Dam.

Although the successful conclusion of the Santa Ana River adjudication helped to increase the natural inflow into Orange County from upstream, other water supply sources remained problematic. State Project water from northern California did not arrive in the quantities anticipated in the early 1970s. Replenishment deliveries finally began during the 1972–73 water year, peaked in 1975, and averaged 25,000 acre-feet per year through 1981–82. State Project water did not become available in Orange County for direct use until 1974–75. Around that time, the energy crisis prompted a rapid escalation in the price of imported water. MWD curtailed water deliveries beyond direct service requirements in order to economize on energy use and production costs. MWD's prices rose 50 percent from 1973 to 1978.

Parties had nearly adjusted to the first round of price shocks by 1975–76 and 1976–77, two of the driest consecutive water years in California history. Colorado River water became unavailable for replenishment after March 1977, and State Project water was unavailable for all uses after March 1977. Pumping in Orange County in these two years was 245,456 acre-feet (a record) and 243,511 acre-feet, respectively, and by the end of the 1976–77 water year, the average water level in the basin was back down to 6.3 feet below sea level.

With the instability of imported supplies and local precipitation, the district's conjunctive management program would need more than the acquisition of a minimum right to 42,000 acre-feet per year from the Santa Ana River. It would entail taking the greatest possible advantage of wet years and heavy river flows in order to store water in the basin, to be drawn down in dry periods. Making this work meant altering the characteristics of the basin itself.

Building Maximum Recharge Capacity

The conjunctive management program triggered a new effort to increase basin recharge capacity. Lands were purchased and excavated to create new spreading facilities, such as the Warner and Kraemer basins and the Burris Pit. In all, the OCWD owns 3,400 acres of land used primarily for conservation and basin recharge. District conservation and recharge plans call for a recharge capacity of 300,000 acre-feet per year to accommodate Santa Ana River base flows and storm flows, and imports. This goal cannot be attained without still more recharge capacity, which has become difficult to acquire in light of the county's economic expansion and high real estate values.

The district's acquisition of additional recharge capacity has considerably improved its ability to replenish the basin. In years of above-normal rainfall and river flow (such as 1969, 1978, 1979, 1980, and 1983), the amount of water stored in the basin increased by 50,000 to 200,000 acre-feet, despite groundwater production in excess of 180,000 acre-feet and total water use of 300,000 acre-feet or more. The district remains short of its goal of 300,000 acre-feet of annual recharge capacity, but its ability to conserve water supplies when they are plentiful has increased markedly, and the essential supply-side component of the conjunctive-use program—the ability to refill the basin when water is plentiful—is largely in place.

Walling Off the Basin

The other required element of a conjunctive-use program is the ability to draw down the basin when water is scarce. Refilling a coastal basin in wet years and mining it in dry years means that in dry years water levels may fall below sea level and encourage more seawater intrusion. The Orange County basin had already demonstrated that it could drop from 10 feet above sea level to 10 feet below sea level in 3 years (1947–1950) and rise back to 20 feet above sea level in just two years (1961–1963). Mining the basin for as little as two or three consecutive dry years could increase saltwater intrusion.

By the late 1960s, district managers acknowledged that seawater intrusion had to be blocked by means other than artificial replenishment of the basin with freshwater. To this end, the OCWD undertook coastal barrier projects at the Alamitos and Talbert gaps. The Alamitos Gap Barrier Project, described in Chapter 7, was constructed jointly with the Los Angeles County Flood Control District and is located at the border of Los Angeles and Orange counties, near the mouth of the San Gabriel River. Seawater intrusion into the Orange County basin had been more extensive along the Talbert Gap between Huntington Beach and Newport Beach. Here the OCWD undertook the Orange County Coastal Barrier Project, a larger operation employing a more complex method. The barrier facilities needed to wall-off the basin at this point were designed to accommodate 20,000 to 25,000 acre-feet of injected freshwater per year. Injections of that magnitude, however, might raise the underground water levels to, or above, the ground surface in that area, re-creating swampy conditions. In addition, there was no guaranteed supply of the additional 20,000 to 25,000 acre-feet of water to feed those injection wells each year.

OCWD made Talbert Gap a two-stage barrier project. Approximately 4 miles inland, twenty-three multipoint injection wells create a freshwater mound against the sea. Between these injection wells and the shore, about 2 miles inland, a series of extraction wells pull brackish water moving inland and return it to the ocean through surface channels. Construction of the Talbert Gap project began in 1967, and the first units became operational in 1969. The OCWD also secured a drought-free, lawsuit-free supply of freshwater for the injection wells at the Coastal Barrier Project. Adjacent to the injection wells at Talbert Gap, the district constructed Water Factory 21, which converts wastewater into high-quality reclaimed water that is injected at the barrier project. Additional water injected there is pumped from a deeper aquifer not affected by seawater intrusion and from which other pumpers do not extract groundwater. The Alamitos Barrier and the Talbert Gap Barrier have walled off the basin so that it can be used as a storage reservoir.

A New Attempt at Demand Management: Penalties and Rewards

In 1968, the Orange County Water District sought and obtained another amendment to its enabling legislation, authorizing the OCWD Board of Directors to establish a "basin production percentage," a proportion of total water production to be produced from groundwater withdrawals. The basin production percentage applies to pumpers producing more than 25 acre-feet of water per year for nonirrigation use.[3]

The basin production percentage was coupled with a new pump tax, a "basin equity assessment." This assessment is levied on each acre-foot of water produced in excess of the basin production percentage. Basin equity assessment funds collected by the OCWD can be used to satisfy reimbursement claims by pumpers who comply with district requests to pump less than the basin production percentage for their total water needs. The assessment therefore is not applied uniformly to all pumpers. Its purpose is to equalize pumping costs by compensating those who pump less groundwater for their higher costs of procuring imported water for direct use, while taxing those who produce a greater share of their water by pumping from the basin. The OCWD Board of Directors establishes the basin production percentage and the basin equity assessment rate each year, taking into account basin conditions and the availability of imported water throughout the basin. With this information, the board adopts a basin production percentage that will, in its prospective view, maximize productive use of the basin without encouraging overdrafting. In setting the basin equity assessment rate, primary consideration is given to the cost differential between pumping groundwater and importing MWD water.[4]

In the early 1980s, MWD's in-lieu and interruptible-water programs made direct use of surplus imported water more attractive to Orange County water users, while OCWD's basin equity assessment program made excessive reliance on groundwater less attractive. Although the

OCWD does not control the MWD programs, between the basin equity tax and the MWD programs, the district does have some demand-side component to its conjunctive management program now. The OCWD has implemented its conjunctive management program through four main steps: (1) an established guaranteed minimum inflow from the Santa Ana River; (2) an increased recharge capacity for filling the basin during periods of more abundant supply; (3) "walling off" the basin on the ocean side, allowing basin levels to be drawn down in dry periods without increasing seawater intrusion; and (4) a system of rewards for those who cooperate with district requests for pumping restraint and penalties for those who rely too heavily on groundwater production.

Analysis

The natural water system in Orange County resembles that of the Central and West basins in Los Angeles County. The Orange County basin lies at the downstream end of a watershed and thus is vulnerable to the actions of upstream users. It is also exposed to seawater intrusion below the Newport-Inglewood Uplift. Some areas in the basin south of Prado Dam are capable of significant recharge, but a pressure area farther south is not suited to percolation.

Unlike the Los Angeles County basins, however, the basin-management program in Orange County has continually emphasized improving supply rather than curtailing demand through the assignment of pumping rights. Orange County water users chose to develop basin governance and management without an intrabasin adjudication and limitation of pumping rights and even prohibited the Orange County Water District from initiating such an adjudication.

Eliciting Information

The Orange County Board of Supervisors procured the first shared picture of basin conditions with the Lippincott report in 1925. A series of reports by the state Division of Water Resources from 1927 through 1930 confirmed the information in the Lippincott report. The Irvine litigation in the 1930s and the suit against the four upstream cities in the 1950s provided additional information about Orange County's water supply situation.

The redesign of the Orange County Water District completed in 1953 included new institutional arrangements for eliciting information about water production. The pump tax entailed metering all wells and reporting production to the OCWD, with the district auditing wells and meters to ensure accuracy. The district began publishing yearly reports from the district engineer on basin conditions and use, as well as an annual report on district activities and finances. These reports notified water users and other interested parties of the operation and performance of the management program. Similarly, annual reports issued by the Santa Ana River Watermaster inform water users of operations under the Santa Ana River judgment.

Institutional Design

Orange County water users have engaged in a considerable amount of institutional design, redesign, and innovation. The Orange County Water District may have been formed to assist with the Irvine litigation, but it also was southern California's first water replenishment district, charged with implementing a program of groundwater supply management through conservation and recharge. In the early 1950s the OCWD was redesigned to accommodate artificial replenishment activities, and the region's first sustained artificial replenishment program financed by a pump tax thus came into being. The pump tax has since been adopted in most other southern California basin management programs. A subsequent redesign of the OCWD authorized the imposition of different pump tax rates within the basin through the addition of the "basin equity assessment."

Orange County water users followed the West Basin example in instituting barrier projects to combat seawater intrusion, including the jointly funded and operated Alamitos Gap project. With the construction and operation of Water Factory 21, Orange County added to the barrier project concept the use of purified wastewater for injection and reuse.

The San Gabriel River adjudication provided the example for the third Santa Ana River suit, including the concepts of a guaranteed inflow and a multimember, representative watermaster. Santa Ana River users built upon the San Gabriel design, adding a calculation of water quality to that of quantity in determining the upstreamers' obligation to the downstreamers, and establishing the Santa Ana Watershed Project Authority as a joint-powers agency to augment supplies and protect and restore quality throughout the watershed.

Integration with Other Governance Systems

Like the basins in the San Gabriel River watershed, Orange County basin has a governance structure that is embedded within a polycentric system connecting it and the basin management program to several other organizations. The watershed governance system is perhaps the most obvious example. As early as 1909, Orange County was part of the Tri-Counties Water Conservation Association. That association dissolved, and after decades and lawsuits passed, another watershed governance system was established, composed of the Santa Ana River judgment, the Santa Ana

River Watermaster, the continuing jurisdiction of the Orange County Superior Court, and SAWPA. Administration of the Santa Ana River judgment also depends heavily on the operation and maintenance of Prado Dam by the U.S. Army Corps of Engineers and gauging stations along the river by the U.S. Geological Survey.

Although not quite as intricately interdependent as some of the basin management programs in the San Gabriel River watershed, the basin management program in Orange County is not operated solely by the OCWD. The district's conservation and recharge program was developed in close cooperation with the Orange County Flood Control District and its program of improvements to the Santa Ana River channel. The artificial replenishment program relies on imported supplies, to which the OCWD has no direct access. There are, however, five MWD members within OCWD's territory—Anaheim, Fullerton, Santa Ana, Coastal Municipal Water District, and the Municipal Water District of Orange County. OCWD purchases most of its imported replenishment water from MWD through the Municipal Water District of Orange County. The seawater intrusion component of the basin management program also involves cooperation with other organizations. Although the barriers at Talbert and Sunset Gaps are OCWD operations, the Alamitos Gap project is jointly funded with the Central and West Basin Water Replenishment District and jointly operated with the Los Angeles County Department of Public Works.

Operation and Performance of the Management Program

Compliance with the Orange County basin management program has been high. Pumpers face no limitation on extractions, but do have to report their production to the district and pay taxes on it, and so far there has been no need to sanction offenders.

The basin management programs have certainly proved adaptable. The district has implemented policy changes throughout the past four decades in response to changes in basin conditions and new ideas about basin management. The Santa Ana River watershed management program contained in the Santa Ana River judgment is also flexible enough to respond to variable water conditions, and the continuing jurisdiction of the court provides the water users with an institutionalized means for modifying the watershed program.

Orange County basin management has proved effective in turning the basin away from critical overdraft and destruction through dewatering and seawater intrusion. Furthermore, the management program takes advantage of the basin's value as a low-cost water storage and distribution facility, relying on the underground system primarily for storage and distribution of imported water purchased by the OCWD.

At the same time, the decision not to assign and limit pumping rights in Orange County has resulted in some loss of efficiency and some increase in risk. Without defined and transferable pumping rights, basin users have no means of moving groundwater production from lesser- to higher-valued uses. Users who stop pumping from the basin benefit other users but receive nothing in return.

Without a limitation of pumping rights, the Orange County basin management program has had to accommodate unlimited groundwater production. The OCWD has responded by expending considerable sums on acquiring and operating extensive replenishment facilities, which in an ordinary year have substantial excess capacity. The decision not to limit pumping has also left basin users heavily dependent on the availability of imported replenishment water to maintain basin conditions, and more exposed to importers' decisions to curtail water deliveries in dry periods. The Orange County management program therefore may exhibit some vulnerability in an extended drought.

NOTES

1. The pump tax is not a very precise tool of demand-side management. Perhaps counterintuitively, a successful replenishment program financed by a pump tax may lower pumping lifts and costs by raising water levels, thereby encouraging more pumping. The question becomes one of relative additions to production costs: if the replenishment assessment per acre-foot is less than the additional cost per acre-foot imposed by longer pumping lifts, the net effect of the replenishment assessment is to lower pumping costs and encourage pumping. If the replenishment program does not reduce pumping costs enough to offset the cost of the pump tax, the tax's effect on pumpers will depend on whether they retail the water they produce and (for those who do) on their ability to pass along the cost of the pump tax to their customers. Those who sell water and can pass along the pump tax to their customers while benefiting from restored water levels and smaller pumping lifts will experience no disincentive to pump.

2. Civil Case 117628 in the Superior Court of the State of California in and for the County of Orange, 1969. Complaint filed October 18, 1963. Judgment entered and filed April 17, 1969 by Judge John P. McMurray.

3. Irrigators and small pumpers accounted for such a small percentage of water production in the basin by the end of the 1960s that they were exempted.

4. In some years, the basin equity assessment has been set lower than the estimated cost differential; for example, during the drought years of 1975–76 and 1976–77, the board lowered the basin equity assessment and raised the basin production percentage, since the drought had severely curtailed MWD's available water supply and producers in Orange County responded (in accordance with the policies of MWD and OCWD) by drawing down groundwater reserves.

12

Chino Basin
Governance for Land-Use Transition

Chino Basin, immediately upstream from Orange County Basin in the Santa Ana River watershed, supplies water for half a million southern Californians in one of the region's most rapidly growing areas—western San Bernardino and Riverside counties. As the most recently adjudicated basin in southern California, Chino Basin reflects the experiences of water users in the adjudicated basins of the San Gabriel River watershed and the impact of the California Supreme Court's decision in the *San Fernando* case. New ideas about groundwater management, and growing concerns about water quality have added to the complexity of the still-evolving governance and management arrangements in this area.

Water Problems in Chino Basin

The emerging tensions in the Santa Ana River watershed in 1930 spurred the area's water users to create the first institutional arrangements for governance in Chino Basin. They organized the Chino Basin Protective Association on February 9, 1931, as they forthrightly stated, to fight off any attempts by "outsiders" to encroach upon their water supplies and water rights. The association's constitution and by-laws indicated that, although members could not be sure of the precise boundaries of the Chino Basin, they knew that it existed, they knew that they relied on its waters, and they shared a common purpose in defending it.

There followed a fairly detailed description of the assumed boundaries of the Chino Basin, with a provision that these boundaries could be altered by vote or written consent of members representing two-thirds or more

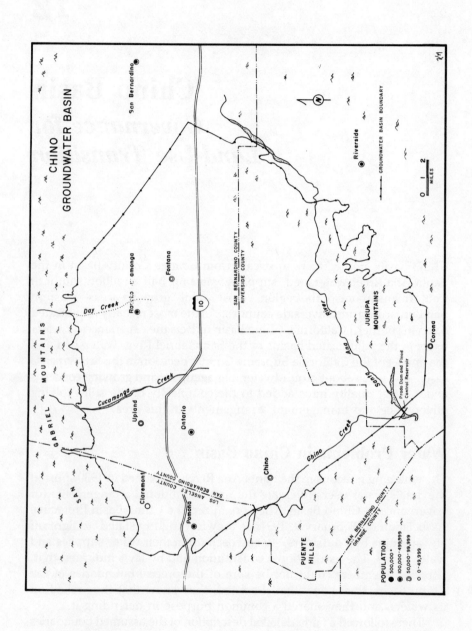

of the total acreage included in the association. Members agreed to contribute dues to the association based on their ownership of overlying lands, and to report their water production monthly and allow one another to inspect their production reports. They established an elected Board of Directors, which would appoint executive officers, and authorized it to "prosecute and defend all litigation concerning said association . . . and take all measures necessary to defend its operations and the rights of the individuals and corporations in said basin," provided that the initiation of litigation required an affirmative vote of members representing two-thirds of the acreage.

In 1932, the Irvine litigation brought into the open what had become widely suspected in the Santa Ana River watershed for years: local water supplies were insufficient to satisfy everyone's demands in an area with a developed economy based on irrigated agriculture. The Chino Basin Protective Association could attempt to defend against the encroachments of outsiders, but that could at best keep the water supply-demand imbalance within the basin from growing worse. A 1930 bulletin by the state Division of Water Resources confirmed the water supply problems: "Annual recharge [in the Santa Ana River watershed] averaged over the past thirty-six years is less than the present demand. . . . The shortage is concentrated in Chino Basin and the Coastal Plain" (California DPW, 1930a: 13). The bulletin suggested that only the importation of water would balance the water supply situation in the Santa Ana River watershed. Acquiring imported water from the recently formed MWD would "involve the organization of the area into one or more districts" (California DPW, 1930a: 17–18). In 1934, another Division of Water Resources bulletin reported that increased pumping and decreased inflow to Chino Basin since 1904 had depressed the water level as much as 50 to 80 feet in parts of the basin. Groundwater still rose to the surface at the southern end of the basin, but that rising water outflow would likely disappear if depletion of the basin continued (California DPW, 1934a: 197).

After a brief recovery as a result of the wet years from 1938 through 1944, water levels again dropped and the supply became overdrawn following the Irvine litigation in 1942 and the onset of another dry cycle in 1945. From 1944 to 1951, water levels fell 20 to 50 feet in the central part of the basin, 10 to 20 feet throughout most of the remainder, and 150 to 200 feet north of Red Hill Dike. The Division of Water Resources estimated that annual overdraft had reached about 21,000 acre-feet as of 1945 (California DPW, 1947: 76). In 1959, the Department of Water Resources projected that under 1948 conditions of development, Chino Basin would require 23,300 acre-feet supplemental water per year to balance supply and demand, and that ultimately it would need approximately 144,300 acre-feet per year (California DWR, 1959a: 63). The conclusion reached in 1930 still stood:

balancing water supply with water demand would require imported water, and access to imported water meant creating water districts.

The Creation of Water Districts in the Upper Santa Ana River Area

Several water districts important to water management in Chino Basin were formed between 1939 and 1954. The 1938 floods prompted the creation of the San Bernardino County Flood Control District in 1939. Since then, the flood control district has gradually assumed the operation of most of the major water impoundment and spreading facilities in the county, including those in Chino Basin.

On December 6, 1949, the Chino Basin Protective Association voted to support the organization of a Chino Basin water conservation district to pursue a more active water conservation program within the basin. The new district, in cooperation with the San Bernardino County Flood Control District and the Los Angeles County Flood Control District, acquired land and excavated additional basins to collect storm runoff and imported water for artificial replenishment of Chino Basin. Today, there are more than thirty spreading grounds along the Cucamonga, Day, Deer, Etiwanda, Lytle, San Antonio, and San Sevaine creeks and the Santa Ana River in the Upper Area, many of which were developed by the Chino Basin Water Conservation District and most of which are operated by the San Bernardino County Flood Control District.

After establishing the water conservation district, the association supported the establishment of the Chino Basin Municipal Water District (CBMWD) to gain access to imported water supplies through membership in MWD. The CBMWD was established June 6, 1950, with a territory of about 92 square miles in the west end of San Bernardino County, but has since expanded its territory to about 242 square miles. In 1951, the CBMWD annexed to MWD by special election. The Chino Basin Protective Association disbanded shortly after the creation of the water conservation district and the CBMWD.

Because of restrictions in the Municipal Water District Act, municipal water districts in California may not cross county boundaries. Therefore, even an expanded Chino Basin Municipal Water District could not encompass the entire basin. The Los Angeles County portion of Chino Basin was organized into the Pomona Valley Municipal Water District in 1950, which subsequently annexed to MWD and is now named Three Valleys Municipal Water District. The Riverside County portion of Chino Basin was organized into the Western Municipal Water District of Riverside County (WMWD) and annexed to MWD in 1954.

The mere creation of water districts, some of which annexed to MWD and acquired access to imported water supplies, was not enough to restore a water supply balance to the Santa Ana River system. The drought that began in 1945, and the greater demands placed on upstream supplies, reduced the outflow from Chino Basin to Orange County. In 1951, the Orange County Water District began the second Santa Ana River litigation. None of the four cities named in the action was located in Chino Basin. One of the Orange County Water District's principal purposes was to force some of the larger municipal water users in the Upper Santa Ana River area into MWD. The fact that the Chino Basin Municipal Water District and the Pomona Valley Municipal Water District had already been created and annexed to MWD in 1951 kept Chino Basin cities out of this suit.

Designing a Chino Basin Management Program

Natural and artificial recharge in the Upper Area declined through the 1950s, pumping continued to increase, and rising water reaching Prado Dam dwindled further, leading to the third Santa Ana River litigation in 1963. As recounted in Chapter 11, this third suit was settled on a different basis, leaving Upper Area water users free to capture, conserve, produce, and consume local water supplies as they wished, as long as they guaranteed a minimum flow through Prado Dam to Orange County. The two prior Santa Ana River watershed judgments restricting upstream conservation and water production activities were suspended.

The Santa Ana River judgment focused the attention of Chino Basin water users on the issues involved in managing their local supplies. Basin users remained almost completely dependent on overdrafted groundwater supplies. The Chino Basin overdraft was somewhere between 25,000 and 50,000 acre-feet per year by the end of the 1960s. Although this situation could not be sustained over the long term, most users remained unwilling to reduce their pumping as long as groundwater remained substantially less expensive than imported water from MWD. Observing neighboring southern California basins, Chino Basin water users and agencies had learned that imported water would be substituted for groundwater only if pumping were limited in some way.

A new water users' association, the Chino Basin Water Association (CBWA), and the Chino Basin Municipal Water District became the focal points of basin governance and the discussion of a Chino Basin management plan. Early negotiations were unsuccessful. The CBMWD proposed an assessment against all water production (that is, a "gross pump tax") to fund studies toward the development of a management plan and to purchase replenishment water as part of an adjudicated settlement. This idea met with opposition from the many agricultural water users in the basin. They had the longest history of basin use and laid claim to their water rights based on ownership of the overlying land. In their view, the increased demands on the basin's water supply were coming primarily from the appropriators—the cities and the water companies and water districts—serving the growing population that had accompanied the area's urbanization. To the agricultural users, an equal tax on all pumping shifted costs onto them that the appropriators should have to pay.

Investigation of a wider range of management plans ensued, led by the CBWA and the CBMWD staff. In December 1970, the district staff prepared some basic details on a proposed basin management plan and submitted them to the CBWA. The CBMWD also agreed to furnish staff assistance for studying the feasibility of a basin management program that would include a stipulated adjudication to define and limit pumping rights. A negotiating committee, composed of the thirteen members of the CBWA Executive Committee and a representative each from the state of California (for the correctional institutions located in the basin), Pomona Valley Water Company, agricultural producers in the San Bernardino County area of Chino Basin, and agricultural producers from the Riverside County area, was formed to review the possibilities.

A 1971 working memorandum of the Negotiating Committee reviewed the management options used in neighboring basins. The mutual-prescription approach to adjudicating pumping rights by stipulated judgment adopted in the Raymond, West, and Central basins formed a basic premise for the plan. The discussion on financing replenishment operations drew upon the programs used in the Central and West basins and the Orange County Water District. The possibilities entertained for organizing the replenishment and ongoing management and monitoring of the basin were based on the examples of the Central and West Basin Water Replenishment District, the Orange County Water District, and the emerging plan for the management of the Main San Gabriel Basin.

Chino Basin water users could have avoided adjudication, but they "wanted vested rights protected and accorded an economic value" (Lipson, 1978: 75). They explicitly considered and rejected the Orange County model (the "utility" approach, they called it) of relying almost entirely on supply-side management of the basin, without a limitation on pumping rights. The committee memorandum observed: "Adjudication appears to offer the only decisive method of meeting and resolving the question of ownership and control of unused ground water storage capacity." That adjudication was to be based on mutual prescription, administered by a watermaster under continuing jurisdiction of the court.

The Negotiating Committee memorandum offered some procedural guidelines for an adjudication, in order to avoid some of the difficulties experienced in other basins:

> Basically, the approach should be to develop a plan for implementation of the management program which would be incorporated in the form

of a stipulated judgment. *Only after the form of judgment had been essentially agreed upon would the complaint be formally filed and legal proceedings undertaken.* In this way, the trial time should be restricted to a matter of days. After the general agreement on approach to the solution, those parties willing to do so should furnish their attorneys for participation in a committee organization to work quickly on finalization of the stipulated judgment. . . . Since the fact of overdraft in Chino Basin is long standing and of general notoriety, no major factual or hydrologic issue should be involved. (Negotiating Committee, 1971)

An appendix to the Negotiating Committee memorandum contained a draft of a stipulated judgment. The draft assumed that the Chino Basin Municipal Water District would act as the plaintiff bringing the adjudication, with all known pumpers joined as defendants. It also laid out assumed prescriptive rights of the parties based on production from 1953 through 1969 reported under the 1955 Recordation Act.

The Negotiating Committee recommended financing basin management through the use of property tax revenues for capital projects only, a gross pump tax to pay administrative costs and to finance improvements of benefit to all water users, and a net pump tax to finance purchases of replenishment water to replace water pumped in excess of adjudicated rights. The committee recommended eliminating "minimal producers" from reporting and assessment.

With respect to administering the judgment and setting basin management policy, the Negotiating Committee was obviously watching the developments in the pending Main San Gabriel Basin adjudication closely. It noted that users there had developed a broadened concept of the use of the stipulated decree and physical solution, relying on the idea of a policy-making watermaster under the continuing supervision of the court. The committee endorsed this approach, viewing it as the one best suited to overcoming Chino Basin's jurisdictional complexity. According to the Negotiating Committee's 1971 memorandum, with a court-appointed policy-making watermaster, "political boundaries no longer are of consequence. The exterior geographic boundaries of the Watermaster's jurisdiction are defined by the hydrologic unit adjudicated."

The committee also concluded that a watermaster with policy-making powers, especially the power to set an operating safe yield tied to changes in basin conditions, would make the basin management program more flexible. It concluded that control and management of the basin's storage capacity required some means of determining rights and of allowing water users to be represented in the making of storage decisions. In all, the committee expressed a strong preference for a management mechanism that would provide for self-governance by basin water users:

The basic distinction is in the control of the exercise of discretion by the managing agency. In the case of the political solution, control resides in the entire community and is exercised through the registered voters. This compares to the adjudicated solution wherein the control lies in the court, subject to petition and appeal from the producers and water right owners. (Negotiating Committee, 1971)

Committee members considered designating one of the basin's overlying special districts as the basin policy-making authority, or forming a water replenishment district fitted to the basin boundaries. Both options presented problems. As in the Main San Gabriel Basin, no existing special district covered the whole basin. It would be difficult to create a water replenishment district to match the basin boundaries in part because any modifications of, or amendments to, the Water Replenishment District Act would have to be coordinated with the Central and West Basin Water Replenishment District. Moreover, some legislators, voters, and the Local Agency Formation Commission (LAFCo) would be reluctant to approve any new overlapping special districts with additional taxing and regulatory powers. The Negotiating Committee therefore recommended the Main San Gabriel Basin approach of having a watermaster constituted separately by the judgment.

The Chino Basin Adjudication

The Negotiating Committee's recommendations were reviewed through 1972 and 1973. In 1974, the Chino Basin Water Association adopted a memorandum of agreement on the Chino Basin Plan calling on the Chino Basin Municipal Water District to proceed with an adjudication and with the remaining studies needed to develop a practicable management program, in consultation with the CBWA. It recommended using a temporary gross pump tax to fund the studies and the development of the management program. State Senator Ruben S. Ayala of Chino, a very active member on water issues, introduced Senate Bill 222 in January 1975, authorizing a temporary levy of $2 per acre-foot. The bill passed the legislature and was signed into law in June 1975. It also required the CBMWD Board of Directors to appoint an advisory committee of water users to develop the details of the Chino Basin management plan.

In the meantime, the CBMWD Board of Directors filed a complaint on January 2, 1975, formally initiating the adjudication process. The complaint in *Chino Basin Municipal Water District v. City of Chino et al.* sought "an adjudication of water rights, injunctive relief and the imposition of a physical solution."[1]

An advisory committee of more than 100 representatives was formed and met regularly. Three producer subcommittees were established to consider how to allocate pumping rights and management costs among the different types of water users within the basin. These subcommittees represented agricultural water users with overlying water rights, non-agricultural (primarily industrial) water users with overlying water rights, and water purveyors (primarily cities, water companies, and water districts) with appropriative rights acquired by actual diversion and use. The subcommittees came to be known as the Overlying (Agricultural) Pool Committee, the Overlying (Nonagricultural) Pool Committee, and the Appropriative Pool Committee.

The Chino Basin adjudication was certain to be complex. There were 1,300 named parties and 93 attorneys involved—more pumpers and lawyers than in any of the previous adjudications. Nevertheless, early agreement among the advisory committee members on the presence of the overdraft in Chino Basin and on the basic theory of the adjudication—that is, mutual prescription—offered hope of a relatively smooth resolution of this large and multiparty adjudication. Within a few months, however, it became clear that the process would not be as smooth as originally hoped.

The Impact of the San Fernando Decision

On May 12, 1975, four months after the Chino Basin adjudication began, the California Supreme Court issued its *Los Angeles v. San Fernando* decision, reversing the trial court's application of a mutual-prescription solution to the determination of water rights in the San Fernando Valley. The Supreme Court ruled that the water rights of overlying landowners could not be reduced to a specific quantity but were limited only by "beneficial use" and the "correlative rights" of other overlying landowners. Therefore, the water rights of overlying landowners could not be lost by "prescription." This opened the door for any overlying landowner to refuse to go along with a stipulation that would limit his or her water right on any basis other than the doctrine of correlative rights.The decision also held that mutual prescription could not be imposed on public water purveyors because California Civil Code Section 1007 barred the acquisition of a prescriptive water right against public entities.

The *San Fernando* decision precipitated the restructuring of the planned stipulation in Chino Basin. Its impact was especially great in this instance because of the large proportion of water rights claimed by overlying landowners. Overlying agricultural and nonagricultural users still accounted for most of the pumping from the basin in 1975. Effective basin management could not reasonably have been implemented without them.

The appropriators in Chino Basin continued to press for some adjudication and limitation of rights and provisions for the purchase of supplemental water, despite the uncertainty created by the *San Fernando* decision. The problem of growing water demands was greatest for them, and they had a greater capacity to spread costs across their customers, so they were willing to bear a disproportionate share of basin management costs. Appropriators preferred any resolution that provided them with firm rights to part of the local groundwater supply to having to shift entirely to surface and imported water supplies and surface water storage and distribution (Lipson, 1978: 78). The appropriators also were willing to accommodate the agricultural interests in the short term, as long as the resolution provided for future transfers of water from agricultural uses to urban uses as the area continued to change.

Therefore, movement toward a stipulated judgment and physical solution continued despite the *San Fernando* decision. The organizational structure of the advisory committee and its subcommittees led the way: water users and water rights were divided up by type of production. The three-pool approach, involving an overlying (nonagricultural) pool of primarily industrial users, an overlying (agricultural) pool, and an appropriative pool dominated the remainder of the negotiations. Efforts focused on crafting a solution that would offer each pool benefits that exceeded the costs they would experience.

Water production by the overlying (nonagricultural) pool was small relative to the basin's total yield. The nonagricultural users could be guaranteed rights equaling virtually all of their production, and a smaller share of the basin management costs than paid by the appropriators. This arrangement secured their support.

The appropriators bypassed strict mutual-prescription language and instead stipulated that all of their *appropriative* rights in the safe yield of the basin were of equal priority. This avoided the Section 1007 problem. Their remaining problem was to persuade the overlying (agricultural) pool members to agree to a share in the safe yield of Chino Basin that would leave a substantial portion available for the appropriators. They arranged a division of safe yield that would be just high enough so that agricultural users would rarely (if ever) have to pay net assessments for basin replenishment, while appropriators often would. Agricultural users, however, would benefit from the higher water levels and shorter pumping lifts produced by basin replenishment.

As the arrangements within and between the pools developed, the physical solution for the Chino Basin "became more attractive as a compromise that benefited each producer group enough to gain their support" (Lipson, 1978: 78). The emerging agreement on the physical solution coincided with the 1976–77 drought and moved the process back into court with a new stipulated judgment at the end of 1977. The stipulation was agreed to by a majority of the parties, with a majority of the water rights. After a brief trial in December 1977 focusing on some issues concerning nonstipulating parties, Judge Howard B. Weiner signed the final Chino

Basin judgment on January 27, 1978, only three years after the filing of the original complaint.

The Chino Basin Judgment and Its Operation

The Chino Basin judgment declared the basin's safe yield to be 140,000 acre-feet per year. The parties stipulated that their water production had exceeded this safe yield and that the basin had been in overdraft for each of the five years preceding the beginning of the adjudication.

Categories of Producers and Rights

The judgment established overlying water rights for the overlying (agricultural) pool and the overlying (nonagricultural) pool, limiting them in the aggregate. Individual rights of the 1,178 named overlying (agricultural) pool members were not specified. Their aggregate overlying rights were 82,800 acre-feet per year, or 414,000 acre-feet in any five consecutive years in order to provide flexibility for the agricultural water users to respond to basin conditions. The rights of the producers in the overlying (nonagricultural) pool totaled 7,366 acre-feet per year. Individual rights were determined for each of the twelve members of this pool.

After the production rights of overlying users were defined and limited, the judgment stated that none of the basin's safe yield remained available to satisfy any other unexercised overlying rights, and that any unexercised overlying rights had been lost. The judgment further specified that overlying rights were appurtenant to land ownership and could not be transferred apart from the land. Ironically, Chino Basin water users had originally chosen their adjudication course out of a desire to see their water rights determined, quantified, and made transferable so that those rights would have economic value. This desire was thwarted by the *San Fernando* decision's reiteration of the status of overlying water rights in California groundwater law.

The judgment listed twenty-two appropriative pool producers and defined their appropriative rights as percentages of the safe yield remaining after the satisfaction of overlying rights. The appropriators' shares of the safe yield totaled 49,384 acre-feet per year. Three provisions of the judgment could enlarge the appropriative pool's rights over time. First, any subsequent modification to the judgment adjusting the basin's 140,000 acre-foot safe yield would be debited or credited to the appropriative pool rather than overlying users. Second, the watermaster could set an operating safe yield each year, making it possible to take basin replenishment into account and to apply the pumpers' shares of the appropriators to a somewhat larger figure. Third, the judgment allowed for the reallocation of unpumped safe yield by the overlying (agricultural) pool to the appropriative pool, after five consecutive years had passed in which members of the overlying agricultural pool had produced less than their share of the basin safe yield. This provision would gradually transfer the safe yield from agricultural users to appropriators as the basin continued to urbanize.[2]

Appropriative rights can be transferred, and unused appropriative rights may be carried over from one year to the next. In addition, appropriators who are favorably situated to do so may contribute to basin replenishment through participation in in-lieu programs that reimburse appropriators for taking imported surface water instead of pumping groundwater.

Like the Main San Gabriel Basin judgment, the Chino Basin judgment explicitly recognizes the basin's storage capacity as a valuable resource to be used and managed under the supervision of the watermaster. Parties in the appropriative and overlying (nonagricultural) pool have rights to store water in the basin. Unlike the Main San Gabriel Basin judgment, the Chino Basin judgment opens the use of that storage capacity to persons other than the watermaster and the parties. With an estimated one million acre-feet of available storage capacity, Chino Basin was viewed by both the state Department of Water Resources and MWD as a possible water storage reservoir. Any use of the Chino Basin for water storage would have to be under a signed agreement with the watermaster.

Production Assessments

Pump taxes finance the Chino Basin management program. All pumpers pay an administrative assessment; the rates may differ across pools depending on the portion of the watermaster's administrative budget that goes to the administration of the three pools. Replenishment assessments are designed to cover the costs of replacement water and of spreading that water. The replenishment assessment formulas (and their actual amounts from year to year) vary by production pool (see Table 12.1).

Because there is no quantification of individual production rights among the members of the overlying (agricultural) pool, the judgment provides for the use of a modified gross pump tax to purchase replenishment water for this pool. If the overlying (agricultural) pool members overpump their share of the safe yield (414,000 acre-feet in a five-consecutive-year period), the watermaster calculates the cost of replacement water to be purchased in the ensuing water year and divides that cost equally across every acre-foot of agricultural pool production, so all members pay to replace their collective overproduction.

Within the overlying (nonagricultural) pool, where production rights are quantified for each producer, the replenishment assessment takes the form of a net pump tax. Each pumper pays the full cost of purchasing and spreading the amount overpumped by it during the previous water year. Individual members of the pool thus replace their overproduction, acre-foot for acre-foot.

TABLE 12.1
Assessments in Chino Basin, 1978–1989 (dollars)

Year	Agricultural pool	Nonagricultural pool	Appropriative pool
Production assessment rates, 1978–1989			
1978	0.2872	0.3179	0.4169
1979	0.6539	1.2865	0.7673
1980	0.5427	0.1966	0.5106
1981	0.3200	0.0000 [a]	0.0000 [a]
1982	0.1000	0.0000	0.0000
1983	0.1000	0.0000	0.0000
1984	0.1000	0.0000	0.0000
1985	0.1000	0.0000	0.1000
1986	0.1000	0.0000	0.4543
1987	0.1000	0.0000	0.4060
1988	0.1000	0.0000	0.2547
1989	0.0940	0.0000	0.6711

	Agricultural pool	Nonagricultural pool	Appropriative pool	
			Gross	*Net*
Replenishment assessment rates, 1979–1989				
1979	1.2150	51.00	1.1600	43.3499
1980	0.0000	56.20	2.3495	47.7700
1981	0.0000	62.51	2.6140	53.1330
1982	0.0000	63.78	2.7900	54.2130
1983	0.0000	81.46	2.6278	69.2410
1984	0.0000	102.18	3.6010	86.8530
1985	0.0000	154.00	3.9380	130.9000
1986	0.0000	149.39	5.1320	126.9810
1987	0.0000	155.10	4.6400	131.8350
1988	0.0000	155.42	4.5780	132.1070
1989	0.0000	155.33	3.5549	132.0305

(continued)

TABLE 12.1 (continued)

	Agricultural pool	Nonagricultural pool	Appropriative pool	Total
Assessments billed, 1982–1989[b]				
1982	7,540.93	72.76	1,224,316.65	1,298,840.34
1983	7,124.42	92.58	989,291.23	996,508.23
1984	6,466.96	90.65	1,348,689.84	1,355,247.45
1985	6,607.77	121.60	1,868,968.17	1,875,697.54
1986	6,181.13	164.57	2,417,313.04	2,423,658.74
1987	5,886.52	153.06	2,120,118.99	2,126,158.57
1988	6,660.43	137.71	2,434,084.76	2,440,882.90
1989	0.0	122.13	2,254,066.37	2,254,188.50

a. In 1980–81, 1981–82, 1982–83, and 1983–84, a flat administrative fee of $5.00 was assessed against each appropriative and each nonagricultural producer, rather than an assessment against pumping. In 1984–85, 1985–86, 1986–87, 1987–88, and 1988–89, the flat fee method was used for the nonagricultural pool but not for the appropriative pool.
b. Assessments are billed during the water year shown on the basis of water production in the previous water year.
SOURCE: Chino Basin Watermaster Annual Reports.

Within the appropriative pool, there was some disagreement about whether to use a gross pump tax or a net pump tax for assessments to replace overproduction (Lipson, 1978: 82). A resulting compromise has some appropriators paying a net pump tax to replace their overproduction on an acre-foot by acre-foot basis, whereas other appropriators use a 15/85 formula that spreads 15 percent of replacement water costs across the participating appropriators in the form of a gross pump tax, and assigns the remaining 85 percent to individual appropriators who overpumped their share of the operating safe yield.[3]

The Chino Basin Governance Structure

The constitution for Chino Basin governance is the basin judgment, which provides a structure for taking collective management decisions and actions under the continuing jurisdiction of the court. Basin governance involves the three producers' pools, their selection of representatives to a watermaster advisory committee, and the designation of a Chino Basin watermaster. The judgment appoints the five-member Board of Directors of the Chino Basin Municipal Water District (which overlies about 75 percent of the Chino Basin) to serve as the Chino Basin Watermaster.

The court appoints the watermaster, which serves at its pleasure. The initial appointment was for five years. After that, the watermaster could be reappointed or could be changed at any time at the direction of the court or a majority of the members of the Watermaster Advisory Committee.

The Chino Basin Municipal Water District has been reappointed by the court as Chino Basin Watermaster twice and is now serving its third five-year term.[4] The offices of the Chino Basin Watermaster are the offices of the Chino Basin Municipal Water District in Rancho Cucamonga, California. Four persons at the CBMWD spend at least part of their time on watermaster services, and one staff member is devoted to watermaster services full-time. One CBMWD staff member is designated the chief of watermaster services. The first chief, Frank Brommenschenkel, served until 1980. His former assistant, Donald Peters, served as chief of watermaster services from 1980 to 1991. The Chino Basin Watermaster also uses the CBMWD to purchase imported replenishment water for the basin, reimbursing the district for those purchases. The CBMWD does not place any surcharge on the replenishment water.

While agreeing to have the Chino Basin Municipal Water District Board of Directors act as the Chino Basin Watermaster, the producers insisted that the watermaster have a representative structure and placed a number of conditions on watermaster operations—for example, Advisory Committee approval must be obtained before the watermaster takes any substantive basin management actions. This allows Chino Basin water users, whether located in the CBMWD or not, to exercise a check on the district's actions as watermaster.

The judgment directs the watermaster to organize a pool committee of water user representatives for each of the three pools. The pool committees are the governing bodies for the producer pools and may decide matters affecting the internal administration of their respective pools. The producers in the overlying (agricultural) pool annually elect a twenty-member pool committee, with voting based on one vote per 100 acre-feet of recorded production in the previous year. The Overlying (Nonagricultural) Pool Committee consists of the entire pool, which had only twelve members at the time of the judgment. Voting is on a one-member, one-vote basis. All producers in the appropriative pool (twenty-two at the time of the judgment) are members of the Appropriative Pool Committee. Voting in the Appropriative Pool Committee is allocated by a scheme totaling 1,000 votes, with 500 votes apportioned by pumping right and 500 votes apportioned by assessments paid. To prevail in a weighted vote, one must have the support of a majority of the votes and at least one-third of the members. When no members object, the pool committee may conduct business on the simpler one-member, one-vote basis, but the weighted method must be used when called for by any member.

The pool committees select representatives to the Watermaster Advisory Committee. The overlying (agricultural) pool has ten representatives, the overlying (nonagricultural) pool has three, and the appropriative pool has ten (eight of which are designated in the judgment: the cities of Chino, Ontario, Pomona, and Upland, the Cucamonga and Monte Vista County Water districts, and the Fontana Union and Pomona Valley Water companies). On the Watermaster Advisory Committee, total voting power is 100 votes allocated among the pools in proportion to the assessments paid during the preceding year, provided that the least the overlying (agricultural) and appropriative pools can have is twenty votes each and the least the overlying (nonagricultural) pool can have is five. The reason for this voting scheme is that the appropriative pool pays most of the costs of the management program (see Table 12.1).

The completion of the adjudication and the institutionalization of the pool committees and the Watermaster Advisory Committee to represent water users largely eliminated the need for the continuing presence of the Chino Basin Water Association. On August 4, 1982, the association unanimously voted to dissolve.

Basin Storage, Water-Quality Concerns, and the Changing Role of the Watermaster

As already mentioned, among the innovations in Chino Basin is the wider array of possibilities for water storage. Since the entry of judgment in 1978, the watermaster has implemented three programs to make use of the basin's storage capacity: the local storage program, the cyclic storage program, and the water exchange agreement program. Under the local storage program, water users may enter into agreements with the watermaster to store water in the basin, either for later use by the party itself or for sale to another party.

Basin Storage

In November 1978, the Chino Basin Watermaster approved a standard form local storage agreement and a cyclic storage agreement and submitted them to the court for review and approval. The watermaster also approved forms for the sale of water in local storage between parties. Uniform groundwater storage rules and regulations were adopted by the watermaster in May 1979. The first local storage agreement was executed in the 1978–79 water year with the Conrock Company to preserve the unused portion of its pumping right of 1.589 acre-feet. By the end of the 1988–89 water year, forty local storage agreements had been executed, totaling 277,928.44 acre-feet of potentially stored water, with 126,264.272

acre-feet of water actually in storage pursuant to those agreements. As of the end of the 1988–89 water year, ten sales of local storage water, totaling about 50,000 acre-feet, had been transacted among parties.

In December 1978, the watermaster entered into a cyclic storage agreement with MWD. This five-year agreement, which has been renewed since, allows MWD to store up to 100,000 acre-feet of surplus water in the basin. The stored water guards against any future lack of availability of replenishment water in years when the watermaster might wish to purchase it from MWD and guarantees MWD the future sale of the surplus water. The watermaster does not purchase or pay for the water when it is placed in the basin, although the watermaster does pay the water-spreading costs. Later, the watermaster may request that water in storage be used for replenishment purposes and pays for it then. As of the 1988–89 water year, approximately 70,000 acre-feet of water had been placed in storage by MWD. In 1988–89, the watermaster asked that some of that water be used to make up for the reduced availability of replenishment water.

In 1986, the watermaster and the court approved forms for water exchange agreements, another type of water storage and replenishment program. The water exchange agreement program allows Chino Basin appropriators to enter into agreements with MWD, with the watermaster serving as trustee, to exchange part of their share of the operating safe yield for supplemental water from MWD. In 1987–88 and 1988–89, the Cucamonga County Water District and the city of Ontario both participated in the program, exchanging a combined total each year of about 6,000–7,000 acre-feet.

After the first ten years of operation under the judgment, some members of the appropriative pool began to press for additional studies to review basin conditions and basin management. The pool's initial approach was to persuade the Watermaster Advisory Committee to form an ad hoc committee to address the need for a water-quality study, a water reclamation study, an optimum basin management plan, a review of socioeconomic conditions within the basin, and a facilities equity assessment, all of which are provided for in the Chino Basin judgment. The ad hoc committee first met in July 1988. After directing the watermaster to award a contract to Montgomery Engineers for a groundwater monitoring program, the committee referred the issue of a socioeconomic review back to the appropriative pool. The Appropriative Pool Committee considered the issue of an optimum basin management plan for Chino Basin at its May 1989 meeting and recommended that a management study task force be formed by the Watermaster Advisory Committee, the CBMWD, WMWD, MWD, and the Santa Ana Watershed Project Authority (SAWPA).

These recommendations reflect dissatisfaction on the part of some members of the appropriative pool with the direction of the basin management program in the years since the judgment. That program has been oriented toward restoring water levels and increasing water storage in the basin. Although considerable activity has occurred on those fronts and substantial results have been achieved, some water users (especially appropriators in the lower part of the basin) do not think that enough attention has been paid to issues of water quality. They have emphasized the close connections between water levels and water quality in Chino Basin.

Water-Quality Problems in Chino Basin

The most widespread water-quality problem in the Chino Basin is nitrate concentrations, which are a fairly common groundwater contaminant in heavily developed agricultural areas. As mentioned in Chapter 8, excessive nitrate concentrations are a threat to human health.

Although widespread, nitrate concentrations in Chino Basin are greatest in the basin's northwest and southern areas. Since nitrates from fertilizers, manure, and wastewater do not pass directly from the land surface into the underground water supply, those areas with the highest nitrate concentrations in their groundwater also have the highest nitrate concentrations in their soils. When the water table rises nearer the land surface in these areas, the groundwater (which may already exhibit above-average nitrate concentrations) mingles with the more contaminated soils and absorbs even more nitrates. The nitrate concentrations in these areas rise still higher.

Although the Chino Basin management program has succeeded in storing water in the basin and raising water levels, the benefits and costs of this success have not been evenly distributed within the basin. In many areas, water users have benefited without reservation from the shorter pumping lifts associated with a rising water table. In other areas, a rising water table has increased the water-quality problems.

Water users at the southern end of Chino Basin have felt the negative consequences of the rising water table. Depths to water have always been smallest in this part of the basin, generally 50 feet or less. When water levels in the lower part of the basin recovered as much as 10–15 feet under basin management, water users in the southern end of the basin saw higher nitrate concentrations in their water supply.[5] They do not want their water table raised still further and have begun to oppose the management practices of the Chino Basin Watermaster.

In addition, some members of the appropriative pool are concerned about the delay in formulating an optimum basin management plan, including water-quality and socioeconomic studies, as provided for by the judgment. Members of the Appropriative Pool Committee have been trying to promote action on such a plan, arguing that the Chino Basin Watermaster has ample authority to undertake these studies and is obligated under the judgment to develop such a plan but has failed to use that authority or fulfill that obligation.

On November 9, 1988, the cities of Norco and Chino, and San Bernardino County Waterworks District No. 8, all members of the appropriative pool, filed a "Notice of Motion and Motion for Review of Watermaster Actions and Decisions" before Judge Don A. Turner in the Superior Court for San Bernardino County. The motion charged:

> Watermaster has failed and continued to fail to abide by its responsibilities and duties under the Judgment by failing to undertake and implement an Optimum Basin Management Program for Chino Basin, by failing to conduct the socioeconomic Study and Survey mandated by the Judgment, by failing to provide proper, responsible, equitable and fair water management policy, and by failing to comment on the proposal by the Metropolitan Water District (MWD) for Groundwater Storage at Chino Basin.

Judge Turner directed the Chino Basin Watermaster to undertake the water-quality and socioeconomic studies as soon as possible.

A disturbing report of results from a $1.2 million study coordinated by the Santa Ana Watershed Project Authority was released in September 1990. It indicated that nitrate concentrations throughout the Upper Area of the watershed, especially in Chino Basin, are more widespread and moving more rapidly than previously believed. If the estimated rates of movement continue, much of the water supply in the Upper Area may exceed the state's safe drinking-water levels for nitrates within the next twenty-five years.[6]

The greatest challenge in Chino Basin today is to balance water production and water storage decisions with water-quality considerations at a time when groundwater-quality standards appear likely to grow more stringent and alternative sources of supply (such as imported water) appear likely to grow more scarce. According to the attorney for the down-gradient appropriators in the recent hearing,

> the role of the watermaster in the Chino Basin adjudication is yet to be tested in the more difficult water quality questions that are beginning to become evident in that basin. The watermaster is being called upon to administer the physical solution by providing the adjudicated amounts of water of suitable quality. The shift in management emphasis is towards resolving quality issues, as pumpers receiving increasingly degraded water realize that quantity rights mean little when the water is of inadequate quality. (Trager, 1988:59)

Analysis

Chino Basin's polycentric governance structure is constituted under the provisions of the Chino Basin and Santa Ana River judgments and involves the Superior Courts of Orange and San Bernardino counties, the Chino Basin Watermaster, Watermaster Advisory Committee, and water producer pools, the Chino Basin Municipal Water District, the Western Municipal Water District of Riverside County, the Santa Ana River Watermaster, and the Santa Ana Watershed Project Authority. Development of this governance structure was shaped by the actions of Orange County water users, the Orange County Water District, and the adjudications over the Santa Ana River. The development of the Chino Basin governance structure and management program was strongly influenced by the examples of the adjudicated basins in Los Angeles County, particularly the conjunctive management programs in the Main San Gabriel and San Fernando Valley basins. The governance structure and management program in Chino Basin today reflect the whole evolutionary course of water management in southern California, from the Irvine litigation to SAWPA, and from *Pasadena v. Alhambra* to *Los Angeles v. San Fernando*.

Eliciting Information

The constitution of the Chino Basin Protective Association in 1931 contained an extensive description of the basin boundaries, stating the members' shared understanding of the resource and its users. The association's requirement of monthly water production reports from its members, open to inspection by other members, instituted a system for gathering information on water use. Bulletins from the state Division of Water Resources in 1930, 1934, and 1947 supplied information about past and present basin conditions, along with projections of future water demands.

Later, the 1955 Water Recordation Act and the Chino Basin Water Association renewed the processes of regular reporting of water production and occasional investigation of basin conditions. The Santa Ana River adjudication yielded further information about area water supplies, and the Santa Ana River Watermaster produces and distributes annual reports for water users about operation under the judgment. As a result of the Chino Basin adjudication in the 1970s, all basin water users are now identified and classified into pools, and the Chino Basin Watermaster monitors and reports annually on basin conditions and use, and on its own activities. The Chino Basin Watermaster structure, with its Advisory Committee and pool committees, also provides various forums for identifying and discussing water conditions and concerns within the basin.

Institutional Design

Chino Basin water users have devoted considerable effort to designing and implementing institutional arrangements in response to perceived needs and problems, within the constraints of evolving water law and policy. The Chino Basin Protective Association's self-financing and self-governing processes for gaining members, eliciting information, and taking collective action represent important institutional arrangements that later allowed water users to participate in the development of a Chino Basin water-spreading program, and to contribute to the formation of the San Bernardino County Flood Control District and the Chino Basin Water Conservation District to operate and finance that program. The association also helped organize the Chino Basin Municipal Water District to obtain access to supplemental water for most of the basin. The CBMWD was in turn instrumental in settling the litigation with the Orange County Water District over the Santa Ana River.

In the 1960s and 1970s, a new Chino Basin Water Association contributed to the formulation of the complex set of rules known as the Chino Basin judgment. The Negotiating Committee reviewed examples of institutional arrangements at work in other basins, compared those with the physical and political circumstances of Chino Basin, and evaluated them in light of the changes wrought by the *Los Angeles v. San Fernando* decision in 1975. This committee suggested the unusual pool arrangements, with different types of water users and water rights integrated into a representative watermaster structure, with flexible safe-yield determinations, limited transferability of pumping rights, rights to store water in the basin, and rights to transfer stored water. This set of rules for managing Chino Basin has deservedly been named "the most complex and sophisticated adjudication yet devised" (Lipson, 1978: 83).

Integration with Other Governance Systems

Not surprisingly, given its physical position in the middle of the Santa Ana River watershed and its political position in three counties, Chino Basin's governance and management arrangements are connected with several other water resource organizations. The Santa Ana River judgment links Chino Basin water users through the CBMWD and WMWD to the San Bernardino Valley Municipal Water District, the Orange County Water District, the Santa Ana River Watermaster, and the Orange County Superior Court. As noted in Chapter 11, those arrangements in turn involve the U.S. Army Corps of Engineers, the U.S. Geological Survey, and the Riverside and Corona City Sanitation districts. The four water districts involved in the Santa Ana River judgment are also linked via their joint-powers creation, SAWPA.

The CBMWD, WMWD, and Three Valleys Municipal Water District are member agencies of MWD, supplying imported water for direct use and basin replenishment. Basin replenishment through water spreading is coordinated with the San Bernardino County Flood Control District.

Water-quality monitoring and efforts to clean up contaminated water involve the San Bernardino County Department of Public Health, the Regional Water Quality Control Board, the California Department of Health Services, and the U.S. Environmental Protection Agency.

Operation and Performance of the Management Program

The Chino Basin experience establishes two important points. First, it makes clear that basins can still be managed through adjudication in the aftermath of the 1975 *San Fernando* decision. Such adjudications are clearly more complex, but they are possible and do not have to be excessively time-consuming and costly; even with the complications of the *San Fernando* decision, the Chino Basin adjudication involving the water rights of 1,300 parties was completed within three years. Second, the Chino Basin case demonstrates the inefficiencies arising from the California Supreme Court's interpretation of water rights law in the *San Fernando* decision, especially regarding the rights of overlying landowners. The *San Fernando* decision robbed California groundwater basin management of one of its most efficiency-enhancing aspects: the ability of water rights owners to exchange, lease, and sell their rights. The Chino Basin judgment contains numerous provisions for accounting manipulations that have been implemented in order to allow water production to move from agricultural to urban and suburban uses, in the absence of the marginal and voluntary adjustments that come from simply allowing an appropriator to make an agricultural user an offer for part or all of its pumping right.

Chino Basin management has effectively reduced the supply-demand imbalance that threatened the basin's long-term viability twenty years ago. The increase in pumping in the basin has been halted, and water users rely to a greater extent on supplemental water supplies. Table 12.2 shows water production by producer pool, total production, and replenishment water purchased, and in-lieu replenishment participation for the last few years before, and all years since, the first year of the judgment. Table 12.3 shows pumping, imports, and total water use in the basin for the last few years before, and all years since, the judgment. Pumping has declined from 170,000–180,000 acre-feet to 125,000–150,000 acre-feet per year, while imported water use has risen from 50,000–60,000 acre-feet to 115,00–135,000 acre-feet per year.

Compliance with the pumping limitations has been high. The Chino Basin Watermaster has set the operating safe yield at 145,000 acre-feet each year, and pumping has exceeded this figure in only three years of operation under the judgment. The overlying (agricultural) pool and the overlying (nonagricultural) pool exceeded their 81,800 and 7,366 acre-foot

TABLE 12.2

Water Production and Replenishment in Chino Basin, 1975–1989 (acre-feet)

Year	Overlying (agricultural) pool	Overlying (nonagricultural) pool	Appropriative pool	Total
Production by pool, 1975–1989				
1975	96,567	8,878	70,312	175,757
1976	95,349	6,356	79,312	181,017
1977	91,450	9,198	72,707	173,355
1978	83,934	10,082	60,659	154,675
1979	74,026	7,127	60,597	141,750
1980	70,377	7,363	63,834	140,566
1981	68,040	5,650	70,726	144,416
1982	65,117	5,684	66,731	137,532
1983	56,759	2,395	63,481	122,635
1984	59,033	3,208	70,558	132,799
1985	55,543	2,415	76,912	134,870
1986	52,061	3,193	80,859	136,113
1987	59,847	2,559	84,662	147,068
1988	57,865	2,958	91,579	152,402
1989	46,762	3,619	93,617	143,998

	Imported replenishment purchases	In-lieu replenishment
Replenishment, 1978–1989		
1978	6,977.8	8,832.9
1979	12,638.4	4,911.1
1980	2,184.9	5,327.2
1981	15,248.8	7,139.4
1982	19,062.9	13,670.0
1983	13,187.7	11,480.0
1984	13,776.9	12,088.0
1985	12,188.0	11,705.0
1986	16,322.0	11,278.0
1987	10,086.3	10,140.0
1988	2,493.7	10,391.0
1989	7,407.2	18,487.0

SOURCE: Chino Basin Watermaster Annual Reports.

TABLE 12.3

Chino Basin Production, Imports, and Total Water Use, 1975–1989 (acre-feet)

Year	Production	Imports	Total water use
1975	175,757	49,383	225,140
1976	181,017	57,686	238,703
1977	173,355	55,765	229,120
1978	154,675	61,567	216,242
1979	141,750	75,864	217,276
1980	140,566	70,727	211,293
1981	144,416	77,765	222,181
1982	137,532	67,491	205,023
1983	122,635	76,000	198,635
1984	132,799	99,257	232,056
1985	134,870	92,952	227,822
1986	136,113	114,624	250,737
1987	147,068	126,493	273,561
1988	152,402	116,175	268,577
1989	143,998	135,626	279,624

SOURCE: Chino Basin Watermaster Annual Reports.

respective annual shares of the basin safe yield only in the first year of operation under the judgment.

At the same time, the monitoring task in Chino Basin, with its hundreds of parties, has been considerably more challenging than in other adjudicated basins. The initial installation of meters on all wells has proved problematic. Originally, all wells were supposed to be metered by June 30, 1979, the end of the second year of operation under the judgment. The process of metering has taken much longer. In the 1988–89 water year, the appropriative pool offered to pay all of the overlying (agricultural) pool's assessments in exchange for the transfer of all of the unpumped safe yield water of the overlying (agricultural) pool. In order to verify the amount of unpumped safe yield water, however, the appropriative pool established a compliance procedure for meter installation, testing, and repair required by watermaster regulations. The California Attorney General's office offered to assist in informal enforcement proceedings against 142 noncomplying members of the overlying (agricultural) pool, before the initiation of legal proceedings by the watermaster's attorney. In May 1989, the Watermaster Advisory Committee accepted the offer of assistance (Chino Basin Watermaster, 1990: 18).

Table 12.3 shows the anticipated conversion of water production from the overlying (agricultural) pool to the appropriative pool. In 1977–78, the respective percentages of water production from the basin by the overlying (agricultural), overlying (nonagricultural), and appropriative pools were 54.3, 6.5, and 39.2 percent. In 1988–89, those percentages were 32.5, 2.5, and 65.0 percent. Transfers of unpumped safe yield from the overlying (agricultural) pool to the appropriative pool have allowed the latter to increase its annual groundwater production by about 30,000 acre-feet since the first transfer in 1983–84 without having to pay for 30,000 acre-feet of replacement water purchases each year.

These transfers have moved water production in Chino Basin from lower- to higher-valued uses. Regardless of one's opinion of the water-master's practice of allowing MWD to store tens of thousands of acre-feet of water in the basin, allowing the parties to store and transfer water also promotes efficient use of the resource.

The Chino Basin management program has accomplished supply-management objectives at very low costs to water users. The costs of the three-year Chino Basin adjudication have been estimated at $750,000–850,000. This works out to about $5 or $6 per acre-foot of adjudicated right for each water right owner (Lipson, 1978: 83). Spread over thirteen years of operation thus far, the adjudication has cost each water rights owner less than 50 cents per acre-foot per year. Administrative costs in Chino Basin have been small per acre-foot, as well. The administrative expenditures of the Santa Ana River Watermaster and of the Chino Basin Watermaster have each amounted to less than a dollar per acre-foot over this period. Table 12.4 shows the

TABLE 12.4
Chino Basin Watermaster Budget and Expenditures, 1978–1989 (dollars)

Year	Revenues	Total expenditures	Administrative expenditures	Replenishment expenditures
1978	608,765	339,310	38,310	300,472
1979	802,085	750,771	82,029	668,742
1980	941,576	860,185	55,362	804,823
1981	1,088,781	1,066,265	50,354	998,031
1982	1,299,049	1,287,098	41,853	1,225,245
1983	1,088,781	1,066,265	40,029	998,031
1984	1,407,763	1,497,503	119,813	1,377,690
1985	1,991,828	1,977,597	112,910	1,864,687
1986	2,471,719	2,541,405	124,550	2,416,855
1987	2,178,907	2,196,169	114,007	2,082,162
1988	2,797,852	2,481,282	57,257	2,427,983
1989	2,377,938	1,272,871 [a]	83,869	1,153,069 [a]

(continued)

TABLE 12.4 (continued)

	Administrative budget	Administrative expenditures	Administrative expenditures per acre-foot	Administrative expenditures per acre-foot
1978	53,800	38,310	0.25	0.18
1979	107,700	82,029	0.58	0.38
1980	80,275	55,362	0.39	0.26
1981	96,950	50,354	0.35	0.23
1982	80,075	41,853	0.30	0.20
1983	91,575	40,029	0.33	0.20
1984	73,675	119,813	0.90	0.52
1985	128,760	112,910	0.84	0.50
1986	128,300	124,550	0.92	0.50
1987	120,325	114,007	0.78	0.42
1988	96,030	57,257	0.38	0.21
1989	131,435	83,869	0.58	0.30

a. Purchases of some replenishment water were deferred in anticipation of a new and more advantageous MWD pricing structure to take effect during the 1989–90 water year.
SOURCE: Chino Basin Watermaster Reports.

revenues and expenditures of Chino Basin Watermaster operations; nearly all expenditures have been for replenishment water purchases.

Chino Basin continues to urbanize. The number of pumpers, especially in the overlying (agricultural) pool, has declined since 1978 in the wake of continuing urbanization. A recent "Notice of Motion" to parties was sent to 462 addresses. At one time, there were 3,000–3,500 production wells in Chino Basin; today, there are about 900–1,000.

Basin governance and management in the Chino Basin and in the other basins of southern California continue to evolve, but the evolutionary process is not always smooth, and the management programs are not self-executing. Numerous possibilities remain for making mistakes. Basin governance and management continue to demand skillful artisanship and careful attention to basin conditions and circumstances.

NOTES

1. Civil Case 164327 in the Superior Court of the State of California in and for the County of San Bernardino.

2. The reallocation provisions included a land-use conversion process allowing an appropriator serving an area previously devoted to irrigated agriculture to report the land-use and water-service change to the watermaster. The watermaster verifies the change, calculates the location's average annual water use during the previous five-year period, and allocates the unused safe-yield water to the affected appropriators, up to half of the average annual amount of water actually applied to those lands during the previous five years. This allows unused water rights to "change hands" without really doing so (which would be in violation of the law of water rights), but to do so at a rate that still reduces overall demand on the basin.

3. In addition, the judgment provides for appropriative pool members to be charged a "facilities equity assessment," to finance any additional facilities needed to import water and to make in-lieu replenishment payments to appropriators who take imported water instead of pumping groundwater.

4. The first reappointment of the Chino Basin Municipal Water District was made with the unanimous support of the Watermaster Advisory Committee. The second reappointment was endorsed by a majority, but not all, of the Advisory Committee members, reflecting some water users' discontent. Still, the district appears likely to continue to serve as Chino Basin Watermaster. When asked in 1988 about the prospects for continued reappointment of the district as watermaster, the chief of watermaster services at the district replied, "Who else would do it?"

5. It should be noted that having the water table near the land surface creates additional concerns: swampy conditions may develop, water may seep into building basements and other excavations, and soil liquefaction may occur in the event of an earthquake (obviously a matter of particular concern to southern Californians—the March 1, 1990, earthquake, which registered 5.5 on the Richter scale, was centered just north of Upland along the fault zone that forms the northern boundary of Chino Basin).

6. Jenifer Warren, "Water Peril Cited for Two Counties," Los Angeles Times, September 12, 1990, p. A-3.

PART 3

Why They Prefer "Chaos"

13

Evaluating Performance
Can "Chaos" Work?

The basin governance and management systems described in Part 2 are certainly complex. In evaluating their performance, however, the relevant question is whether and how well they achieve certain outcomes— in other words, whether this "chaos" works. Answering that question involves assessing and comparing the performance of the seven management programs described in Part 2 (nothing that can be called a "management program" has been developed and implemented in the Mojave River case). Three key performance issues will be addressed:

1. Whether management arrangements developed through evolutionary processes and crafted by local water users perform well, where performance is assessed on the basis of several criteria.

2. Whether management arrangements that preserve the yield and storage capacity of basins are more efficient than the alternative approach of depleting the basins and replacing them with other supplies and storage.

3. Whether basin management under a single agency without an adjudication and limitation of pumping rights performs better than basin management that relies on complex interorganizational arrangements and the adjudication and limitation of pumping rights.

As in the discussion of individual basins in Part 2, the order in which performance criteria are examined does not reflect a ranking of their importance. Compliance comes first, principally because users must comply to

301

some extent with the management programs before their effectiveness, efficiency, equity, or adaptability are relevant questions.

Compliance

Compliance is measured indirectly, by how often water users have failed to meet requirements or have violated limitations that management arrangements place on them. By these measures, compliance in the seven managed basins has been extraordinarily high. In the seven basins with operational management programs, compliance has been so high that sanctions have never yet been assessed, even though thousands of operators have been involved and in some cases up to forty years have passed since management programs were adopted. The one lingering difficulty in compliance with a part of one of the basin management systems was described in Chapter 12, concerning the metering of wells in the Chino Basin. Enforcement proceedings may be undertaken there.

This high rate of compliance seems to be due primarily to two factors, which can be mentioned briefly here but will be elaborated in the next chapter. First, management programs in the seven basins were generally perceived as fair and worthy of compliance because they had been developed by the water users. Second, each management program included some form (and sometimes multiple forms) of monitoring, which encouraged compliance by making previously unnoticeable actions noticeable to fellow users. For example, in an annual report, the Central Basin Watermaster noted the repeated tardiness of a couple of users in submitting groundwater production reports during the management program's first five years of operation: "Of the number of parties who have been guilty of not submitting their reports on time, two parties, namely Frank J. Ross and Oriental Foods, Incorporated, have been chronic offenders. Continued laxity . . . could result in Superior Court proceedings for contempt" (1970: 8). The reporting of the failure to observe the rules apparently sufficed, and the backup threat of sanctions was not employed. The next annual report indicated no difficulty in receiving production reports from these or other parties.

Effectiveness

As stated in connection with West Basin in Chapter 6, water users in most of these basins originally undertook collective action not in order to enhance efficiency of water use or to implement an "optimal" management regime, but to keep the water supplies on which they depended from being destroyed altogether. Water users had to work hard in most cases just to keep conditions from worsening as a result of depletion or degradation. Therefore, before we evaluate how well the basin management programs have operated with respect to the kinds of efficiency and equity criteria economists and political scientists tend to focus on, we should assess whether and how well those programs have achieved the results intended by the people who designed and implemented them— in other words, whether they were effective.

The risk of depletion can be reduced by augmenting local water supplies, by restricting demand on local supplies, or both. Water users in all seven managed basins have augmented local water supplies by instituting natural and artificial replenishment programs, and by acquiring access to imported water for direct use. Several southern California communities formed the Metropolitan Water District of Southern California (MWD), which conveys California's share of Colorado River flows to the region. Virtually all of the territory within the seven managed basins has been annexed to MWD, which has made Colorado River water available in southern California for fifty years now. Southern California water users' associations, municipalities, and special districts also supported the development and construction of the State Water Project, which has conveyed northern California water to the south for twenty years now, supplementing the imported supplies from the Colorado.

Users in particular basins or watersheds have taken other actions to augment local supplies. Clearly, the city of Los Angeles increased local water supplies to the ULARA with the construction of the Los Angeles Aqueduct to Owens Valley and Mono Basin. Water agencies in the San Gabriel and Santa Ana River watersheds have relied on reclaimed wastewater as a replenishment water source. Also, the interbasin adjudications in the San Gabriel and Santa Ana River watersheds guaranteed minimum inflows to their lower areas, which improved the local supplies available to downstream users by ensuring that deficiencies in flows from upstream would be "made up" in later years.

By successfully augmenting their water supplies, users have accommodated the growth in total water use in the seven managed basins without depleting the natural local supplies. Total annual water use in the seven basins as of 1985 was close to 2,450,000 acre-feet. Approximately 1,030,000 acre-feet of this use was met from local groundwater supplies. More than half of total water use in the seven managed basins is met by imported and reclaimed water supplies. If the augmentation efforts had been ineffective, current water use rates would be depleting local groundwater supplies at a rate in excess of one million acre-feet per year (in which case they almost certainly would have been destroyed by now), or it would have been necessary to restrict total water use in the region to less than that of 1945.

Augmentation has been coupled with a reduction or limitation of demand on local supplies in six of the seven managed basins. This combination of improving supply and limiting demand has reduced the risk of depletion in those six basins. In the Raymond, West, and Central basins, pumping was limited to a fixed amount corresponding to some estimate of what those basins could sustain. Groundwater extractions in those three basins have remained steady or declined since the determination and limitation of pumping rights took effect. In the three more recent adjudications—Main San Gabriel Basin, Chino Basin, and ULARA—pumping is limited to an annual operating safe yield set each year in accordance with water supply conditions. Groundwater extractions in those three basins exhibit greater variability from year to year, but are maintained within certain ranges. Groundwater production has risen slightly in the Main San Gabriel Basin, declined slightly in the Chino Basin, and fluctuated about a mean in the ULARA.

The limitation of demand in these six basins demonstrates clearly that the risk of depletion has not been reduced by relying solely on what Trelease (1980: 685) described cynically as the "California solution" to water supply problems, namely, pouring some water on them to make them go away. In each of the six basins except Raymond, supplemental water supplies became available a decade or more before the limitation on demand, but pumping continued to increase. Demand limitations negotiated by the water users in the six adjudicated basins forced them to rely on more expensive imported water supplies rather than deplete the local groundwater sources.

Of the cases included here, only Orange County has relied entirely on the augmentation of water supplies to reduce the risk of depletion of local supplies. Pumping rights have not been determined and limited in Orange County. Although the Orange County Water District's pump tax authority theoretically enables it to curtail demand by raising the cost of pumping, in practice it has chosen to use the pump tax to generate enough revenue to purchase and spread imported water to offset the overdraft caused by groundwater extractions in excess of the basin's 150,000 acre-foot safe yield. Pump tax rates have not been high enough to curtail demand effectively; groundwater production in Orange County has fluctuated in response to basin conditions, but the overall trend has been upward.

Orange County water users have not been induced to switch their base supply from groundwater to imported direct service water to the degree that users in Central and West basins (which are similarly situated physically) have been. Instead, Orange County water users have relied primarily on groundwater while purchasing replenishment water to make up the overdraft. This has worked so far, but the last five years have been extremely dry in southern California, and the question that remains for

Orange County is what would happen in a longer or more severe drought. With no limitation on pumping, with groundwater less expensive than imported water for direct use, and with imported replenishment water less available and more expensive, the Orange County basin faces a greater risk of depletion during an extended dry cycle.

Degradation of water quality also has been checked in the seven managed basins. In large measure, the institutional arrangements in the seven managed basins have done so by establishing a governance structure for taking collective decisions and actions on behalf of water users, by developing some degree of control over pumping, and by taking steps to reduce and prevent groundwater depletion.

In the three coastal basins—West, Central, and Orange County—the depletion of local groundwater supplies resulted in seawater intrusion that threatened to degrade groundwater quality and render the basins unusable. In each case, water users and the jurisdictions they created and supported devised and implemented barrier projects along the coast that have operated effectively to halt the intrusion. The Orange County Water District "drought-proofed" its freshwater barrier by developing its Water Factory 21, which provides purified wastewater for barrier operations. This has reduced Orange County's risk of further saltwater intrusion to a greater extent than in the Central and West basins, where the barriers are still operated with treated imported water, which is very expensive and also could be cut back in a severe drought. The Central and West Basin Water Replenishment District, which is responsible for the barrier projects in those two basins, has sought authority to use reclaimed wastewater in the barriers, which would reduce operating costs and more nearly ensure water availability.

Incidents of groundwater contamination in the Main San Gabriel, Chino, and San Fernando (ULARA) basins can be traced to overlying land-use practices that preceded basin management programs; so at a superficial level those programs did not *prevent* the contamination of water supplies. What they did do, however—by augmenting water supplies from different sources and controlling pumping—was mitigate the dangers associated with the contamination incidents. If water consumers in those three basins had depended entirely on local groundwater supplies that were still being depleted, the contamination problems discovered over the past decade or so would have been even more serious. Moreover, the presence of governance systems charged with maintaining basin water conditions has provided a substantial part of the institutional capacity for redressing water-quality problems.

Efficiency in Administration: Basin Management Costs

Of course, compliance and effectiveness in the seven managed basins say little about whether they operate efficiently. If the high compliance and effectiveness of these management programs are purchased at an excessive cost, there may be strong reasons for questioning the quality of their "performance." Efficiency has different meanings, two of which are used in this chapter. This section examines the costs of the basin management programs per acre-foot of water obtained from each of the seven managed basins. Such figures provide some indication of the magnitude of basin management costs in absolute terms, and some basis for comparing the costs of basin management in the seven managed basins.

The costs of particular interest here are those incurred by water users in preserving and managing the groundwater basins. Therefore, basin management costs are assumed to include watermaster service expenditures (where applicable), water replenishment expenditures (where applicable), and adjudication costs (where applicable). Despite the importance of supplemental water supplies to these management programs, property taxes paid to MWD and its member agencies are not included in the calculations of basin management costs, for two reasons. First, since essentially all of the area of the seven managed basins is annexed to MWD and some MWD member agency (either a city or a municipal water district), including the taxes paid to MWD and its members would not help to distinguish among the basins. Second, since the entire area would have to be annexed to MWD and some member agency if local groundwater supplies had been destroyed and all water in the region came from imports, including property taxes paid to MWD and member agencies does not distinguish between the situation with basin management and the situation without basin management.[1]

Watermaster expenditures for the Raymond, West, Central, Main San Gabriel, San Fernando, and Chino basins are taken from the annual watermaster reports in those basins. Similarly, water replenishment expenditures for the West, Central, Main San Gabriel, San Fernando, Chino, and Orange County basins are taken from the annual watermaster reports and the annual reports of the Central and West Basin Water Replenishment District and the Orange County Water District. Expenditures cited below are all for 1985, except of course for the adjudication costs, which were incurred earlier.

Deriving the adjudication costs for the adjudicated basins requires some calculation. Even though the court costs, reference costs, and legal and engineering fees have long since been paid in the adjudicated basins, simply treating all adjudication costs as having been paid in the past and therefore no longer affecting basin management costs would provide an unfair comparison with a nonadjudicated basin such as Orange County. There is no disputing that adjudication is expensive, and Orange County water users have avoided this expense, on the theory that "adjudication never produced a drop of water." Their approach to basin management should be compared with the situations in which adjudication expenses were incurred in order to see the savings realized by Orange County. Therefore, adjudication costs have been included by amortization. Taking the best estimates available of the total adjudication costs for each adjudicated basin ($300,000 in Raymond, $3,000,000 in West, $450,000 in Central, $1,000,000 in Main San Gabriel, $2,000,000 in San Fernando, and $850,000 in Chino), suppose that the parties had borrowed the money to pay the entire cost of the adjudication up front, and then made annual payments each year to pay off the loan. Using a fifty-year loan period and a conservative interest rate of 5 percent (reflecting the years in which the money would have been borrowed—1937, 1945, 1955, 1962, 1968, and 1975), we obtain an annual payment for the adjudication that can be divided by 1985 groundwater extractions to obtain a current adjudication cost per acre-foot of groundwater in those basins.[2] These adjudication costs are presented in Table 13.1.

The adjudication costs can be combined with the other basin management costs to produce a total basin management cost per acre-foot. The other basin management costs were calculated by dividing total 1985 expenditures for administration and replenishment by the number of acre-feet of groundwater produced that year. (In the Main San Gabriel Basin, however, where the structure of the management system introduces much greater variability in replacement water and makeup water expenditures, a five-year average for the period 1983–1987 was used instead, because 1985 was an exceptionally low-expenditure year and would have artificially understated basin management costs there.)

TABLE 13.1
Amortized Adjudication Costs and Basin Management Costs of Groundwater Production, 1985 (dollars per acre-foot per year)

Basin	Amortized adjudication costs	Basin management costs
Raymond	0.46	3.50
West	3.18	77.40
Central	0.13	73.77
Main San Gabriel	0.22	15.47
San Fernando	0.92	15.23
Chino	0.34	15.00
Orange County	NA	151.79

NA = Not applicable.
SOURCE: Author's calculations.

Comparisons are presented in Table 13.1. We are unable to make efficiency determinations of the type that would indicate whether basin management costs are as low as they can possibly be in each of these basins, and there is no reason to presume that they are, but we can conclude that the basin management costs being paid in each of the basins are reasonable in relation to the replacement cost of $240.00 for each acre-foot of water in 1985.

It would not appear that Orange County water users have saved themselves much money by forgoing an adjudication and limitation of pumping rights. As noted at the end of Chapter 11, by avoiding a limitation on pumping, Orange County has had to invest much more heavily in additional spreading facilities to provide enough replenishment capacity to meet the annual overdrafting of the groundwater supply and has had to purchase more imported replenishment water, the cost of which has escalated sharply in the past decade.

It bears noting that the Orange County basin management costs, stated in amounts per acre-foot, should not be read as indicating that groundwater producers actually *pay* $151.79 per acre-foot in addition to their direct production costs. If that were the case, Orange County pumpers would probably rely on imported water much more than they do. The Orange County Water District still raises a considerable portion of its revenue from property taxes, so property owners still subsidize pumping. When district expenditures are divided by total groundwater production, one obtains the $151.79 per acre-foot figure as the cost of basin management per acre-foot produced. Pumpers actually pay their direct production costs (estimated at $134.00 per acre-foot) plus the pump tax of $32.00, for a total of $166.00 per acre-foot, rather than $285.79 per acre-foot, which would be the cost if all basin management costs were paid by taxing pumping.

Orange County basin management costs are best compared with basin management costs in the similarly situated Central and West basins. In West and Central basins, however, the replenishment district has maintained very few staff and relatively modest office space and contracts with the county Department of Public Works for operation of the barrier projects and the artificial replenishment programs, and with the County Sanitation Districts for purchases of reclaimed wastewater. The Orange County Water District operates these programs with its own facilities and personnel.

Raymond Basin and San Fernando management costs are especially low because there is neither a barrier project nor a basinwide artificial replenishment program there (some parties conduct their own water-spreading operations in return for pumping credits). Management costs in the Main San Gabriel and Chino basins also are lower because there are no barrier projects in those basins, and because purchases of imported water for the artificial replenishment programs in those basins are not as large each year as in West, Central, and Orange County.

Efficiency in Resource Use

Even if basin management costs are fairly low, the question remains, are they worth it? This question pertains to another aspect of efficiency. Some economists have argued that overpumping a groundwater basin to the point of destruction, rather than restraining use and preserving the basin for a discounted future, may represent a rational choice. Having maximized their wealth through short-term exploitation of the resource, pumpers can confront the task of acquiring a replacement water supply source later.

Similar thoughts were expressed by a committee of the California legislature in 1962:

> The major impact of destroying a basin beyond any possible use is that all the water supply will have to be imported. Even in the West Coast Basin about 70 percent of the water used is now imported so that a shift of the remaining 30 percent from ground water to an imported supply would not be catastrophic, provided the surface supply is available (California Assembly Interim Committee on Water, 1962: 39)

As noted in Chapter 2, these views tend to focus solely on the value of a groundwater basin as a water supply source, and on the replacement of water supplies. On their own terms, then, they make some sense: if southern Californians had to replace their groundwater supply (at approximately $125-150 per acre-foot production costs) with treated imported water (at $250 or so per acre-foot), the entire region probably would not suffer an economic collapse.

Groundwater basins have value not only as sources of water supply, however, but also as water storage and distribution facilities, regulating the variability of surface water supplies and providing water for peak and emergency use while base supply needs are met from surface and imported supplies. There is strong reason to believe that these uses of groundwater basins are their more valuable uses.

Given the growth in total water use in the seven managed basins, if southern California water users simply relied on their groundwater resources to meet daily supply needs, most (perhaps all) of those basins would have been destroyed by now. Had this occurred, the provision of a water supply to the population and commerce of these areas would have required importing direct-service water to meet 100 percent of total water use, as the Assembly Interim Committee on Water stated. Because imported supplies are variable, however (that is, there are wet and dry seasons in each year and there are wet and dry years), and because water demand is variable (that is, water needs at the peak hour of the peak day of the peak season may be as much as twenty times the average rate of use), considerable investment in storage and distribution facilities would have been needed to provide southern Californians with all their water from imported supplies. Surface water storage facilities would have been needed to replace those provided naturally by the groundwater basins.

In order to evaluate whether the price that has been paid for preserving the groundwater basins has been worth it to the local users (that is, whether the management systems they have designed and implemented have been "efficient" interventions), we must compare the costs they have incurred with the costs they would be incurring for their water supply if they had allowed the basins to be destroyed. Each year, the Orange County Water District publishes estimates of the direct costs of pumping groundwater, as well as the cost of treated imported MWD water. Assuming that the cost of pumping an acre-foot of groundwater is the same whether a well is located in Orange County or in Los Angeles, Riverside, or San Bernardino counties, we can adopt the OCWD 1985 estimates of $134.00 per acre-foot for pumped groundwater, and $240.00 per acre-foot for treated imported water.

In order not to overstate the case, take the lowest estimate of the amount of surface storage capacity required to make up for the loss of the underground system. This is a Los Angeles County Flood Control District estimate, that storage facilities would have to be constructed equivalent to 16 percent of total water use. The lowest estimate available of the capital cost of constructing that amount of surface storage in each of the basins is also a Los Angeles County Flood Control District estimate of $57,440 per acre-foot ($16,000 per acre-foot in 1960 adjusted upward to 1985 by the all-item Consumer Price Index [CPI], which is a conservative adjustment since the price of land that would have to be acquired for the construction of such facilities in southern California has escalated faster than the all-item CPI). This construction cost can then be amortized at 5 percent per year over a fifty-year period, as was done with adjudication costs earlier, to obtain an annual cost of the construction of the required surface storage. As a final conservative measure, no costs are included for annual maintenance of these surface storage facilities—that is, it is assumed that they never need cleaning, repainting, or repairs—and therefore they are treated as being equivalent to natural underground storage.[3]

The results of these calculations are presented in Table 13.2. The calculations for Raymond Basin can be used to review how the cost estimates were made. In Raymond Basin, the current mix of groundwater and imported water is 54 to 46 percent. Calculating groundwater at $134.00

TABLE 13.2

Comparisons of Water Costs with and without Management, 1985 (dollars per acre-foot)

	Average cost with basin management	Estimated cost if all groundwater supplies and storage replaced by imported water and surface storage
Raymond	184.65	748.68
West	235.71	739.30
Central	224.85	739.94
Main San Gabriel	153.86	740.69
San Fernando	228.73	740.69
Orange County	267.93	740.21
Chino	192.46	740.69

SOURCE: Author's calculations.

per acre-foot plus the $3.50 basin management costs and imported water at $240.00 per acre-foot, an average acre-foot of water in Raymond Basin in 1985 cost $184.65.

If Raymond Basin water users relied entirely on treated imported MWD water, they would have paid $240.00 per acre-foot for it, but they also would have required 8,571 acre-feet of surface storage capacity (0.16 times total water use of 53,567 acre-feet), which, at $57,440 per acre-foot, would have cost $492,318,240.00. Annual payments for this construction would be $27,248,400.00, or $508.68 per acre-foot of water used. Adding this to the $240.00 per acre-foot cost of treated imported water yields a total of $748.68 per acre-foot of water in Raymond Basin. Since an acre-foot of water is the average annual demand for a five-person household, we can translate the difference between $184.65 per acre-foot under the current system and $748.68 per acre-foot under the alternative one as the difference between an average monthly water bill of $15.00 and an average monthly water bill of $62.50.

Even with conservative estimates of the cost of replacing the groundwater basins in this study with surface storage and imported water, it appears that basin preservation has been an extraordinarily good bargain. Water costs are considerably less than the costs the water users in these areas would be facing by now if the basins had been destroyed.

Preservation of the groundwater basins has been a good bargain, but to what extent are basin users taking advantage of it? Efficiency also involves allowing resources to shift from lower- to higher-valued uses over time, and taking advantage of a basin's valuable storage space. In four adjudicated basins of the San Gabriel River watershed, pumping rights were quantified, assigned to individual entities as property rights, and made transferable. Water users in those four basins can exchange, lease, or sell their pumping rights. During the operation of the management programs in those basins, water rights markets have been active, allowing pumping rights to move through marginal and voluntary adjustment from those who valued them less to those who valued them more. In those basins, the current distribution of pumping rights must be regarded as more efficient than the original distribution would be if it had been frozen in place and maintained through the present.

The ULARA adjudication provided for a fairly intricate physical solution that allows users to pump in places where they do not have recognized rights in return for compensating others, but this does not provide for the transfer of pumping rights from one rights owner to another. The owners of overlying water rights in the ULARA can transfer their pumping rights along with their land, but this is a less efficient way of transferring water rights.

The Chino Basin adjudication improves upon the ULARA adjudication by providing for the occasional transfer of unpumped safe yield from the agricultural pool to the appropriative pool. Also, members of the appropriative pool are allowed to transfer pumping rights among themselves. As noted at the end of Chapter 12, these provisions allow water to move from lower- to higher-valued uses, but not through voluntary and marginal transfers among the full set of rights owners. Apart from the provision for the transfer of unpumped safe yield between pools, overlying water rights still have to be transferred with the land in order to be transferred from one individual to another, which is less efficient.

Because the Orange County management program has not included any quantification and assignment of pumping rights, those rights in the Orange County basin are not transferable at all, except by sale of the overlying land to which they are appurtenant. The effect of this system will be discussed further below in connection with distributional equity.

Finally, with respect to efficiency in resource use, the conjunctive management programs in the Main San Gabriel, San Fernando, Chino, and Orange County basins make more efficient use of their respective storage capacity than do the fixed-yield management programs of the Raymond, West, and Central basins. Storing water underground in wet years for use in dry years, and encouraging water users to take more surface and imported water when it is plentiful and to pump more groundwater when it is not, capitalizes on one of the strengths of the groundwater resource. Restricting pumping to the same amount each year regardless of basin conditions does not. There is evidence that water users in the Raymond, West, and Central basins are interested in modifying their management programs to take better advantage of the ability to raise and lower allowed pumping amounts and to store water in the basin for later use, but they have not yet enacted such modifications. The ULARA, Main San Gabriel, and Chino basins have included provisions allowing individual water users or overlying districts to store water in the basin for later use. Raymond Basin has selectively allowed the cities of Sierra Madre and Pasadena to save water in the basin. The Chino Basin Water-master allows parties to exchange their stored water. All of these are efficiency-enhancing arrangements.

Equity: Fiscal Equivalence

The first question in considering the equity of the basin management programs is who pays the costs of basin management and whether basin management costs are apportioned in some relation to benefits received. This is the equity dimension known as "fiscal equivalence." The cost-sharing problem is not trivial; indeed, it is both vital and difficult if users are asymmetric (Blomquist and Ostrom, 1985: 388; Nunn, 1986). It has been argued that cost-sharing formulas are best worked out before decisions are taken regarding share assignments or supply levels, because cost-sharing arrangements worked out after benefits have been obtained or restrictions have been set in place take on the aspect of a zero-sum game, where participants seek to minimize their contributions at the expense of others (Hardin, 1982: 91). In the adjudicated basins, cost-sharing formulas were developed either before or at the same time as basin management programs, so users could anticipate the effects of various alternatives.

In the Raymond, West, Central, Main San Gabriel, San Fernando, and Chino basins, management costs, including the costs of replenishment and injection water purchases, are paid by water users through assessments on pumping. These systems therefore appear to meet a basic criterion of equity, that the principal beneficiaries of the basin management systems should bear the costs of their operations.

There are some variations on this general practice. The Raymond, Main San Gabriel, and San Fernando basins come closest to having all basin management costs borne by water users in proportion to their reliance on the basins. In the West and Central basins, the capital costs of the construction of the spreading grounds and the injection barrier projects that protect those basins from seawater intrusion and enhance their freshwater supply have been paid by property owners within the basins. In the Chino Basin, the appropriators pay virtually all of the costs of the basin management program, whereas overlying agricultural users pay little or none of the administrative costs.

As noted previously, the operating costs of the Orange County Water District are recovered from pumping assessments and from taxes on real property. At least a portion of the operating (as well as the capital) costs of the Orange County basin management program are borne by property owners rather than directly by water producers.

Equity: Distributional Considerations

Another question of equity is whether the benefits of basin management have fallen equitably across water producers. In each of the basins, the number of groundwater producers has declined—the water industries in the basins have become more concentrated, as it were. The question now becomes how to evaluate such phenomena.

There is no doubt that in the adjudicated basins, the adjudication process itself eliminated many of the small producers. They abandoned pumping rather than pay the costs of defending their right to a few acre-feet or less of groundwater. This occurred despite the fact that the pumping in most of these basins was sufficiently concentrated that a smaller group of larger pumpers could have curtailed their use and preserved the basins by their own actions. The impact of the production by small pumpers on aggregate groundwater production would have been minimal, and in the later adjudications of the Main San Gabriel and Chino basins, minimal pumpers were specifically identified and exempted.

In most of the basin adjudications, however, the parties sought to define the rights of all pumpers and to spread the costs over all of them, even though many smaller ones were eliminated as a result. Those small pumpers, had they not been eliminated, could today still be pumping their 1 or 2 acre-feet per year and enjoying the lower cost and (in most places) higher quality of the groundwater instead of using more expensive imported water. This is reflected by the fact that more small water users have continued pumping in Orange County, where there was no intrabasin adjudication of rights.

If the criterion one uses to evaluate the distributional consequences of the actions in the various basins is the effect on the small as opposed to the large producers, one would conclude that Orange County's approach has been considerably more equitable than that of the adjudicated basins. Small producers have not been chased out of the groundwater industry in Orange County and continue to derive substantial benefits from being able to pump their own groundwater rather than having to purchase water from others.

Not all of the reduction in the number of small pumpers can or should be attributed to the adjudication process, however. Many small pumpers in southern California during the middle decades of this century were agricultural water users. As the region urbanized, many of these water users sold their farmland to developers and would not have been pumping groundwater any more, regardless of the onset of adjudications. This is reflected in the fact that the number of small producers in Orange County has declined over time as well. And in each adjudicated basin, the number of parties owning rights has continued to decline since the adjudication. In other words, parties who acquired decreed pumping rights nevertheless have disposed of them subsequently.

This raises another distributional consideration. In addition to the issue of whether large pumpers could have suffered the smaller ones to continue pumping by omitting them from the assignment of rights (which they could have), there is the issue of whether the value of pumping rights has been reflected appropriately in the various basins. As noted in Chapter 12, Chino Basin water users were rather emphatic about wanting their pumping rights defined and assigned as property rights so those rights would have economic value. In Orange County, the absence of an assignment of pumping rights means that those rights in Orange County remain usufructuary and hence untradable. Small pumpers continue to pump, but it is unclear whether they do so because they prefer their groundwater rights to whatever compensation they could receive for them or because the current system does not allow them to receive anything in exchange for giving up their right.

Conclusions are therefore mixed on the distributional consequences of the actions taken in the basins. Adjudication undoubtedly eliminated several small pumpers who could have been exempted, and the absence of an adjudication in Orange County likely accounts for the continued presence of 250 relatively small pumpers there. The number of Orange County basin users pumping 25 acre-feet per year or less nevertheless declined from 780 in 1970 to 250 in 1985. All that can be said of the 530 small producers who gave up pumping in those fifteen years is that they received no compensation when they stopped, even though their stopping benefited other pumpers.

Adaptability

All of the basin governance and management systems devised thus far in the seven managed basins have proved adaptable to changed conditions and new ideas about basin management. In the six adjudicated basins, the courts have retained continuing jurisdiction to oversee and modify the judgments. The first basin to develop its basin governance and management system—the Raymond Basin—already has modified its judgment twice to change the management program and the basin governance structure.

Governance structures have changed within basins and from one adjudicated basin to another. In the Raymond Basin, the Southern District office of the California Department of Water Resources originally served as watermaster, and the role was purely that of a monitor of the judgment and an accountant for water production and exchange. In the West and Central basins, the Department of Water Resources plays a role similar to its original role in Raymond Basin, accounting for water production and transactions, but the water producers also established the Central and West Basin Water Replenishment District as a policy-making body to coordinate basin replenishment and the work on the saltwater intrusion barriers. In the San Fernando Valley, the accounting and policy-making roles were united in an individual watermaster chosen by the court with the approval of the water producers, who operates with the advice and consent of an advisory committee composed of water producer representatives. In the Main San Gabriel Basin, a multimember court-appointed watermaster composed of representatives of water producers and overlying water districts serves as the policy-making and accounting body for the basin, and in turn contracts out the accounting functions to one of the overlying water districts. The Raymond Basin water producers then followed this example, replacing the Department of Water Resources as watermaster with their own Raymond Basin Management Board consisting of producers' representatives and contracting out the accounting function. In the Chino Basin, the board of directors of an overlying water district serves as the watermaster with both policy-making and accounting responsibilities and is advised by a committee of producer representatives on policy while delegating most of the accounting functions to the district staff.

Adaptability has emerged as a conscious element of institutional design in basin management programs. The basic approach to basin management has changed dramatically from Raymond Basin to Chino Basin. The conscious effort to build adaptability into institutional design is best seen in the more recently developed arrangements—the Main San Gabriel, Chino, and San Fernando (ULARA) basins. Use of the concept of operating safe yield has allowed water users in those basins to respond to changed conditions of water supply, including both severe drought and relative abundance, by adjusting the demands they place on the natural water supply system. This provision contributes to the "ultra-stability" of the management systems in those basins.

Adaptability to particular problems and circumstances may be one of the strengths of self-governing arrangements designed and implemented by those who must live with them. In the governance and management of groundwater supplies in California, what some perceive to be ad hoc and uncoordinated arrangements may appear to others as "a well-developed and diverse system" (Lipson, 1978: 1) that has "developed . . . under laws and institutions adapting to changing conditions and circumstances" (Phelps et al., 1978: 2). A number of "innovative concepts developed" by local efforts "to meet a wide variety of water supply and waste disposal needs" have also been identified (Peters, 1972: 196). A choice in favor of local self-governance therefore may represent a preference for adaptability and innovation, rather than either a no-action groundwater management system or mere chaos.

NOTES

1. The 1992 MWD property tax rate has been declining anyway, and as of 1992 is $0.0087 per $100 assessed valuation, or about $17.40 per year on a $200,000 house.

2. This is a long loan period, but the Raymond Basin adjudication began in 1937, so we cannot use a shorter period if we wish to compare basin management costs as recently as 1985.

3. To indicate how conservative this estimate is, the California Department of Water Resources in 1963 published the following estimates of the capital costs and *annual maintenance costs* of a 500,000-gallon (approximately 1½ acre-foot) elevated storage tank: capital costs, $125,000; annual costs, $6,000. (California DWR, 1966a: 239) Adjusted upward for inflation, these estimated costs would be substantially higher than the ones used here.

The Three Valleys Municipal Water District (which overlies parts of the Main San Gabriel and Chino basins) has been constructing a lined and covered earthen surface storage reservoir with a capacity of 8 million gallons (approximately 24 acre-feet) on 2½ acres of district-owned land. Construction of the reservoir costs approximately 20 cents per gallon, or $1.6 million—$66,000 per acre-foot. If the district had not already owned the land for the reservoir, it would have had to purchase it at about $500,000 per acre, which would have added another $1.25 million to the cost of the reservoir and raised the per acre-foot cost to about $120,000. The lined and covered earthen reservoir is less expensive to construct than other surface storage methods: steel tanks cost 27 to 48 cents per gallon, and concrete tanks 32 to 57 cents per gallon.

14

Institutional Development and Human Action

The southern California institutions compared in Chapter 13 seem to demonstrate surprising performance and adaptability. This small number of cases cannot prove any general proposition, but they do appear to refute some of the blanket propositions discussed in Part 1 such as that there is no groundwater management in California, or that effective groundwater management requires a central public manager, or that the alternative to "regional master plans" and "water czars" is "chaos." At a minimum, it seems clear that these diverse institutional arrangements should not be simply written off as chaos.

Since the basin governance and management systems developed by southern California water users do not involve a regional master plan or a water czar, they challenge our understanding. How can they seem to perform so well when confronted with relatively daunting problems of resource use and preservation? This question is especially acute since comparison suggests that the most successful and sustainable cases are those in the San Gabriel River watershed, which has no watershed authority, no regional superagency, and no dominant user.

The institutional arrangements described in Part 2 evolved from processes of human problem solving over a number of years. The conceptual framework used here to explain their development characterizes it in terms of deliberate choices made within constraints by human beings with limited capabilities in a changeable world. In this view, institutional arrangements are designed, redesigned, adapted, and eliminated over time as part of a problem-solving process.

Institutions as Human Artifacts

Institutional arrangements and their performance are often analyzed with the aid of models that represent ideal arrangements. To assess institutional performance as "suboptimal," for instance, means having some conception of "optimality." Where does this conception of optimality come from? Typically not from direct observation, since it is a sobering fact of life that analysts of human social behavior, especially human political behavior, rarely observe optimality occurring in actual situations. Usually, an analyst's conception of optimality comes from a model, an idealized representation of a situation. This is among the most useful functions of models in the social sciences: they offer glimpses of various optima, such as "efficiency," or "equilibrium," or "Pareto-optimality," or "justice as fairness."

Models often tie concepts of optimality to a particular institutional structure, which is itself idealized. For example, optimal allocation of resources occurs in a system of private property rights combined with a perfectly competitive market in equilibrium. Or, optimal groundwater management results from a "comprehensive" groundwater management program efficiently administered by a central public authority.

These optima linked to institutional structures sometimes become the basis for policy prescriptions (Ostrom, 1990). The result can be a kind of structural determinism: fix the structure and reap optimality. A model may demonstrate that, *given* a system of private property rights and a competitive market (*and* perfect information *and* participants who never make mistakes, and so on), an efficient equilibrium will ensue. Policy analysts translate: if you want an efficient equilibrium, create a system of private property rights and a competitive market, and an efficient equilibrium will follow. Another model demonstrates that, *given* an integrated legal-rational hierarchy (*and* disinterested top decision makers with complete, undistorted information *and* individuals who follow the rules, and so on), efficient policy making and administration will ensue. Policy analysts translate: if you want efficient policy making and administration, establish an integrated legal-rational hierarchy.

What can be puzzling about these prescriptions is that the optimal outcomes apparently will be achieved *regardless of what people think and do*. In the actual development and implementation of institutional arrangements for resolving problems in actual settings, imperfect information, uncertainty about present and future states of the world, and the presence and unpredictability of people cannot be assumed away. Often, these matters are the very essence of the problematic situation people are trying to resolve.

To borrow from an old joke, this is like applying to the problem of opening a can a model that begins, "Assume a can opener. . . ."

Resource policy prescriptions based on models that assume that the resource is unproblematic and that all individuals already know everything are not so much wrong as they are fundamentally irrelevant. Statements such as "Effective management policies need to be simple, flexible, equitable and inexpensive to administer" (Knapp and Vaux, 1982: 61) send researchers and policy makers on a quest for the public policy equivalent of the Holy Grail. Demsetz (1969: 1) has contrasted this *"nirvana* approach" with *"a comparative institution* approach in which the relevant choice is between alternative institutional arrangements." Alchian (1950: 220) adds: "What really counts is the various actions actually tried, for it is from these that 'success' is selected, not from some set of perfect actions."

An important implication of the cases presented in Part 2 is that it is preferable to proceed from a conception of intelligent but fallible human beings having to figure out what is happening in a problematic situation and attempting to work through solutions within a context of previous actions and existing institutional arrangements. In such a world, it matters tremendously what people think and do. Although more complicated, this approach may be more appropriate.

The problem is not just one of prescribing actions based on an assumed ideal set of institutional arrangements. At a deeper level, the problem resides in trying to explain the development and performance of institutional arrangements while assuming away the processes by which human beings struggle to create them. Another important implication of the cases is that neither institutional structure nor contextual factors (nor even their combination) determine the actions that will be taken or the success of those actions. The development of institutional arrangements for solving collective problems, and the implementation and performance of such arrangements, still depend to an irreducible degree on what people do. This leaves elements of indeterminacy in all explanations (and certainly in all predictions) of situations involving human behavior (Nelson and Winter, 1982: 370). Explanations that regard institutional arrangements as "given" or exogenous, as "induced" or determined, as mere instruments of manipulation and dominance or the "congealed preferences" of a dominant interest, or as the results of a random process of trial and error will not suffice for our purposes.

The actions in the San Gabriel and Santa Ana River watersheds, especially in the Coastal Plain basins in Los Angeles and Orange counties, indicate that even in physically similar, neighboring basins facing similar threats over the same period, individuals can develop substantially different responses, and both can work reasonably well. The 1955–1975 San Fernando Valley adjudication illustrates what extreme turns events can take, first in one direction and then the opposite, as a result of decisions made by a few individuals. And perhaps best of all, the Mojave River case shows the possibility that a program that is within an eyelash of being implemented may be derailed because of mistakes made during its development and hostility between its proponents and opponents.

This indeterminacy in human affairs is not amenable to smoothing out with the assumption that it results from random processes. There is more to human action than mere trial and error. Conceiving of institutional development as an evolutionary process of problem solving with a significant role for entrepreneurial skill incorporates adjustment to changed conditions and correction of earlier errors over time, while leaving open the possibility that some changes may be too wrenching and some flaws fatal.

I am not attempting to mount a critique of the use of simplification and assumptions in explanations. But what can be simplified or "assumed" depends on what one is trying to understand and explain (Field, 1979: 66). If we are interested in understanding the creation and transformation of institutional arrangements, we must employ conceptual tools that allow us to treat institutions as endogenous and problematic entities. Economists who have attempted to study technical and economic change have found that they could not do so within a framework of analysis that treated technology as a "given" (Nelson, 1987), capital structure as determined (Lachmann, 1978), and the problem of equilibrium as finding the optimal allocation of resources once all information is known (Hayek, 1945). It may be useful to assume a "given state of technology" when constructing a static equilibrium model, but not when constructing an explanation of economic change (Alchian, 1950: 220n).

Similarly, in political theory and policy analysis, it may be useful for some purposes to assume a given set of institutions, as when calculating the likely effect of a proposed policy on individual behavior, but not if one is attempting to understand and explain the development and performance of institutional arrangements over time (Runge, 1984: 154; Bromley, 1989: 252; Eggertsson, 1990: 282; Ostrom, 1990: 50). Understanding institutional development and change entails thinking about institutional arrangements as the deliberate creations of human beings oriented toward some purpose or purposes and operating at multiple levels of action.

Human Action as Intentional Problem Solving under Constraint

Human beings are conceived here are acting intentionally to try to solve problems. This conception accords with Jon Elster's (1983: 20) characterization that the "basic building block of the social sciences, the elementary

unit of explanation, is the individual action guided by some intention,"
and with Ludwig Lachmann's (1986: 49) assertion that "all human activity,
unless prompted by ingrained habit of mind or guided by routine, is
problem-solving."

Intentionality and Problem Solving

If neither structure nor context determines outcomes, and it still matters
what people think and do, then analysts cannot make normative evaluations of degrees of success or failure in an indeterminate human realm
without attending to what it was that individuals were attempting to
accomplish or avoid. To assess one of the cases presented here as a
"failure," for example, implies an understanding of how the participants
approached each other and what they were trying to do. Were they trying to accomplish something, and if so, what? If they were trying to
accomplish something, did they fail because of mistakes they made or
because of changes in circumstances that rendered it impossible for them
to accomplish what they intended? Moreover, were different participants
trying to accomplish contradictory purposes, and to what extent does that
account for the outcome? The answers to questions such as these have
considerable significance for the conclusions we draw, and the applica-
bility of those conclusions to other situations.

These observations apply to evaluating apparent successes, as well.
A groundwater basin may be managed very effectively, but the distribution of pumping rights is highly concentrated. Does this represent a fair
distribution based on historical use, or a "water grab" during the development of the management system? Did the smaller users agree to the
distribution of pumping rights, or were they coerced? Did the water users
organize and use public sector institutions to facilitate and administer an
equitable management plan, or out of a "rent-seeking" motive to enhance
their own value at the expense of the general welfare? The answers to
these questions would affect profoundly an analyst's evaluations, and
the answers depend on inferences about participants' intentions.

Although it is unwise to accept unquestioningly the declared intentions of actors in social situations, it is equally unwise to ignore such
declarations. Social scientists must develop an understanding of the
intentions of actors, and in so doing must find ways to take into account
actors' statements of their intentions without being taken in by them.
Actors' declarations of their intentions need to be considered and should
be taken seriously if matched by their actions and rejected if not.

Social scientists stand in a different relation to their subjects than,
say, entomologists do with a colony of ants. Human subjects are not just
engaged in social behavior. They are engaged in *self-conscious* social

behavior. Human beings, except when engaged in reflexive or purely habitual behavior, tend to be engaged simultaneously in acting, analyzing their actions, and trying to explain their actions. This is especially the case when people are engaged in more challenging endeavors that require interpersonal communication and coordination. Frohock (1987), in trying to modify the interpretation of "rational" behavior to make it more broadly applicable to associational behavior, refers to "reason-giving" rationality: the tendency of rational actors in social settings to base their actions upon choices for which reasons can be supplied that make sense in a particular context.

When people appear to have been engaged in self-conscious social behavior, especially arduous behavior over a long period of time, their own analyses and explanations of what they are doing and what they are trying to do provide important insights into their behavior. If their actions comport with their explanations, both can be taken seriously. If their actions do not comport with their explanations, this, too, is important in developing an explanation of what is occurring or has occurred.

The southern California cases provide examples of individuals who worked for years (sometimes decades) to develop and implement basin governance structures and management systems. These individuals frequently and repeatedly attempted to articulate what they were trying to do, how successful their efforts were, what impeded their progress, and when they erred. The attorneys who worked in several of the cases—such as Kenneth Wright, James Krieger, Arthur Littleworth, Donald Stark, and Susan Trager—have written descriptions and evaluations of the arrangements worked out in the basins. Likewise, engineers and geologists such as Harvey Banks, Max Bookman, John Mann, and Thomas Stetson, have contributed several addresses and writings reflecting on the governance and management systems, the reasoning behind them, and how they have performed. Association members, board members, district managers, and other participants—such as Carl Fossette, Ben Haggott, Alfred Jorgensen, Mel Blevins, and Duncan Blackburn—have written, testified, and spoken at conferences about their experiences, accomplishments, and frustrations in devising the institutional arrangements in the cases presented here. Their observations and reflections have been incorporated into my explanations of what transpired in the cases.

Constraints on Individual Problem Solving: Bounded Rationality

Viewing human activity as intentional problem solving refers only to the purpose of behavior, not the outcome. It does not mean that people solve problems automatically, consistently, or optimally. While human beings engaged in processes of institutional development are conceived as purposeful and self-interested, and intelligent and capable of learning, they are also constrained by limits on their capabilities and limits imposed by the physical world, and are therefore prone to error. The institutional arrangements they create in attempting to solve collective problems have intended and unintended consequences and often fall short of optimality when measured against models in which constraints have been removed or assumed away (Ostrom, 1990: 14).

People make their institutions, but they do not make them just as they please. The physical world imposes limits that individuals apparently cannot change even if they wish, and even if they try (gravity, mortality, and so on). Other aspects of the physical world are subject to change without warning, and without regard to whether the changes are desired by human beings or compatible with their plans (weather, natural disasters, and the like). Human problem solving involves navigating within a physical world that offers opportunities, obstacles, and uncertainties.

Other constraints arise in the capabilities of human beings. On the whole, people are neither as smart as they think they are nor as dumb as they sometimes look. The human organism is "a choosing, decision-making, problem-solving organism that can do only one or a few things at a time, and that can attend to only a small part of the information recorded in its memory and presented by the environment" (March and Simon, 1958: 11). There is what Ronald Heiner (1983) has called a "gap" and what Charles Lindblom (1990) has called a "tragic discrepancy" between the competence of human beings and the difficulty and complexity of the tasks they face. People never have all the information they need, and yet they are unable to process all the information they have. They are capable of understanding, and of misunderstanding, themselves, each other, and the physical world.

This "bounded-rationality" approach differs in important ways from others employed in analyzing collective problem-solving situations, especially the neoclassical view of "economic man." Among the key points of Hayek's critique of that view was that its assumption of identical, fully informed, flawlessly calculating individuals collapsed the task of modeling collective problem solving into the modeling of individual problem solving. He argued that this could not be done effectively. Not only does all of the information needed to solve collective problems not exist in a single mind, it cannot be given to a single mind (Hayek, 1945).

Other analysts have added that these shortcomings are not redressed by plugging "costly information" or positive transaction costs into the modeling of situations still animated by economic man. Nelson and Winter (1982: 66) point out that costly information makes only a quantitative rather than a qualitative difference if individuals still are viewed as "perfect mathematicians" with unlimited information-processing capabilities. Such individuals still could make unerring investments in acquiring additional information, then reduce all uncertainties to maximum likelihood estimates, and proceed on the basis of their common best estimate to define and implement optimal strategies. Again, collective problem solving reduces to individual problem solving.

The concept of transaction costs, vital to understanding social behavior and the emergence of nonmarket institutional arrangements such as the firm, nevertheless does not provide an adequate understanding of institutional development if it remains coupled to the conception of economic man. As the literature reviewed and summarized by Eggertsson (1990: 102n) points out, the actions of economic man are always efficient, even with the presence of positive transaction costs. If institutional arrangements are developed and sustained, their benefits will have exceeded the costs; if not, the costs will have exceeded the benefits. Of this sort of analysis, Field (1979: 57) stated succinctly, "In accounting for both, it explains neither" (see also Bromley, 1989: 5).

To examine institutional development with a conception of human action as boundedly rational problem solving brings into focus additional difficulties, as well as opportunities. Boundedly rational individuals do not optimize in the general sense of surveying all possible alternatives and anticipated consequences and then selecting the best option (Alchian, 1950: 211; Eggertsson, 1990: 77). This does not mean that we must drop the assumptions that individuals are rational and self-interested; we still can assume that people are rational in Popper's sense of "acting in accordance with the situation" and self-interested enough to choose their best option if they know the alternatives and their consequences. Rather, we need to recognize that the best option is generally not known in advance, nor is the situation fully understood, and individuals usually have to expend effort in finding out what it is (Lachmann, 1978: 3).

There are two hindrances here for boundedly rational individuals. The first is not knowing in advance the desired outcome or solution. As jazz artist Humphrey Lyttelton reportedly said, "If I knew where jazz was going, I'd be there already" (Elster, 1983: 9). The second hindrance is not knowing what actions will lead to the desired state of affairs even if it were foreknown. Armen Alchian (1950: 218n) offers a different analogy: "The situation is parallel to trying to control the speed of a car by simply setting by hand the indicator on the speedometer." Instead, the challenge of learning to drive a car is to operate its various components so as to reach and maintain the desired speed.

As several analysts have described, boundedly rational individuals attempt to overcome the hindrances created by the lack of knowledge of their situations, options, and likely consequences by searching for additional information. Because their information-gathering and information-processing capabilities are limited, individuals typically engage in limited searches (see, for example, March and Simon, 1958: 140; Nelson, 1987: 21; Lindblom, 1990: 7; Ostrom, 1990: 209).

Although limited, search activity in effective problem solving is not blind (March and Simon, 1958: 140). Search activity tends to focus on other situations or experiences that appear nearby in place or time. Similar-looking problems experienced in the recent past by oneself or by neighbors are likely to shape the understanding an individual has of a situation and to bias the selection of alternatives for action. Actions that seem to have been successful in the past or for someone else are likely to be copied in the hope they will yield success again (Alchian, 1950: 218).

Limited search is quite rational, but still can result in decisions being taken on faulty premises, and individuals still will be prone to error. Seizing upon the similarities between two situations, individuals may overlook a crucial difference that causes a successful strategy in one to yield failure in the other. Actions taken at one time may be attempted again at another but executed differently, and the difference in execution may produce a different outcome. Out of these variations come frustration, failure, surprise, improvement, success, confusion—in varying degrees and combinations. These outcomes were certainly realized by those in the San Fernando and Mojave River cases who tried to apply a formula from neighboring basins.

Collective Problem Solving

In developing institutional arrangements—rule structures for coordinating the behavior of multiple individuals—human beings are engaged in collective problem solving. All of the problems and opportunities involved in individual problem solving with bounded rationality are radically compounded in collective problem-solving situations.

When the situation is not fully known, how it is understood can (and likely will) differ from one individual to another, even after some search activity (Alchian, 1950: 216). "Some individuals simply see things about a problem, or about a possible solution, that others don't see; what is seen may or may not be actually there" (Nelson, 1987: 118). Interaction between such individuals can be constructive ("two heads are better than one"). It also can be conflictual ("too many cooks spoil the broth"). In any given collective problem-solving situation, "there is inevitable disagreement about what is the best course of action to take, and about who will be right about the matter this time" (Nelson, 1987: 119), and a considerable proportion of the process will be devoted to reconciling alternatives or choosing among them.

Communication therefore becomes essential for disseminating information and signaling intentions in collective problem-solving situations. Yet, communication among individuals with imperfect information and imperfect information-processing capabilities also is a source of difficulties. Communication methods must be established among participants in interdependent situations; it cannot be assumed that communication is immediate, perfect, and without cost (Blomquist and Ostrom, 1985; Blomquist, 1987a).

In the water resource arena, empirical observation has established that the "first response in most areas to some type of water problem is the creation of a water association to provide a forum for discussion" (Coe, 1986: 15). Certainly, that was the case in several of the basins described in Part 2. One Central Basin participant even stated that the "primary purpose" of the development of basin governance structures was "to reduce friction and increase rapport among water users of a water supply that is in critical demand" (California DWR, Central Basin Watermaster Report, 1970: 1).

Coping with Constraint

Uncertainty is significantly greater in collective problem-solving situations if the problems are not fully understood, if individuals differ in their perceptions of the problems and which actions to pursue, and if communication is problematic—all of which are reasonable expectations. Under such circumstances, participants in an interdependent situation may also be expected to become concerned about the unpredictability of other participants' actions.

Reliance on Rules and Norms for Ordering Behavior

The fact that human behavior is indeterminate presents as great a problem for human beings dealing with each other as for analysts. In order to make plans and choices, actors need to reduce indeterminacy (including the gap between stated intentions and actual behavior) to a manageable level.

Several analysts have proposed that it is precisely this indeterminacy that encourages people to develop and rely on norms and rules for ordering their behavior and making their actions predictable. Heiner (1983) identifies "the origin of predictable behavior" in the effort to deal with uncertainty and unpredictability. Alchian (1950) suggested that boundedly rational individuals may be more likely to cope with uncertainty by adopting relatively persistent "modes of behavior" in dealing with a certain problematic situation rather than making continuous marginal adjustments in each period based on some optimization criterion. March and Simon (1958: 4) point to the functional utility of organizational "roles" for enhancing predictability in an interactive environment: "Not only is the role defined for the individual who occupies it, but it is known in considerable detail to others in the organization who have occasion to deal with him." Runge (1984: 155) emphasizes the incentive of individuals who might reap advantages from collective action to establish institutional arrangements to coordinate their expectations about each others' behavior. Over time, uncertainty is reduced as institutions coordinate expectations and their operational qualities become known (Eggertsson, 1990: 72).

There seem to be strong incentives in human social life to develop means for making behavior predictable and binding people's behavior to their stated intentions. Rules are developed, sometimes evolving from convention and sometimes from reflection and choice, for regularizing conduct. Thus is the game of chicken turned into the flow of traffic. Contracts are used, whereby parties consent to be coerced into performing in accordance with their stated intentions. Thus are the taking of property and the making of promises turned into enforceable exchange. Through these processes of making behavior predictable, neither indeterminacy nor the need for human choice is eliminated (contracts are still breached, accidents still occur), but both are reduced.

Problem Solving as an Evolutionary Process

People also cope with uncertainty and unpredictability by exploring alternatives and taking actions cautiously and incrementally, adding experience to their information base as they proceed. Rather than aim for "a solution," the problem solver "tries a step toward amelioration, a step very likely containing a significant element of failure but leaving the situation open for another, now better informed step" (Lindblom, 1990: 219). Ideas are confronted with experience. How one's actions affected and were affected by the characteristics of the physical world can be reviewed to see if the outcomes were desirable, and to revise estimates of the physical world. Expectations about the behavior of others are confirmed and reinforced, or contradicted and revised. Feedback is obtained from experience and experimentation, through a process that is not "mere" trial and error, but "trial-and-error learning" (Ostrom, 1990: 34). People "do what they have learned and then learn what they have done" (Lindblom, 1990: 221).

Many questions are embedded in any collective problem-solving process: what do we know, what do we need to learn, how can we find out, how do we communicate, how do we decide, who goes first, how do we make assurances with each other, how do we check each other, and so forth. Much like the search process described above, people involved in a collective problem-solving process are likely to rely on some previously created, familiar, and workable institutional arrangements for addressing some of these questions (for example, alphabetical order, majority rule, seniority, raising hands, drawing lots) while devising new means for others. In the course of making changes, interacting with each other, and learning from experiences, people engage in problem solving and in revising their equipment for doing so.

These means of coping with the uncertainties involved in collective problem solving, through the sequential development of institutional arrangements, suggest a path dependence to institutional development analogous to evolutionary processes (Ostrom, 1992). Nelson and Winter (1982) proposed evolutionary explanations for understanding technical and economic change, which Elinor Ostrom (1990) compares with institutional change. Elster suggests that when, as in technical and institutional change, radical uncertainty and games without solutions are added to situations animated by rational-choice models of individuals, "the result is close to chaos. Out of this chaos the evolutionary theories emerge as the more likely to explain actual technical progress" (Elster, 1983: 12).

Careful consideration of context becomes especially important, as it is vital to know where action is occurring in terms of process as well as time and place. Abstractions from context can lead to faulty analysis, because differences in context are likely to influence the institutional arrangements established by people engaged in problem-solving processes: "Different rules are established and modified for different communities; the fact that many rules appear to evolve or appear to be culture bound or appear to be inappropriate for the current state of technologies reflect these contingent characteristics of rules" (Sproule-Jones, 1989: 53).

One of the most important conclusions of this study is that *there is no formula* for governing or managing groundwater basins, in southern California or elsewhere. It is easy to conclude from a study of the San Gabriel River watershed that water users in the Raymond, West, and Central basins developed the answers for problems of overdraft and degradation, and to evaluate as faulty any other systems that departed from that approach. Water users elsewhere in southern California did this, and so did I. Careful examination of the successful but different governance structures and management systems in the Main San Gabriel, San Fernando, Orange County, and Chino basins helps to dispel the notion that there is a formula. Nothing more powerfully dispels that notion, however, than the fate of the attempts to apply the San Gabriel formula in the San Fernando and Mojave River cases.

An evolutionary perspective on problem solving and institutional development implies neither teleological explanations of what has occurred to date nor predictions of convergence to a single form. While "the process of institutional development is an evolutionary process . . . in which the conditions of each day arise from the actual circumstances of the preceding day and in which uncertainty abounds" (Nelson and Winter, 1982: 404), the ideas of intentional problem solving, experimentation, and learning from search and experience leave prospects for creativity, as well as for gradual learning through the accumulation of experience and the continual limited search of the environment.

Conceived as an evolutionary process of deliberate choice within constraints, institutional development follows the normal course of economic and political life, in which some behavior is adaptation and "muddling through," but also in which intentional efforts at problem solving, building on experience, and coping with uncertainty and constraints produce new methods and designs. In the applied context of water resources, "while the management process appears to be largely inductive, the fact is that many of the rules, principles and standards that influence the outcome of incremental water management decisions and actions are deductive, even innovative, in character" (Weatherford, 1990: 13). In the cases in Part 2, water users adapted existing practices and institutional arrangements to their needs but also developed new arrangements tailored to their circumstances, including new legal doctrines and organizational forms. Water users crafted new types of governmental organizations to encompass groundwater basins and watersheds, and nongovernmental water associations that crossed jurisdictional boundaries and encompassed numerous organizations as members. For example, enumerating the membership of the West Basin Water Association and the Central Basin Water Association, Fossette (1961: 91) placed their combined membership at "105 member agencies, including representatives from 27 cities, 9 public water districts, 24 water companies, and 45 industries." Existing organizations thus became the component features of these new organizations.

Social Capital and an Institutionally Rich Environment

The idea of "social capital" (Coleman, 1987) enriches the understanding of institutional development as an evolutionary process. At each level of action, people draw upon, and add to, the stock of social capital when engaging in collective problem solving through institutional development. Social norms and shared values are important components of social capital, permitting social interactions to take place more predictably and productively and requiring fewer investments in explicit rule design and less reliance on policing arrangements. Institutional arrangements developed and experiences accrued in the course of collective action are other important components of a community's social capital.

The process in Figure 14.1 illustrates the development of information about a problem and the design of institutions for collective response. When first confronted with a change in their conditions and circumstances, or with an incompletely understood problem, individuals engage in a limited search of the environment (including the recent past as well as similar or familiar situations in the present). In so doing, they draw on previously created instruments and procedures for gathering, classifying and storing, disseminating and retrieving, and pooling information. The information developed about their own problem, and any innovation in the means by which they acquired it, then constitute additions to the set of instruments and procedures for gathering, classifying and storing, and disseminating and retrieving, information.

As their understanding of the problem they confront improves, individuals may attempt to design new institutional arrangements for ordering their relations with each other and responding to the problem as they understand it, or they may adapt existing institutional arrangements to their circumstances in light of the revised understanding of the problem. Frequently, they do some of both. In devising and adapting institutional arrangements for response to the problem, individuals again draw on existing institutional arrangements for assistance, for ideas about what to do or what to avoid. This may range from copying an existing institutional arrangement (such as a contract) essentially unchanged to using existing institutional arrangements (such as legislative or judicial procedures), to creating new arrangements suited to the particular circumstances as they

FIGURE 14.1

A Segment of an Evolutionary Process of Institutional Design

	Drawing Upon/Making Additions to Stock of Social Capital		
	↑	↓	
Awareness of Problem →	Search*/Seeking of Needed Information →	Institutional Design/Redesign →	Revised Awareness of Problem

*Search is limited, likely to be affected by recent experiences and by experiences of neighbors in addressing similar, though nonidentical, circumstances.

are understood by the individuals involved. The institutional arrangements designed at this stage, as well as the experiences gained in adapting existing institutional arrangements to a different set of circumstances, become additions to the stock of social capital.

With this conception of institutional arrangements as a form of social capital that individuals draw on and add to as they engage in problem solving, the idea of "an institutionally rich environment" acquires real significance. Individuals in an institutionally rich environment—where considerable investments have been made in diverse institutional arrangements for learning about and responding to problems—are likely to have considerable advantages in understanding and responding to collective problems (Nunn, 1986).

Heckathorn and Maser (1990) refer to a "transaction resource frontier" representing the limits of a group's ability to resolve coordination, division, and defection problems. They incorporate within that concept the prospect that group members may invest in incremental additions to their transaction resources, thereby shifting their "transaction resource frontier" outward and enlarging their ability to resolve problems. This seems closely related to the idea of social capital that can be invested in and drawn upon in collective problem-solving efforts, and to the advantages gained by individuals in an institutionally rich environment. A group in an institutionally rich environment has a transaction resource frontier farther from the origin than a group in an institutionally poor environment. In an institutionally rich environment, individuals with limited information-processing and communication capabilities coping with a changeable world should be able to perceive and employ more ways of acquiring needed information, more means of sharing costs and distributing benefits, and more possibilities for overcoming problems.

Institutional Change and the Levels of Action

Conceiving of institutional development as an evolutionary process that occurs incrementally, depending upon and taking advantage of contextual factors and existing social capital, does not imply that the process is accidental. The conception remains within the framework of human action as purposeful, intentional problem solving. Evolution in a social perspective includes notions of selection through filtering and deliberate choice, rather than through random or uncontrolled processes (van Parijs, 1981: 51–52). Harvey Mansfield, Jr., (1991: 9) states the contrast usefully and provocatively:

> When the institutionalist reflects on the staying power of institutions,
> he must admit the possibility that they were formed for a purpose. The

> purpose may indeed have been an immediate response to provocation.
> . . . But what happens by accident can happen by intent. . . . The
> possibility of constitutional design must be seriously investigated and
> not quickly dismissed or referred to another desk at which someone does
> political theory.

One of the several important distinctions between evolutionary processes involving human action and those involving biological structures is that human beings are both the objects and the artificers of institutional arrangements. Human beings are able to alter their social behavior, their social organizations, and even the "rules of social organization," "unlike biological phenotypes which are stuck with their original set of genes" (Nelson, 1987: 14). In developing institutional arrangements, human beings operate at different "levels of action" (Kiser and Ostrom, 1982).

The conception of levels of action is essential to an analytic understanding of institutional change as a deliberate process. This conception entails recognizing that all rules for coordinating individual behavior are nested within rules that specify how those rules may be changed (E. Ostrom, 1991: 8). Human beings endeavoring to solve problems may find that prevailing rules or practices are inadequate for coordinating their behavior and may alter those rules or practices. If they change those rules or practices, they have taken action at one level designed to influence behavior at another level. Moreover, human beings engaged in collective problem solving may find that they lack adequate means for taking collective decisions at all. If they respond by forming a collective organization—by constituting an association, a club, a unit of government—with the ability to arrive at collective decisions, then they have taken action at still another level in order to authorize actions to be taken at another level that will influence actions at a third.

These three levels of action are identified by Kiser and Ostrom (1982) as the operational, collective-choice, and constitutional levels. (Bromley (1989) identifies three nearly identical levels of action, naming them operational, organizational, and policy.)

The operational level of action encompasses most of the ordinary behavior of individuals: production, exchange, driving down a street, pumping from a groundwater basin, playing baseball. The collective-choice level encompasses actions that set the rules for operational-level actions: establishing environmental regulations, consumer protection laws, traffic rules, pumping rights, the designated-hitter rule. The actions taken at the constitutional level establish the mechanisms and capabilities for taking decisions at the collective-choice level: creating and empowering a national or state legislature, a city council, a basin management board, the American League.

It should be relatively clear that changes in rules at the operational level are expected to occur more frequently than changes in rules at the collective-choice level, which in turn are expected to occur more frequently than changes in rules at the constitutional level (Ostrom, 1990; see also March and Simon, 1958: 170). It is equally vital to recognize, however, that changes can and do occur at all levels. People have preferences not only concerning outcomes at the operational level, but also about the terms on which choices are available, and the means by which decisions about those terms are made (Bromley, 1989: 6).

Remaining clear about the levels of action is a challenge when analyzing the behavior of a group of individuals confronting complex problems. Different levels of action do not imply different individual actors. The same individuals can switch back and forth among operational, collective-choice, and constitutional levels of action. They may do so without recognizing that the level of action has shifted, and analysts may not catch the shift, either (Ostrom, 1990: 50, 1991: 2).

In the cases in Part 2, individuals took actions at all three levels in all eight basins. Associations and units of government were constituted to permit collective choices to be made among users of common water supplies. Collective-choice mechanisms were used to establish rules governing pumping rights, contributions to acquisition of additional water supplies, and sanctions for failure to comply. At the same time, individuals continued their operational-level activities: producing and purchasing water, growing crops, producing goods and services, paying taxes.

Elinor Ostrom has associated certain types of decisions and actions with the levels as defined by Kiser and Ostrom. Like production and exchange, activities such as appropriation, provision, monitoring, and enforcement occur at the operational level. Policy making, the taking of collective decisions about operational rules, and what is normally referred to as "management" occur at the collective-choice level. Governance, and the formulation and modification of collective decision rules, are decisions and actions at the constitutional level (Ostrom, 1990: 53). These classifications help, especially for our purposes, in distinguishing between "basin governance" and "basin management," but understanding the levels of action remains challenging.

Environment, Context, and Constitutional Choice: The Importance of a Facilitative Political Regime

The idea of actors operating at multiple levels, including a constitutional level of action, underscores the importance of contextual factors and the environment in which action occurs. The latitude of legitimate constitutional-level action available is particularly context-sensitive.

Part 1 of this study focused considerable attention on the physical, historical, and legal contexts in which the actions in Part 2 unfolded. Key additional factors should be recognized that have not been as thoroughly elaborated in the discussion of the cases in Part 2. These include the role and attitude of state officials in California during most of the period of institutional development, the characteristics of the water user communities in southern California, and some particularly favorable aspects of groundwater basins.

The attitude of California state officials toward local government in general and local management of water supplies in particular was important to the development of the management systems in southern California. In general, California has had a commitment to "home rule" in local affairs (Proposition 13 notwithstanding). In the management of groundwater supplies, this commitment translated into the state's willingness to refrain from adopting a statutory framework into which all management systems must fit, or forcing action in areas where delicate negotiations might be in progress. This forbearance was matched by a willingness to authorize arrangements that were developed and supported by local water users—what Elinor Ostrom refers to as "a facilitative political regime" (1990: 137).

The Institute of Public Administration (1987: 66-67) offered the following characterization of California's approach with regard to authorizing new water districts, and the reasoning behind it: "California leads the way in this area and authorized the creation of special districts specifically to deal with groundwater problems in the belief that the complexities of groundwater management can best be dealt with by specialized units of government operating at the local or regional rather than the state level." The accuracy of the institute's characterization is affirmed by the following statement included in the 1962 report of the California Assembly Interim Committee on Water, in the midst of a period of active institution building in southern California groundwater management:

> Water agencies expressed a strong desire to solve their problems themselves and to manage the ground water basins locally. The committee agrees that local management is desirable and, as noted earlier in this report, provides simplified solutions to many of the ground water management problems. *The water users have a choice of solutions available to solve their problems, and their preferences in choosing solutions will assist them in fashioning a management program that will be locally acceptable and financially within their means.* (California Assembly, 1962: 46, emphasis added)

As stated in Chapter 1, California's preference for local management did not reflect an attitude that groundwater resources were unimportant to the state. Indeed, the chairman of the above-quoted committee was

Assemblyman Carley V. Porter, who cosponsored the Burns-Porter Act (1959) authorizing the financing of the State Water Project; the Porter-Dolwig Ground Water Basin Protection Law (1961) authorizing the Department of Water Resources (DWR) to conduct investigations of groundwater basins within the state and recommend to the State Water Resources Control Board (SWRCB) instances in which the SWRCB should initiate an adjudication; and the Porter-Cologne Water Quality Control Act (1969) authorizing the formation and implementation of water-quality control plans in each of nine regions of the state.

The legislative legacy of Assemblyman Porter reflects the state's role as active facilitator of local management. In particular, the state's investment in the Department of Water Resources and its activities represents a substantial commitment not just to allowing local management of water supplies, but assisting it. A state water agency like the DWR, with a staff of nearly 500 persons—including professional engineers, hydrologists, planners and managers—"is not common," to say the least (Weatherford et al., 1982: 17). In addition to its hydrologic investigations, the DWR assisted with the development of the prototype barrier project in West Basin, acted as fact-finding referee in the early adjudications, and shares the cost with the water users of the watermaster service in the West and Central basins.

California's facilitative political regime contributed significantly to the prospects for successful collective action by southern California water users, especially in their constitutional-level actions to form basin governance structures for taking collective decisions about basin management. The supportive attitudes of state officials, and the organizations established within state government to assist local water users in learning about and addressing their problems, are key elements of the institutionally rich environment in which water users designed and developed their institutional arrangements. The view of institutional development as human action must be informed by a recognition that actors' prospects for developing well-tailored and successfully performing institutional arrangements are a function not only of their own capabilities, but also of the environment in which they make their efforts.

Understood within this conceptual framework, institutional development involves evolutionary processes of individual and collective problem solving under constraint, and at multiple levels of action. In some cases, individuals may succeed in crafting institutional arrangements that are well-adapted to contextual exigencies. In other cases, they may fail owing to limitations on their capabilities that cause them to misperceive their situation or misapply the heterogeneous elements of physical, human, and social capital involved in collective problem solving. In still other

cases, individuals' attempts to develop successful institutional arrangements may be blocked by environmental factors, such as a paucity of
physical, human, or social capital or the presence of arrangements that
inhibit flexibility or diversity in the creation of new arrangements or the
adaptation of existing ones.

In most of the cases in Part 2, large numbers of water users coped
with complex problems over an extended period of time. They generally
identified problems one at a time, in situations where information was
extremely impacted and considerable investments had to be made in
figuring out what was happening and who was involved. Many of the
problems turned out to be interrelated, especially in the San Gabriel and
Santa Ana River watersheds. Water users also worked under institutional
constraints: the law of water rights exacerbated problems of overuse, the
boundaries of existing political jurisdictions did not match basin boundaries, the laws governing the creation of special water districts did not
allow them to overlap certain jurisdictional boundaries, and procedures
for acquiring access to additional water supplies were time-consuming
and expensive (see Lipson, 1978: 3–5).

As they worked on the problems they identified, water users in
different basins reached different solutions. In some instances, they confronted institutional constraints and altered them, moving to a constitutional level of action to obtain the passage of new laws or amendments
to existing ones, and using the courts to ratify agreements negotiated
among themselves and to constitute basin governance. In other instances,
they tailored institutional arrangements within the constraints and lived
with them, compromising more desired outcomes in order to maintain
progress, avert disaster, and live to fight another day. And most of the
basin governance structures and management programs have been
modified at least once, to correct a flawed aspect of the original design
or to adapt to changed conditions and new ideas (Phelps et al., 1978: 2).

The southern California cases suggest that all of these possibilities
and outcomes of institutional development are best understood in terms
of deliberate problem-solving action by boundedly rational individuals
making deliberate choices within constraints. This conception offers
greater prospects for real comparative analysis, allowing us to distinguish
among problem-solving situations and account for differing outcomes
without having to assume that human beings in some institutional environments are geniuses or angels while those in other environments are
dolts or thieves.

15

Polycentricity, Entrepreneurship, and Performance

The institutional arrangements for governing groundwater in southern California were deliberately created. Although they are diverse and complex, there is an order to them. They are polycentric, self-governing systems.

The use of the groundwater basins, and the allocation of water supplies between basins in the same watershed, are governed by rules that were fashioned by the water users and their representatives and formalized in court judgments. Water users participate in the selection of members of boards that constitute, govern, or check watermasters or water districts that promulgate rules and regulations governing the behavior of the water users. Most of these water users are also members of associations that discuss basin conditions and management options. Several of the associational memberships overlap; there is a network of water associations.

The basin governance systems are nested within watershed governance systems and integrated with other governance systems. Los Angeles, Orange, and San Bernardino counties have provided needed services and facilities. The Metropolitan Water District of Southern California (MWD) wholesales imported water in the three watersheds; governed by a board composed of representatives of water districts and municipalities, MWD has adopted water pricing policies that have complemented local basin management efforts. The California legislature has played a crucial role in facilitating basin governance and management through the passage of laws drafted by local water users to create specialized jurisdictions and to elicit information about water conditions and use. The California courts assisted in compiling needed information through the use of reference and discovery procedures, and made the basin- and watershed-level constitutions that water users wrote enforceable and adaptable through their continuing jurisdiction and the appointment of watermasters to administer the judgments. The California Department of Water Resources, the U.S. Geological Survey, and the U.S. Army Corps of Engineers have also provided information and physical facilities. The more recent water-quality problems in the basins and watersheds have involved yet another set of actors, among them the Regional Water Quality Control Boards, the California Department of Health Services, and the U.S. Environmental Protection Agency, with whom basin governance structures and management programs must now be integrated if they are to move beyond identifying problems toward implementing solutions.

Advantages of Polycentric, Self-Governing Systems

Southern California water users invested heavily in supplying themselves with institutions that would link decision makers and the information they possessed together in ways that created a governance structure for the local water systems and that generated the additional information and communication required to deal with future changes in the environment. In so doing, they crafted a polycentric order that takes advantage of specialization and scale, solves complex problems within the constraints of limited human information-processing capabilities while at the same time enhancing their problem-solving skills through experience, connects individual behavior by coordinating their expectations reinforced by perceptions of fairness, and increases the prospects for innovation, adaptation, and learning.

Specialization and Scale

Evidence from the growing body of literature on the organization and performance of public economies demonstrates that the governance of metropolitan areas can benefit from the presence of multiple providers and producers of services (for example, U.S. ACIR, 1987). As in private economies, advantages can be gained from functional specialization and from organizing activities on different scales, in accordance with their characteristics. Wade (1987) found similar benefits among the separate and specialized organizations in irrigation systems in Asia.

Perhaps the strongest examples of polycentric systems among the cases in Part 2 are in the West and Central basins of the San Gabriel River watershed. At a minimum, the management system for these basins includes the West Basin and Central Basin Water Associations, the West Basin and Central Basin Municipal Water Districts, the Central and West

Basin Water Replenishment District, the Los Angeles County Department of Public Works, the County Sanitation Districts of Los Angeles County, and the Southern District Office of the California Department of Water Resources. The involvement of this number of organizations could easily appear to represent "chaos," or at the very least, inefficiency due to wasteful duplication and overlap.

But the governance structure and management programs in the West and Central basins do not reflect chaos or wasteful duplication and overlap. Rather, they reflect functional specialization. There is considerable specialization in the public economies of the Los Angeles, San Gabriel, and Santa Ana River watersheds, yet there is little true "duplication" of services. Duplication would occur if the several agencies, water districts, watermasters, and water users' associations performed the same tasks, but they do not. In the West and Central basins, for example, there are water suppliers, project operators, two trade associations, a management group, and an auditor. The activities of these service providers and producers are coordinated through interorganizational agreements governed by law.

Polycentric systems allow water users to take advantage of differences in scale in the performance of separable tasks. The tasks in managing water supply in southern California and elsewhere have different characteristics. Neither small-scale nor large-scale organizations can be fitted well to all of them. The systems developed by these water users comport with Olson's (1965: 172–73) assessment that "efficient government demands many jurisdictions and levels."

Some undertakings, such as large capital projects, call for large entities: the State Water Project was planned and built and is operated by the California Department of Water Resources, the Colorado River Aqueduct by MWD, the Los Angeles Aqueduct by the Los Angeles Department of Water and Power. Larger organizations also make sense for undertakings requiring professional expertise that may have to be used repeatedly in different situations: most of the hydrologic investigations of southern California watersheds were undertaken by the California Department of Water Resources or the U.S. Geological Survey, each of which maintains a staff of professional hydrologists and engineers who can be dispatched to particular areas. This is more economical than having separate professional engineering staffs at the basin level. At the same time, the engineering aspects of particular basin management plans were usually handled by individual local professional engineers or geologists under contract with a district or association.

At a somewhat less grand scale than the construction and operation of aqueducts hundreds of miles long is the effort that goes into flood control channels, spreading grounds, and smaller dams and debris basins.

Still, the equipment and expertise needed to perform these tasks suggest that economies may be gained by not having them separately organized for each basin. In southern California, county flood control districts typically have performed these functions. Similarly, the construction and operation of water reclamation plants can be organized economically on a scale that overlaps individual groundwater basins but is smaller than the state, or even than the larger counties such as Los Angeles, Riverside, and San Bernardino. Special districts have typically been organized to perform these tasks.

Basin policy decisions—such as how much replenishment water to purchase, how much water in storage to draw down or replace, or where to set the rates for taxing pumping this year—are best made through basin governance structures representative of, and responsive to, water users. When basins are interconnected in a watershed, water users may choose either to achieve watershed governance through the creation of a separate watershed-scale organization (such as SAWPA) or through interorganizational agreements and representative structures such as the San Gabriel and Santa Ana River judgments and their respective watermasters. Either method can work, while leaving basin governance structures in place for taking policy decisions at the individual basin level (Stetson, 1982: 3–4).

Organizing governance and policy making on different scales allows decision-making processes to include all and only those decision makers who are directly affected by the decisions. Important information about preferences and options is not excluded, and extraneous information is not included. Decisions of others in the community are not unnecessarily altered or disrupted (Nunn, 1986: 294).

Because water users have taken advantage of the benefits of functional specialization and appropriate scales of organization, the results gained from these polycentric management systems are the opposite of what might be predicted by analysts who would characterize such systems as "wasteful," "uncoordinated," and "inefficient." Instead, the multiple organizations in the three watersheds contract with one another for the provision of specialized services and the coordination of activities and share facilities and staff in cooperative arrangements. As shown in Chapter 13, the administrative costs of these systems are extremely low.

Administrative overhead tends to be reduced rather than magnified by these arrangements. For three decades, the Central Basin Municipal Water District and the Central and West Basin Water Replenishment District shared an office the size of a small house in Downey and shared a general manager and three clerical employees. The Main San Gabriel Basin Watermaster meets in the offices of the Upper San Gabriel Valley Municipal Water District, and purchases such staff services as it requires from the district. The Raymond Basin Management Board meets in the offices of the Foothill Municipal Water District and contracts with the Southern District Office of the Department of Water Resources for data collection and the preparation of its annual report. The San Gabriel River and Santa Ana River watermasters each have a mailing address, but virtually no overhead; the members are employed in other pursuits and are compensated for their time and travel when they need to meet. The office of the ULARA watermaster is in the Los Angeles Department of Water and Power (DWP), and the current watermaster is a DWP employee. The Chino Basin watermaster is on the Board of Directors of the Chino Basin Municipal Water District, and district personnel provide staff support for the watermaster and the three pool committees. Indeed, among the seven successful cases, basin management costs appear to be highest in the Orange County Water District, which is the closest of any of the seven successful management systems to being an integrated basin management agency—it maintains its own water reclamation plant, its own spreading grounds, its own staff of engineers, its own public information officers, and so on.

This is not an ex post facto rationalization of the organization of the polycentric governance structures and management programs. It is important to remember that, for the most part, *the water users who assembled these systems are the ones who bear the costs of their operation.* Water users had a strong incentive to devise management systems that were not wasteful or inefficient, and they chose to craft them in these ways. Especially during the development of the governance and management systems in the Main San Gabriel Basin, the San Fernando Valley Basin, and the Chino Basin, water users deliberately chose interorganizational arrangements instead of creating new water districts.

Of course, this does not mean that users made no mistakes or compromises in devising these systems, or that there is no fragmentation or duplication anywhere in southern California water supply management. For example, the presence of three municipal water districts in the Main San Gabriel Basin (two of which are MWD member agencies and the other a State Water Project contractor) complicates basin governance and management with no clear offsetting benefits.

Information and Computation

The quality of decision making depends on the availability, use, and quality of the information that goes into this activity. Those attempting to resolve the toughest problems of resource management require considerable information, not only about the resource but about the users and their preferences (Nunn, 1986: 297–302). Institutionally rich environments, such as those found in southern California during the development and implementation of the governance and management systems there, provide a better information base for decision making and greater social capital to draw on in institutional design. Larger and more centralized systems have more difficulty collecting, acting upon, and communicating information, especially about complex problems and are more vulnerable to information losses (Nelson and Winter, 1982: 358–59; see also Hardin, 1982: 182).

Hayek viewed the market as a desirable polycentric system primarily because it was likely to elicit and make fuller use of available information, including both "general knowledge" and "the knowledge of the particular circumstances of time and place" (Hayek, 1945: 21; see also Nunn, 1986: 294). Lindblom (1990: 225) notes that the market mechanism "solves mammoth allocational and distributional problems without their ever appearing on anyone's desk or agenda."

This observation extends to other polycentric forms of collective decision making. Elinor Ostrom (1990: 17) concluded from her study of numerous common-pool resource situations around the world that those who use a resource year after year and depend on it in whole or in part for their life or their livelihood develop detailed and relatively accurate information about it. If this is the case generally, we can expect that, all other things being equal, rules made by the parties directly affected by them will be based on better information than rules imposed from outside or influenced by unaffected parties (Nunn, 1986: 294–95; see also Uphoff, 1986: 23). "This suggests that the implementation of efficiency-compatible rules may be less important than the implementation of institutions that relate decision makers in ways that generate necessary information" (Nunn, 1986: 297; see also Lindblom, 1990: 225).

The actions of individuals attempting to solve problems will obviously be shaped by their understanding of their situation. Full knowledge of their situation is not "given" to them. Among the most instructive aspects of the cases in Part 2 are the ways in which the institutional arrangements devised by water users at different times reflected their changing understandings of their situations, and the learning they acquired along the way.

Decision Making and Compliance: Self-Interest Rightly Understood

The beneficial political effects of these polycentric systems are just as important as their beneficial economic effects. Water users in the successful cases repeatedly and purposefully chose decision-making processes that involved the organization and representation of diverse communities of interest, and they elicited information from several sources in developing a shared understanding of water supply conditions and problems. Water users also repeatedly chose decision-making processes that required a consensus or a near-consensus rather than decision making by simple majority.

The best example of these processes can be seen in the repeated use of the courts and stipulations. Water users usually did not take issues into the courts in order to have them decided by a judge or jury, but in order to take advantage of the information-gathering processes of a lawsuit and the pressure of bargaining "in the shadow of the court" in order to negotiate a resolution of issues among the affected parties. (Indeed, the only adjudication decided by a judge was the botched 1968 decision in *Los Angeles v. San Fernando,* which was reversed on appeal.) Negotiating a stipulation means attaining a consensus or near-consensus of the parties, however conflicting their interests may be initially. Water users repeatedly opted for this process, despite the fact that it often consumed several years and considerable sums of money. Moreover, the stipulated judgments they reached always included continuing jurisdiction by the court, which allows parties who may subsequently become dissatisfied with the judgment or its administration to petition the court for relief or modification.

The basin governance structures constituted by water users in the successful cases also show a preference for decision making by consensus. In the San Fernando Valley and Chino basins, any significant basin policy decisions must have the general approval of representative water producer committees. The three-member San Gabriel River Watermaster includes one member each chosen by the Upper Area and the Lower Area each year, but the two areas have to agree each year on the nomination of the third (and potentially decisive) member. The five-member Santa Ana River Watermaster represents the four major water districts in the watershed, and is obliged under the terms of the Santa Ana River judgment to take decisions unanimously.

These decision-making processes have required water users to take into account, and attempt to accommodate, one another's interests in order to reach any desired outcome. Water users in the San Gabriel River watershed frequently disagreed during the decades they spent constructing the governance and management systems there. Along the way, they developed a norm of "not walking away from the table" (Fossette, 1986). The plainest illustration of that norm was the lock-up session called in order to reach agreement in the San Gabriel River adjudication.

The decision-making processes and polycentric governance structures employed by the water users called on many individuals to play multiple roles over time, which required them to take each other's interests into account. At various times, an engineer might offer consulting services to a water user, represent that water user in negotiations, testify as an expert witness, serve as a district manager or board member or watermaster, and lobby the California legislature on a particular issue on behalf of all southern California water producers. Similarly, local attorneys at times represented water users and districts and also lobbied the legislature, city mayors and utility directors also served as officers of water users' associations, and so forth. Most of the actively involved individuals at one time or another shifted from consultant to advocate, from advocate to manager or board member, and from principal to agent.

These multiple links and multiple roles helped the participants understand one another's circumstances and recognize the importance of cooperation and coordination. In this way, the participants heightened what Tocqueville called the sense of "self-interest rightly understood," that is, self-interest that is informed and qualified by recognizing the need to take the interests of others into account. The many roles played by so many of the participants in these cases had beneficial political effects similar to those Tocqueville observed about the jury system, which places ordinary citizens temporarily in the position of magistrate, requires them to learn something about the law, and obliges them to cooperate with a group of their fellow citizens in reaching a decision requiring consensus. In *Democracy in America,* Tocqueville described the jury system, participation in associations, and involvement in local government as three "free schools" in which Americans learn the behavioral and attitudinal prerequisites of a self-governing democracy. Since the water users in the successful cases presented here spent most of their careers participating in associations and local government, it is not surprising that they developed the skills of which Tocqueville wrote.

As mentioned in Chapter 13, the polycentric, self-governing systems developed by water users are responsible for the extraordinarily high rates of compliance with the basin management programs— which in most of the successful basins are fairly rigorous. Pumpers may not extract more from the basin than their determined share. If they do, they are subject to heavy assessments. In addition, they are taxed on each acre-foot of groundwater extracted within their right in order to support the management program. Economic incentives to violate these rules and attempt to evade assessments can be presumed to be very strong, especially in the larger basins where there are numerous pumpers and no single well's effects on basin conditions would be noticeable (Olson, 1965; Hardin, 1982). In addition, the costs of these basin management programs are borne almost entirely by the users themselves.

Of course, water users have invested in monitoring mechanisms. On the other hand, every well meter in a basin is not tested every quarter, when production reports are usually due. In the basins with the largest numbers of wells, two years or more can pass between tests at a particular well. Monitoring alone cannot account for the fact that no water user in these basin or watershed management programs has yet had to be sanctioned for noncompliance. Water users comply with the requirements of the management programs, accurately reporting their water extractions each quarter, paying their pump taxes, and having defective well meters repaired or replaced, for reasons that cannot be fully accounted for by Posnerian economic calculations of the risk of being caught multiplied by the severity of the sanctions (see Wade, 1987: 178).

The management programs are perceived as legitimate and fair because they are decided on through basin governance structures designed by, and participated in by, the water users themselves. Levi (1988: 2) makes the following observation about rules and rulers: "A distinction exists between the process of making the rules and the process of making decisions within the rules. Rulers participate in both processes. However, they are also responsible for enforcing the rules." In the successfully managed basins of southern California, water users have designed the processes for making the rules, made decisions within the rules, and designed the processes for enforcing the rules. In other words, at the same time that they are governed by the rules, they fit Levi's definition of "rulers." These sorts of reciprocal rule-ruler-ruled relationships (V. Ostrom, 1991) are more likely to be sustainable and to gain compliance than systems based on a sovereign authority and a separation between the rule maker and the ruled (see Clark, 1980).

Margaret Levi's concept of "quasi-voluntary compliance" and Ford Runge's application of the "assurance problem" to common-pool resource management also help explain why water users are so committed to the basin management programs. Quasi-voluntary compliance arises from a combination of factors. First, individuals perceive gains from a particular collective action (such as managing the basin)—in other words, the rules are connected with something the individual wants. Second, individuals perceive some prospect of being sanctioned if caught violating the rules (even if the chance of being caught is thought to be relatively small). Third, individuals have a reasonably founded belief that others will also be sanctioned if caught violating the rules. Under these circumstances, individuals offer their compliance with a sense that others are doing the same.

This reasoning is closely related to the concept of "assurance." In an assurance problem, each individual's preferences depend in part on what others are doing. The individual would prefer to act cooperatively if others are, but not to act cooperatively if others are not. According to Runge (1981), this assurance problem appropriately characterizes most common-pool resource situations: individuals would prefer to see the resource preserved and maintained for a future stream of uses, but are unwilling to make sacrifices toward that end by themselves.

The decision-making processes employed by the water users in the successful cases were designed to assure participants that most—indeed, nearly all—other water users would cooperate with them before any actions were taken or required. Water users developed "contingent contracts" with one another (Hardin, 1982), primarily through negotiated stipulations to which no signer could be held unless 75, or 80, or 90 percent of the others signed as well. The basin governance systems similarly require a high level of agreement before actions are taken to alter the status quo. Individuals respond by offering their compliance, quasi-voluntarily, and water users reap tremendously high compliance rates as a benefit of having capitalized on the advantages of polycentricity and self-governance.

Some of these benefits are unavailable through other processes. Basin management with built-in tendencies toward sustainability and compliance of this strength cannot be replicated by decision-making processes that are not characterized by polycentricity and self-governance. Effective, efficient, adaptable, equitable, sustainable basin management programs that meet with near-perfect compliance cannot be designed in a laboratory and implemented by command and control. They are not attainable merely through better hydrology or better engineering, regardless of how crucial hydrology and skillful engineering are to any basin management program:

> Past history has shown . . . that *developing local management plans is not a simple engineering problem and is as much a product of negotiations as it is of scientific study*. . . . The Southern California experience also strongly suggests the need for the development of local producer organizations similar to the water users associations developed in the West Coast, Central, and Main San Gabriel Basins of Los Angeles County to exercise leadership and utilize existing technical capability in the search for and implementation of a local management plan. (Lipson, 1978: 24, emphasis added)

The sustainability of the basin governance and management systems in southern California is tied as much to the fact that local users designed them as it is to the particular designs they arrived at and adopted. After comparing the basin management systems in West Basin and Orange County, Charles Corker observed that the "important fact appears to be that there was a choice, and each district chose—or perhaps it would be more accurate to say discovered—a pattern which proved to be workable and acceptable" (quoted in Schneider, 1977: 49).

The Crucial Role of Entrepreneurship

It is no small accomplishment to craft a polycentric, self-governing system that is well-tailored to problems, takes advantage of specialization and scale, improves the information base for collective decision making, and attains high levels of cooperation and compliance. Such an effort requires individuals to apply skills and knowledge that are not "given" to them at the outset of a collective problem-solving process. In Vincent Ostrom's (1991: 243) words, "We can rule out the possibility that a polycentric system of order . . . will emerge spontaneously. Instead, it is necessary, as Tocqueville suggested, to draw upon a science and art of association in learning how to put polycentric systems of order together."

Entrepreneurship is a vital aspect of collective problem solving, directed toward achieving complementary combinations of heterogeneous elements of physical, financial, human and social capital, and moving across levels of action. Ideas are not automatically transformed into working innovations, heterogeneous elements of various forms of capital cannot be combined in just any fashion, and not just any outcome will do. Entrepreneurship involves the development over time of skills in collective problem solving, based on experience in particular situations where time and place specificities apply (Hayek, 1945; Lachmann, 1978; Elster, 1983).

In overcoming some of the difficulties of collective problem-solving situations described in Chapter 14, a key problem is one of organizing (Ostrom, 1990: 39). Individuals who develop entrepreneurial skills learn what institutional resources can be drawn upon in gathering information, developing means of communication, taking and implementing collective decisions, and crafting institutional arrangements to ensure the coordination of expectations and sustainability (see Elster, 1983: 78–79). Accordingly, individuals who have developed entrepreneurial skills gain capabilities for diagnosing situations and determining when no existing institutional arrangements can be employed or adapted to address a particular problem, so that new ones will have to be crafted.

Learning and Experience

The local engineers, public officials, businesspeople, attorneys, and farmers who designed and developed the institutional arrangements for governing groundwater in southern California succeeded to the extent they have partly because of the advantages of polycentric, self-governing systems in an institutionally rich environment. They also succeeded because they developed the skills to capitalize on those advantages.

The most vulnerable aspect of polycentric, self-governing systems lies in the ability of people to craft and maintain them in order to capitalize on the advantages they offer. As the cases presented in Part 2 emphasize, people can only develop the kinds of institutions that will resolve problems and improve conditions if they know what they are doing.

Vitally important general knowledge of hydrology and engineering can be communicated to and considered by local water users more readily than a detailed knowledge of local physical, economic, political and other conditions can be communicated to and considered by central decision makers (Hayek, 1945). Local water users have more information about the particular characteristics of the resource and of the community or communities that depend on it (Uphoff, 1986: 36), and this "knowledge of the particular circumstances of time and place" turns out to be of greatest importance in governing a basin or watershed.

Other scholars who have researched groundwater resources in southern California and elsewhere have reached similar conclusions about the capabilities of local users to integrate the knowledge and demonstrate the skills needed to manage groundwater resources effectively, and they have drawn similar inferences from those conclusions. Albert Lipson, author of the groundwater management volume in the 1978 RAND series, *Efficient Water Use in California*, wrote:

> The Southern California experience also strongly suggests the need for the development of local producer organizations similar to the water users associations developed in the West Coast, Central, and Main San Gabriel Basins of Los Angeles County to exercise leadership and utilize existing technical capability in the search for and implementation of a local management plan. (Lipson, 1978: 24)

Susan Christopher Nunn (1986: 299) concluded that the groundwater management experience of New Mexico and the Texas High Plains "illustrates a remarkable ability on the part of nonseparably related decision makers to develop rules to mutual benefit. This suggests that the devolution of authority and responsibility to make rules to such groups is a valuable policy aim." Zachary Smith (1984: 255), who has studied groundwater management throughout the western United States, agrees: "The groundwater users are in a much better position in regard to any outside authority to determine the most desirable mix of measures designed to decrease dependence on groundwater." Elinor Ostrom (1992) and S. Y. Tang (1992) demonstrate these same principles at work in water resources in other parts of the world.

The southern California cases in particular show that expertise and wisdom are not the sole province of central public authority, that innovation in groundwater management is not limited to the public sector nor efficiency to the private sector, that diversity in governance and management systems is not a sign of disorderliness or impending disaster, and that citizens have considerable ability to self-organize and solve complex problems. Consider just the complexity of the Coastal Plain cases—the Orange County Basin, and West and Central basins in Los Angeles County. Analysts should be very cautious indeed about selling short the problem-solving capabilities of local users who could successfully resolve that tangle of interrelated threats.

The value of the experience and expertise acquired over time by water users on the Los Angeles County Coastal Plain were recognized by the California Department of Water Resources in bulletins published in 1966 and 1968:

> Through these pioneering activities—basin replenishment by spreading and injection, and creation of freshwater barriers to prevent saline intrusion—local agencies have acquired a wealth of experience in basin management. (California DWR, 1966a: 1)

> The Coastal Plain groundwater managers can best understand the changes in their water service requirements and the political, legal, social, and organizational forces that influence management decisions. These forces may play a dominant role in the selection of a management plan and often override cost and benefit considerations. For these reasons, basin management must remain in local hands. (California DWR, 1968: 17)

Public Sector Entrepreneurship and Rent Seeking

The emphasis on having water users themselves develop governance structures and management programs raises an important issue: whether their creation of public jurisdictions and employment of public authority in order to achieve their aims constitutes what political economists call "rent seeking." Buchanan (1980: 4) defines rent seeking as the effort to enhance an individual's (or a group's) welfare at the expense of the general welfare, generating social waste rather than social welfare. Such behavior often occurs when organized interests engage the public sector (as in the water supply field).

The distinction between public sector entrepreneurship and rent-seeking behavior is crucial, but unfortunately sometimes blurred. All efforts to engage public authority for collective problem solving are not rent seeking. There is an important difference between the sort of behavior defined by Buchanan as rent seeking and the use or creation of public institutions to solve problems. There remain many kinds of efforts in which groups organize and use public institutions in order to achieve benefits that are not at the expense of the general welfare.

The cases in Part 2 shed light on this distinction. Users of a common resource may experience or anticipate the loss of benefits from its use, as a result of overuse, depletion, or degradation. In responding to these anticipated losses, they may organize and take action to establish firm shares, curtail use, protect and restore the resource, or any combination of these. In so doing, they may need or wish to engage some mechanisms of public authority (a court, a legislature, an agency, a district) and even to sponsor the creation of others. This is properly conceived as *the avoidance of rent dissipation* rather than as *rent seeking*. When groups organize to avoid the dissipation of rents and do so in ways that place the costs upon themselves and match the costs to benefits received, this is not accurately described as rent seeking.

More to the point, however, a group may engage (and even create) public institutions in order to achieve a collective benefit *and* bear the costs of that collective benefit rather than spreading them to others. This is rent creation, in which individuals organize to enhance the value of a common resource (Buchanan, 1980: 7). It is emphatically *not* rent seeking, since the individual or group has achieved a beneficial purpose at its *own* expense.

In the successful cases in Part 2, water users provided themselves with collective benefits (rent creation, and the avoidance of rent dissipation) through the use and creation of public institutions in ways that place essentially the full costs of obtaining the benefits upon themselves. This includes paying the full costs of replacement water brought into the watershed when local supplies are overextracted and must be replenished. In addition, the water users used public institutions and authority to impose restraints on their own water-producing behavior. To describe this as rent-seeking behavior, as one recent study (Hampton, 1989) does, is simply inaccurate. It implies that the southern California water industry is composed of the dumbest rent seekers yet found on the planet—who wanted to use public authority to enhance their welfare at the expense of others but wound up restraining their own behavior and paying the costs of doing so.

A better way of characterizing the use of the public sector by the southern California water users is what Robert Salisbury called "self-regulatory policy." Hart (1974: 126) applied the self-regulatory policy concept to the case of the West Basin Barrier Project and concluded that it "could scarcely better fit." Indeed, the self-regulatory policy concept fits all of the successful cases presented here.

This difference between rent-seeking and self-regulatory policy is not merely the difference between an economist's view and a political scientist's view of the same phenomenon; it is not a case of "you say po-tay-to and I say po-tah-to." There is no question that the concept of rent seeking applies to a great deal of public sector activity, especially to the subsidization game so skillfully played in Washington, D.C. But it does not apply when a community of interest designs institutional arrangements for their benefit at their cost and in the course of so doing generates social welfare rather than social waste.

Mistakes, Unintended Consequences, and Troublesome Tendencies

Even skillful and experienced entrepreneurship is practiced by fallible beings operating under constraints. In the development of the governance and management systems in the southern California watersheds studied here, tactical mistakes have been made and design flaws can be found. Improvements could be made, even in the most successful cases (see, for example, Lipson, 1978: 21).

Unintended Consequences of Changing the Law

Every analyst who has written about the mutual-prescription doctrine devised during the Raymond Basin adjudication has included a discussion of the race to the pumphouse it engendered. This was an unintended, but not unforeseeable, consequence of basing the size of an individual pumper's right on recent historical use. Since the mutual-prescription doctrine would apply only in an overdrawn basin, and overdraft would imply reductions in groundwater use, the clear incentive for pumpers after *Pasadena v. Alhambra* was to escalate their groundwater extractions in order to gain a larger prescriptive right in the event of an adjudication, so that the consequent reduction would still leave one with a "livable" pumping right.

The race to the pumphouse undoubtedly made groundwater conditions in several California basins even worse. Its effects can still be seen in the heavily overdrafted Mojave River area, where cities, industries, and utilities maintain irrigated alfalfa fields to help preserve high historical records of water production, anticipating the day that has now arrived, when adjudication would be attempted again.

Trying to Apply a Formula

The Central Basin adjudication was the third mutual-prescription adjudication. After the prolonged Raymond Basin and West Basin litigations, the one in Central Basin was a rousing success. A long and costly fact-finding reference was avoided. An interim agreement was achieved within nine months, and a final judgment in less than five years. It is a testimony to hubris that the success of the Central Basin adjudication spawned two of the greatest tactical mistakes in the development of groundwater basin management in southern California.

The judge in the Central Basin case moved over to the *Los Angeles v. San Fernando* litigation and issued a judgment imposing a mutual-prescription division of the waters of the San Fernando Valley over the objections of Los Angeles and in contradiction to a long series of cases. This ultimately led to reversal in the California Supreme Court. That 1975 Supreme Court decision left considerable uncertainty over the status of mutual prescription (and basin adjudications generally), helped to finish off the faltering Mojave River Basin adjudication, and produced the pool arrangements in Chino Basin that leave some overlying users without firm, tradable rights.

During the same period, some of the attorneys and engineers involved in the Central Basin adjudication moved north to the Main San Gabriel Basin and the Mojave River Basin. In the Main San Gabriel Basin, the Central Basin formula was adopted, with important modifications. The Mojave River Basin presented a different set of circumstances, however, and the mutual-prescription solution was strongly and successfully resisted by smaller overlying landowners. They did not perceive it as a formula for resolving groundwater problems, but as a water grab by larger upstream ranchers and appropriators. The collapse of the Mojave River adjudication was accompanied by the collapse of the proadjudication majority on the Mojave Water Agency Board of Directors, and the dismissal of proadjudication staff members (the agency manager, engineer, and attorneys). The years since 1976 have demonstrated the difficulty of assembling support for any other management alternative, and the overdraft situation has grown significantly worse in the interim.

Trying to Move Too Fast

The San Gabriel Valley Municipal Water District (SGVMWD) in the Main San Gabriel Basin was created when some water users tried to move the process along too fast. Four cities overlying the Main San Gabriel Basin strongly opposed annexation to MWD, and were convinced that the Upper San Gabriel Valley Water Association intended to push for the creation of a municipal water district and its annexation to MWD.

It is impossible to say whether their opposition to MWD annexation could have been mollified or some compromise could have been worked out. The four cities bolted from the association and formed the SGVMWD, which became and remains a State Water Project contractor independent of MWD. As noted in Chapter 8, the SGVMWD consists of three noncontiguous parcels of land on the west and north sides of the Main San Gabriel Basin. Its existence in addition to the Upper San Gabriel Valley Municipal Water District and the previously created Three Valleys Municipal Water District (both of which annexed to MWD) complicates basin governance and management.

The Mojave River adjudication represents not only an attempt to impose a formula, but to move much too quickly in doing so. In the previous basin adjudications based on mutual prescription, general agreement first existed about the general shape and nature of the water resource. In the Mojave River adjudication, differences persisted *up to the time of the dismissal of the lawsuit* over whether the water resource consisted of a single area of influence, an underground stream subject to the laws governing surface watercourses, or a series of three distinct underground basins. It is impossible to say whether water users could have reached a common understanding about the resource, and beyond that, whether they could have agreed on a plan for allocating rights to its use. Nevertheless, moving forward with an adjudication when users do not even agree about the basic nature of the resource was another significant tactical mistake in the Mojave River case.

Subsidization: Pricing Water at Less than Full Cost

Inefficient consumption decisions are almost certain to be made when prices charged to consumers do not cover the full costs of providing the good or service. This is true even if the consumers are the same people who pay the remainder of the costs in some other form, as when provision is subsidized by public funds paid by the consumers as taxpayers. Once the taxes are paid and the subsidies are conferred, consumers have no reason to respond to costs other than the stated price of the good or service. This general observation applies to the cases presented here through the use of property taxes to fund basin management activities (see also Phelps et al., 1978: 11).

In all of the cases, at least some administrative costs of the overlying water districts are raised by real property taxes. The remainder of the expenditures of the water districts are covered by revenue from water sales, sales of services, or from taxes on water production, each of which are factored into the cost of water to producers and consumers and thus figure into water consumption decisions. In nearly all of the cases, the proportion of administrative costs financed by property taxes is so small that their marginal effect on consumption decisions is nearly negligible. In the Orange County Water District, however, real property taxes have been relied on substantially in the past, in combination with pump taxes, to purchase replenishment water. This practice allows the pump tax on water production to be set at a lower rate. Water production is subsidized by property taxation, and the true cost of the management program is not reflected in water rates charged to customers.

Possible Unfairness of a Gross Pump Tax

A gross pump tax to finance basin management activities has the advantage of being simple to administer and appearing fair. There is, however, reason to question that surface appearance. Generally speaking, if a safe yield or basin production percentage has been established for a groundwater basin, then the producers who exceed their share of the safe yield or who exceed the basin production percentage are the ones who cause additional amounts of replenishment water to be purchased and spread in the basin to maintain water levels. If replenishment water purchases are financed by a tax levied on all pumping, then the burden of the additional replenishment purchases falls equally on all producers and all production (hence the surface appearance of fairness). Under these circumstances, producers who exercise restraint are taxed at the same rate as producers who do not, and the former are in effect subsidizing the latter.

The Orange County Water District modified its single gross pump tax, making it a two-tier pump tax by the addition of the basin equity assessment program. This partly addresses the unfairness problem. The Central and West Basin Water Replenishment District continues to finance purchases of replenishment water and injection water for the barrier projects with a gross pump tax. This design flaw has not caused problems so far because of the extraordinary record of compliance by producers, all of whom either maintain their production within their respective shares of the safe yield or acquire additional pumping rights from other producers.

Politics and the Determination of Flexible Safe Yields and Pump Taxes

When safe yields, basin production percentages, or pump tax rates are discretionary policy decisions of a governing board that is primarily responsive to the water users, the possibility arises that those decisions may be influenced by political considerations as well as basin management considerations. Chapter 11 mentioned the tendency of the Orange County Water District Board to base decisions about pump tax rates on considerations of revenue collection rather than production control, which keeps the pump tax rates lower than would be necessary to have a significant impact on pumping. This is less of a concern in the Main San Gabriel and Chino basins, where the replacement water assessments are set equal to the cost per acre-foot of MWD replenishment water, but the determination of the operating safe yield in those basins affects how many pumpers will have to pay the replenishment assessment.

The tendency to set high operating safe yields or basin production percentages in order to minimize the amount of groundwater production on which extra assessments must be paid is a potential concern in these more flexible management programs. When the 1987–1991 drought caused water levels in the Main San Gabriel Basin to fall, for example, the situation called for a reduction in the operating safe yields. Annual operating safe yields in the Main San Gabriel Basin were nonetheless maintained at 200,000 acre-feet per year while water levels fell toward the bottom of the target management range. This was in contrast to the dry years of 1976–77, when the operating safe yield was cut to as low as 150,000 acre-feet in response to falling basin water levels. The difference in policy response between the 1976–77 drought and the 1987–1992 drought cannot be attributed with certainty to political considerations. The possibility that producers might place their economic interests above the objective conditions of the basin is built into the institutional arrangements in these more flexibly managed basins.

Is this a catch-22 situation? Chapter 13 pointed out some of the problems of being inflexible. Are the flexibly managed basins now being criticized for being flexible? Not at all—the San Gabriel River and Santa Ana River judgments provide excellent examples of flexible management programs that take physical conditions into account, but do so according to an established and agreed-upon rule. This provides the flexibility needed to respond to water supply conditions while making it less likely that annual basin management policy decisions will be affected by political considerations.

Exclusion of Nonproducers

The responsiveness of basin policy decisions to the interests of pumpers raises a question about the exclusion of nonproducers from the policy-making process. This is less of a concern in the Central, West, and Orange County basins, where the governing boards of the principal agencies engaged in basin management activities are elected by all residents. Of course, it is to be expected that nonproducer residents will take less interest in the activities of these agencies, and water producers will still be the principal constituency of the elected boards. Nevertheless, nonproducer residents of the area can exercise a voice in basin policy, should they wish to do so.

The membership of the policy-making entities for the Raymond, Main San Gabriel, Chino, and ULARA basins, however, is controlled by water producers alone. As noted in Chapter 8, this has already occasioned some controversy in the development of responses to groundwater contamination problems in the Main San Gabriel Basin. As primary attention turns to the safety and quality of the drinking water produced from the groundwater basins of southern California, some thought may need to be given to allowing people who do not have producing wells, but nevertheless have a close interest in basin conditions and use, to participate more directly in basin policy decisions.

Polycentricity, Entrepreneurship, and Innovation: Why They *Prefer* Chaos

The basin governance and management arrangements developed by the water producers in the Los Angeles, San Gabriel, Santa Ana River watersheds are not perfect. Mistakes were made along the way, two of which were probably fatal to the development of effective action on the Mojave River. Design flaws remain that could be remedied, and there are a few tendencies in the operation of the institutional arrangements that give reason for concern.

These errors and design flaws are more than offset by the effectiveness of the polycentric arrangements in overcoming serious problems of groundwater depletion, halting saltwater intrusion along the coast, and resolving upstream-downstream conflicts in seven of the eight cases studied. The effective systems in the Los Angeles, San Gabriel, and Santa Ana River watersheds are also generally equitable and adaptable, and tend toward efficiency. The water users prefer the "chaos" of these arrangements, not because they harbor some perverse preference for uncoordinated and ineffective management, but because the diverse systems they designed work reasonably well, and because they would rather govern their basins and watersheds themselves than have someone else do it for them or tell them what to do.

Concluding that the successes of the management systems developed by the water users of southern California more than compensate for their faults explains in part why these users *prefer* their ostensibly chaotic system. But there is more to be said here than simply, "the good outweighs the bad." There is another level of analysis that leads to the conclusion that an institutionally rich environment is preferable because of the way in which it operates, not just because of what it produces.

The diversity of an institutionally rich environment encourages innovation and experimentation. A society that is willing to let individuals and organizations pursue different ideas about solving problems or meeting demands is better off than a society that attempts to establish an optimal system "once and for all." Indeed, in a changeable world, optimal allocation decisions cannot be made either "once" *or* "for all."

The complex market systems of modern society are institutionally rich environments suited to innovation and entrepreneurial behavior. In the long run, this advantage of market systems is seen by some economists as more important than their tendencies toward efficiency or equilibrium (Nelson, 1987: 4). Markets offer entrepreneurs incentives to innovate, differentiate, and resuscitate. It is neither necessary nor useful to view markets as inducing all employments of capital to be efficient. Rather, functioning markets provide incentives to learn from and correct inefficient employments of capital: "A progressive economy is not an economy in which no capital is ever lost, but an economy which can afford to lose capital because the productive opportunities revealed by the loss are vigorously exploited" (Lachmann, 1978: 18).

This is neither an abstract nor a market-bound concept. For instance, one can think of groundwater lost from storage due to overuse as a capital loss. At the same time, the empty storage capacity represents an opportunity revealed by that loss. Water suppliers throughout the complex water economy of California (from the huge suppliers such as DWR and MWD to small suppliers such as the city of Sierra Madre in the Raymond Basin and the several participants in water storage agreements in the Chino Basin) have been devising and implementing ways to take advantage of that new opportunity for decades.

The economist Ludwig Lachmann sees close ties between innovation and diversity, which make diversity desirable for reasons that connect with the previous discussion of information and computation. What at first appears to be a digression on the demise of wholesalers in Lachmann's *Capital and Its Structure* becomes particularly instructive:

> Those economists that are in the habit of denouncing product differentiation as one of the "wastes of competition" and who extol standardization as the hallmark of efficiency, will welcome the decline of the wholesale merchant. They tell us that "distribution costs too much." But *their argument appears to depend on the curious assumption that progress has come to an end, that all possible methods of production and their relative merits are already known today by everybody concerned, and that no further knowledge is to be gained by product differentiation, experiment, and market observation.* . . . Others will doubt whether in a world of unexpected change the gains from standardization will outweigh the social loss. . . . There are "economies" which cost too much. (Lachmann, 1978: 64–65, emphasis added)

Nelson and Winter also contend that what is truly desirable (and sustainable) about market competition in the long run is its ability to "take advantage of, not repress, differences of opinion" (Nelson, 1987: 117) and to translate them into innovations. In a changing world, the notion of an efficient general equilibrium as the principal advantage of a competitive market fades away. What takes its place is the propensity of pluralist structures to encourage innovation.

The institutional diversity that may be viewed by some as a wasteful and inefficient practice perpetrated by wily public sector entrepreneurs on an unsuspecting public is thus seen in a different light. It represents a form of experimentation with institutional arrangements, the technology of collective problem solving. The fruits of that experimentation—the failures and the successes—feed back into the environment and enhance its institutional richness.

The greater information available in an institutionally rich environment is related to its greater innovation and experimentation. The information advantages and the innovation advantages of an institutionally rich environment are properly seen as two sides of the same coin. Consider not only the amount of innovation, but the amount of diffusion of innovation through learning and adaptation that occurred during the development of the institutional arrangements in the Los Angeles, San Gabriel, and Santa Ana River watersheds from the Raymond Basin to the Chino Basin. That diffusion of innovation was enhanced by the polycentricity of the governance and management arrangements. The membership of water users' associations overlapped, some districts overlapped, some individuals served as board members or staff members of agencies in more than one basin, attorneys and private engineers gained experience in several of the basins, and staff from the Los Angeles County Flood Control District, the California Department of Water Resources, and the U.S. Geological Survey provided information and assistance for most or all of the basins included in this study.

One can hardly imagine this level of activity and this extent of innovation, learning, adaptation, and modification if southern California groundwater management had been part of a "comprehensive" program adopted in, and directed from, Sacramento. Even with all the borrowing and adaptation that occurred between and among the basins and watersheds of the Los Angeles area, the fate of the mutual-prescription doctrine in the San Fernando Valley and the Mojave River Basin warn of the difficulties of applying one solution across several cases. Dangerous snares await those who assume on the basis of a few successes that a "magic bullet" has been found, that groundwater management has been "figured out," and all that remains is to implement the optimal program in the remaining basins.

The propensity of the California water industry for innovation and for diffusing its innovations has been evident during the drought that began in earnest in 1987. Responses to the drought have been prolific. Some districts and municipalities have distributed water conservation kits; others have offered residents rebates for the costs incurred in making water-saving improvements to their homes and businesses. In the summer of 1990, hard-hit Marin County in northern California offered residents rebates of up to $245 per household to rip out their lawns and replace them with drought-resistant plants. Districts and municipalities have experimented with voluntary and mandatory water conservation measures, varying by degrees in accordance with the severity of the community's water supply problems. As the drought worsened, MWD set conservation goals for its member agencies; they were offered rebates of up to $100 for each acre-foot of water conserved, or assessed penalties for failing to meet conservation goals. (Their response was so great MWD lost millions of dollars.) Coastal communities are experimenting with desalination technologies on varying scales of production. One interorganizational agreement among MWD, the Los Angeles Department of Water and Power, Southern California Edison Company, the San Diego County Water Authority, and the Mexican state of Baja California may lead to the construction of a large desalination plant in northern Mexico, if Edison and MWD work out their differences. New water reclamation plants are being constructed and existing plants expanded throughout the Coastal Plain and inland valleys: in some communities, dual water systems are being installed—one pipe system delivering fresh potable water for human consumption, the other delivering reclaimed water for landscape irrigation and other outdoor uses. Community by community, district by district, discussions of possibilities ranging from simple conservation measures to iceberg towing have occurred, and the more economically and technically feasible ideas are passing into practice.

In analyzing technical and economic change, Richard Nelson and Sidney Winter have recognized that the prolific innovativeness of competitive systems necessarily implies that bad ideas as well as good ideas are developed and tested. Some are huge successes, and others are colossal flops; most fall somewhere in between. Technological development generally takes place in a pluralistic environment, where several firms are engaged simultaneously in exploring and developing different alternatives. In this way of pursuing improvements in products and processes, some weeding out certainly occurs at the research-and-development stage, but more often "a number of different departures tend to pass into actual practice. . . . Put more generally, in capitalist economies the inherent uncertainties regarding innovation are resolved in large part by actual introduction and trial use of a wide variety of alternative departures" (Nelson, 1987: 8-9).

Similarly, the diversity and pluralism of institutionally rich environments such as federal systems in general and a metropolitan region like that of southern California in particular imply that different ideas about the solutions to collective problems or the provision of public services, and about institutional arrangements for accomplishing these aims, tend to pass into actual practice. Several ideas will be tried: some will fail, while others will succeed.

As Nelson acknowledges about the market: "With the vision of hindsight this looks like a very wasteful process. There ought to be a less costly way of finding out which of a set of alternatives is best other than actually building and trying each" (Nelson, 1987: 9). We could economize on a great deal of the costs and the capital losses involved in experimentation and product differentiation. We could avert the failures and have only the successes if we could know in advance which ideas and plans will succeed and which ideas will fail. We could solve problems "once and for all." We could even have a "comprehensive" groundwater basin management program that could be administered everywhere.

This, of course, is not our situation, regardless of how much we might wish it were. The world is changeable, problems are diverse and inter-related, and it is not at all clear that the savings we would realize from standardization would offset the social losses. Knowledge is imperfect, and human minds are limited—even the minds of experts. One way to attempt to deal with the problem of limitations on human minds is to set several minds to work on a problem. That is what a competitive market system does about the problem of developing better products and processes, and it seems so far to be preferable to waiting for one mind to develop the one best idea (Nelson and Winter, 1982: 366).

This analysis of the strengths of the disorderly market system as a process of developing better ways of doing things echoes Tocqueville's analysis of democracy as a means of organizing society. Tocqueville contrasts the more orderly government of the "single man" with the more uneven "government of all." After recognizing all the defects of the latter, Tocqueville explains why he nevertheless prefers it:

> When the opponents of democracy assert that a single man performs what he undertakes better than the government of all, it appears to me that they are right. The government of an individual, supposing an equality of knowledge on either side, is more consistent, more persevering, more uniform, and more accurate in details than that of a multitude, and it selects with more discrimination the men whom it employs. If any deny this, they have never seen a democratic government, or have judged upon partial evidence. . . . *Democratic liberty is far from accomplishing all its projects with the skill of an adroit despotism.* It frequently abandons them before they have borne their fruits, or risks them when the consequences may be dangerous; *but in the end it produces more than any absolute government; if it does fewer things well, it does a greater number of things. Under its sway the grandeur is not in what the public administration does, but in what is done without it or outside of it. Democracy does not give the people the most skillful government, but it produces what the ablest governments are frequently unable to create: namely, an all-pervading and restless activity, a superabundant force, and an energy which is inseparable from it and which may, however unfavorable circumstances may be, produce wonders. These are the true advantages of democracy.* (Tocqueville, 1945: I, 261–62, emphasis added)

Over the course of a hundred years in the groundwater basins of southern California, an institutionally rich environment has contributed to the intense efforts of several individuals, and their efforts have contributed to it. The polycentric governance structures and management programs they designed and applied are diverse and complex, and some work better than others. That on balance they have worked well is significant; that so much effort has been applied to the tasks and that so much has been attempted is even more significant. In a changeable and challenging world, those are true advantages indeed.

An Integrated Chronology
of the Eight Cases

1769   Expedition led by Don Gaspar de Portola, Spanish governor of California, camps in Santa Ana Valley, naming the river and valley in honor of St. Anne; Portola expedition camps at future site of the pueblo of Los Angeles, and in the San Fernando Valley.

1771   Fra Junipero Serra establishes Mission San Gabriel; earliest recorded use of waters of the San Gabriel River watershed.

1776   Expedition of Fra Francisco Garces from the Colorado River to Mission San Gabriel; Garces expedition reaches Mojave Indian Trail along the Mojave River; Garces expedition reaches Chino Basin floor at Cucamonga Creek.

1781   El Pueblo de Nuestra la Reina de Los Angeles de Porciuncula established, with an area of four square leagues and a population of forty-six persons.

1797   Mission San Fernando established.

1810   Jose Antonio Yorba receives first Spanish land grant in the area, at the confluence of Santiago Creek and the Santa Ana River.

1821   Water from the San Gabriel River first diverted, through a dirt ditch to Mission San Gabriel.

1822   Spanish rule over California ends; Mexican governance begins.

1826   Jedediah Strong Smith crosses the Mojave Desert, giving the river the name Inconstant.

1837   Establishment of ranchos under way in Santa Ana River watershed.

1843   First permanent diversion of water from the San Gabriel River.

1844   John Fremont leads an expedition into the Mojave Desert, giving the river the name Mohave River.

1848   United States acquires California from Mexico, under the Treaty of Guadalupe Hidalgo.

1850   California admitted to the Union as a state; Los Angeles incorporated as a city, with a population of 1,610.

1857   Anaheim founded by German settlers.

1861   Severe flooding of the Coastal Plain.

1863   Great Drought of 1863–64 ends dominance of land holdings by rancheros in Santa Ana River watershed; smaller holdings develop thereafter.

1868   A. B. Chapman and Andrew Glassell receive 40 acres of land in future Orange County, in payment of attorneys' fees; they begin the town of Richland there (name changed to Orange in 1875).

1869   Santa Ana founded by William Spurgeon.

1870   Water users in the vicinity of the Newport-Inglewood Uplift tap artesian wells and springs, primarily for agricultural use; first drill rigs and deep pumps introduced in southern California, allowing access to groundwater supplies in nonartesian areas; first local orange trees raised in Anaheim area; James Irvine begins acquiring land for the original 172-square-mile Irvine Ranch; in Mojave River Basin, the Thirty-Fifth Parallel Association purchases 30,000 acres from the United States in the upstream area just below The Forks of the Mojave River.

1871   San Jose Water District formed in upper San Gabriel Valley, after petition to the Los Angeles County Board of Supervisors by settlers in the Azusa-Duarte area.

1872   First recorded appropriation of water from the Mojave River.

1873   William Spurgeon drills a 340-foot well and constructs a 2,500-gallon storage tank, which serves as the town water works for Santa Ana.

1879   City of Los Angeles acts to destroy ditches of upstream irrigators, who respond by suing the city; City of Anaheim taps an artesian well for municipal supply to supplement private wells during the dry season.

1880   Southern California land development boom begins.

1880s   Landowners on northern side of the Santa Ana River in the vicinity of Santa Ana sue southside users to establish a predominant claim to Santa Ana River water; trial court judgment favors northside users but is reversed by the California Supreme Court on the basis of the riparian right of the Rancho de Santiago de Santa Ana downstream.

1881   First well drilled in Raymond Basin; California Supreme Court holds for City of Los Angeles in *Feliz v. Los Angeles* and *Elms v. Los Angeles*.

1884   Another severe flooding of the Coastal Plain; possible to row a boat overland from Santa Ana to Los Angeles.

1886   In Mojave River Basin, Hesperia Land and Water Company organized; Waterman Junction renamed Barstow.

1889   Orange County established after favorable vote on the question of Orange/Los Angeles County division; in the upper San Gabriel River Valley, Compromise of 1889 established in response to disputes over San Gabriel River waters, San Gabriel River Water Committee (Committee of Nine) formed.

1890   First irrigation districts organized in Chino Basin.

1891   Arrowhead Reservoir Company formed in upper Mojave River area to capture the waters of Deep Creek.

1895   Beginning of severe drought period, lasting until 1904; first water spreading along San Antonio Creek in western portion of Chino Basin; *Vernon Irrigation Co. v. Los Angeles* decided by California Supreme Court; Columbian

Colonization Company organized to irrigate lands in Mojave River Valley below Victorville.

1899   *City of Los Angeles v. Pomeroy* decided by California Supreme Court.

1902   Publication of J. B. Lippincott's studies of water development in the upper Santa Ana River area for U.S. Geological Survey; city of Los Angeles takes over operation of its municipal water supply system; Los Angeles Department of Water and Power established.

1904   Drought completes its tenth year; United States Geological Survey reports over 100 producing wells in West Basin, shrinkage of artesian area, lowered underground water elevations; Los Angeles Board of Water Commissioners votes support of an aqueduct project to bring Owens Valley water to Los Angeles.

1905   Los Angeles voters approve first Owens Valley aqueduct bond issue for land purchases and project design; publication of W. C. Mendenhall's study of hydrology of the San Bernardino Valley for U.S. Geological Survey.

1906   City of Glendale incorporated; Congress and the president award Los Angeles free right-of-way through public lands for construction of aqueduct from Owens Valley.

1907   Los Angeles voters approve second aqueduct bond issue for construction; Orange, Riverside, and San Bernardino counties form the Tri-Counties Reforestation Committee.

1908   U.S. Geological Survey report on Raymond Basin published, showing 141 wells in operation; Santa Ana River rechanneled; early water spreading on Cucamonga Creek in northern portion of Chino Basin; *City of Los Angeles v. Los Angeles Farming and Milling Company* decided by California Supreme Court.

1909   *City of Los Angeles v. Hunter* and *City of Los Angeles v. Buffington* decided by California Supreme Court; Orange, Riverside, and San Bernardino counties form the Water Conservation Association; Arrowhead Reservoir and Power Company organized to assume Arrowhead Reservoir Company's property in upper Mojave River area.

1910   Mojave River Land and Water Company organized to develop lands northeast of Yermo; Cleveland National Forest, a preserve of 390,000 acres, formed for protection of lower Santa Ana River watershed.

1911   Tri-county Water Conservation Association begins water spreading on Santa Ana River; city of Burbank incorporated; city of San Fernando incorporated; Quinton, Code, and Hamlin report on terminus location and distribution system for the Los Angeles Aqueduct issued; Appleton Land, Water, and Power Company organized to take over Hesperia Land and Water Company's water supply system in upper Mojave River area.

1912   Southern California Edison Company abandons Redondo Beach well in West Basin because of saltwater intrusion.

1913   Overdraft of Raymond Basin begins; Los Angeles Aqueduct completed, Los Angeles begins importing Owens River water; San Fernando Valley annexed to city of Los Angeles (except Glendale, Burbank, and San Fernando); Municipal Water District Act and California Water District

Act adopted; Mojave River area settlers form the Victor Valley Mutual Water and Power District Association.

1914   City of Pasadena Water Department initiates water spreading in Raymond Basin.

1915   Hesperia Water Company organized in Mojave River area.

1916   Another flood inundates the Coastal Plain; Mojave River Land and Water Company reorganized as Yermo Mutual Water Company.

1917   Victor Valley Irrigation District formed to irrigate lands in the Baldy Mesa area southwest of Victorville; Mojave River Irrigation District formed to irrigate lands in Apple Valley.

1918   Los Angeles begins pumping groundwater in Owens Valley to augment surface supplies conveyed by Los Angeles Aqueduct.

1920   Beginning of continuing overdraft in West Basin; water levels below sea level at wells along the Pacific coast; water producers note receding water levels in wells in Orange County; San Gabriel Valley Protective Association incorporated.

1920s Early signs of saltwater intrusion along the coast in Orange County.

1922   Wells in El Segundo area of West Basin are shut down because of saltwater intrusion.

1923   Los Angeles begins diverting water from Mono Basin streams into Los Angeles Aqueduct; city of Pasadena purchases all claims to flood waters of the San Gabriel River.

1924   Los Angeles granted rights to 1,500 cubic feet per second of Colorado River water.

1925   J. B. Lippincott report on conditions in the Orange County section of the Santa Ana River watershed issued.

1927   Another flood prompts formation of Orange County Flood Control District.

1928   Metropolitan Water District of Southern California (MWD) established by thirteen southern California cities.

1929   Study for new Metropolitan Water District (MWD) concludes West Basin being invaded by Pacific Ocean water; U.S. Geological Survey publishes David G. Thompson's report, *The Mohave Desert Region*.

1931   City of Inglewood study reports long-term threats from falling water levels and saltwater encroachment in West Basin; Orange County Farm Bureau requests state legislators to seek the formation of a district for conservation and replenishment of the basin; Chino Basin Protective Association formed by individuals and corporations in the basin; San Bernardino Valley Water Conservation District organized; California Legislature appropriates $400,000 for water conservation and flood control in Santa Ana River watershed; Los Angeles begins spreading of Owens Valley-Mono Basin waters in San Fernando Valley; state of California approves Pasadena's plans for a dam site on the San Gabriel River; San Gabriel Valley Protective Association files suit to enjoin Pasadena's dam; agreement entered into by San Gabriel Valley Protective Association, city of Pasadena, U.S. Geological Survey, U.S. Department of Agriculture's Bureau of Agricultural Engineering, and Los Angeles County Flood

Control District for construction and installation of a key well in the
Baldwin Park area of the upper San Gabriel Valley.

1932   Irvine Company in Orange County files suit against water users in the
upper part of the Santa Ana River watershed.

1933   Orange County Water District established; Los Angeles sues Burbank
for declaratory and injunctive relief.

1934   Settlement of Morris Dam controversy between Pasadena and San Gabriel
Valley Protective Association; California Department of Public Works
publishes Bulletin no. 45, *South Coastal Basin Investigation*, and Bulletin
no. 47, *Mojave River Investigation*.

1936   Los Angeles sues Glendale for declaratory and injunctive relief; case consolidated with Burbank suit.

1937   City of Pasadena initiates legal action against other Raymond Basin water
producers; agreement entered into between the San Gabriel Valley Protective Association and the Los Angeles County Flood Control District
for the conservation and spreading of flood flows of the San Gabriel River
and the Rio Hondo, and for measurement of the water table in 100 wells
in the San Gabriel Valley; San Gabriel River Spreading Corporation
organized.

1938   Most destructive flood ever in the Coastal Plain; Los Angeles County
Flood Control District initiates spreading of flood waters in Montebello
Forebay in Central Basin; Orange County Water District Act amended,
more territory included.

1939   Superior Court appoints Department of Public Works as Referee in
Raymond Basin litigation; trial of the *Los Angeles v. Glendale* and *Burbank*
cases, with appeal taken to California Supreme Court; San Bernardino
County Flood Control District established.

1940   Los Angeles Aqueduct extended further into Mono Basin watershed.

1941   First Colorado River water deliveries from MWD arrive in Los Angeles
County; Prado Dam on the Santa Ana River completed by the Army
Corps of Engineers.

1942   Irvine Company's Santa Ana River adjudication settled with an agreement governing upstream spreading activities; Los Angeles County Flood
Control District Chief Engineer and Manhattan Beach City Engineer correspond regarding saltwater intrusion in West Basin and initiate contacts
with other West Basin water producers; continuing overdraft begins in
Central Basin, as groundwater production exceeds 200,000 acre-feet.

1943   Referee's report filed in Raymond Basin litigation; stipulated agreement
reached among Raymond Basin producers; California Supreme Court
decision in the *Los Angeles v. Glendale and Burbank* cases; West Basin Survey
Committee formed, contracts with U.S. Geological Survey to study
groundwater conditions and prospects.

1944   Trial of *Pasadena v. Alhambra*; Raymond Basin Judgment issued; beginning of watermaster service for Raymond Basin.

1945   *Pasadena v. Alhambra* judgment appealed; West Basin Ground Water Conservation Group replaces West Basin Survey Committee, appoints Ways
and Means Committee to organize report for West Basin producers; West

Basin Ways and Means Committee report and recommendations published and distributed; West Basin water rights adjudication initiated by California Water Service Co., Palos Verdes Water Co., and City of Torrance.

1946   West Basin Water Association established, succeeding West Basin Ground Water Conservation Group; West Basin Water Association appoints Engineering Advisory Committee to aid in West Basin adjudication; Order of Reference issued to Division of Water Resources to act as referee in West Basin adjudication; Los Angeles County Supervisor organizes Southwest Water Fact-Finding Committee, later renamed West Basin Campaign Committee, to organize formation in West Basin of a municipal water district to annex to MWD to secure imported water supplies.

1947   District Court of Appeal reverses and remands *Pasadena v. Alhambra*; California Department of Public Works publishes Bulletin no. 53, *South Coastal Basin Investigation: Overdraft on Ground Water Basins*; first special election on formation of West Basin Municipal Water District results in defeat; second special election for formation of smaller West Basin Municipal Water District carries.

1948   West Basin Municipal Water District (WBMWD) annexes to MWD, Gardena annexes to WBMWD; Orange County Water District begins purchases of MWD water from the Colorado Aqueduct for artificial replenishment.

1949   California Supreme Court affirms *Pasadena v. Alhambra*; City of Compton convenes meeting of Central Basin cities to discuss groundwater conditions; city of Long Beach reports appearance of saltwater intrusion in Central Basin, on inland side of Newport-Inglewood Uplift; Chino Basin Water Conservation District established to succeed the Chino Basin Protective Association; amended complaint in West Basin suit names 340 additional parties; MWD water deliveries to West Basin Municipal Water District, and to Chino Basin, begin.

1950   Central Basin Water Association formed, requests investigation of Basin conditions by State Water Resources Board; experimental injection well operates successfully at Manhattan Beach in West Basin; Los Angeles County Flood District Act amended to allow creation of Conservation Zones within the District; city of Pasadena requests redetermination of Raymond Basin safe yield; Pomona Valley Municipal Water District (now Three Valleys Municipal Water District) formed and annexed to MWD; Chino Basin Municipal Water District formed.

1951   Second Santa Ana River adjudication begins, as Orange County Water District sues four upstream cities (Riverside, San Bernardino, Colton, and Redlands) over use of groundwater of the Santa Ana River watershed; Chino Basin Municipal Water District annexes to MWD; state of California appropriates $750,000 for prototype injection barrier in West Basin.

1952   First referee's report issued in West Basin adjudication; West Basin Water Association forms Legal Settlement Committee for West Basin adjudication; construction of prototype injection barrier in West Basin begins; Los Angeles County Flood Control District Zone I created to finance artificial replenishment at Montebello Forebay in Central Basin; California State Water Resources Board Central Basin Investigation report published,

Central Basin Water Association distributes report to Central Basin water producers; Central Basin Water Association campaigns for formation of a municipal water district to annex to MWD; Central Basin Municipal Water District formed; Foothill Municipal Water District formed in Raymond Basin; in Orange County, joint meeting of local water committees and the Orange County Water District Board to discuss increasing purchases of MWD water for replenishment of the basin; Orange County Committee of 12 formed to formulate a water management plan; city of Inglewood and Dominguez area annexed to West Basin Municipal Water District.

1953   Foothill Municipal Water District annexed to MWD; recommendations of Orange County Committee of 12 for amendments to the Orange County Water District Act adopted by the state legislature; Orange County Water District gains more territory, pump tax authority, and authority to require registration of all wells and reporting of groundwater production; injections at prototype West Basin barrier begin; city of Hawthorne annexed to West Basin Municipal Water District.

1954   Draft interim agreement for pumping reduction presented to parties in West Basin adjudication; program of artificial replenishment at Montebello Forebay begins; Los Angeles County Flood Control District Zone II created to finance West Basin barrier; Central and West Basin Committee of 12 drafts Water Recordation Act and Water Replenishment District Act; water producers from the Upper and Lower areas of the San Gabriel River watershed meet in Azusa; Central Basin Municipal Water District annexed to MWD; Western Municipal Water District of Riverside County formed and annexed to MWD; San Bernardino Valley Municipal Water District formed.

1955   Safe yield of Raymond Basin redetermined; Raymond Basin judgment modified to increase the decreed rights of parties; interim agreement in West Basin adjudication presented to court; court in West Basin adjudication issues ex parte order requiring signers to comply with pumping reduction, establishing watermaster service, and beginning water exchange pool; city of Los Angeles files action against Cities of San Fernando, Glendale, and Burbank, and other parties in the Upper Los Angeles River Area (ULARA); state of California enacts Water Recordation Act and Water District Act; MWD Colorado River water deliveries to Central Basin Municipal Water District begin; Upper San Gabriel Valley Water Association formed; Cucamonga County Water District formed.

1956   Reference Continuance ordered in West Basin suit; Second West Basin water rights suit, American Plant Growers case, initiated against new pumpers.

1957   Judge in West Basin adjudications disqualifies himself, voiding all orders and halting operation of interim agreement and reference continuance; second Santa Ana River adjudication (Orange County Water District suit against the four upstream cities) tried, and judgment entered.

1958   New judge reinstates previous orders in West Basin adjudications; State Water Rights Board ordered to investigate and report on physical facts in the *Los Angeles v. San Fernando* case.

1959   San Gabriel River adjudication begins with suit against Upper San Gabriel
        Valley water producers initiated by city of Long Beach, city of Compton,
        and Central Basin Municipal Water District; special election to form Cen-
        tral and West Basin Water Replenishment District (CWBWRD), forma-
        tion passes; second draft referee's report in West Basin adjudication
        circulated; West Basin Water Association Legal Settlement Committee
        begins work on stipulated judgment; Alhambra, Azusa, Monterey Park,
        and Sierra Madre form the San Gabriel Valley Municipal Water District;
        Upper San Gabriel Valley Municipal Water District formed following
        special election; Mojave Water Agency Law enacted by state of California;
        public hearing held on formation of the Mojave Water Agency.

1960   Mojave Water Agency organized, after favorable vote of residents on
        agency establishment and issuance of revenue bonds; draft stipulation
        for West Basin adjudication presented to West Basin Water Association,
        circulated for signatures; negotiating committees organized in the San
        Gabriel River adjudication; city of Pasadena sues East Pasadena Water
        Company for failure to join and comply with Raymond Basin judgment.

1961   Stipulation in West Basin adjudication presented to court, judgment
        entered; Hawthorne appeal of West Basin Judgment begins; Central and
        West Basin Water Replenishment District begins operations, assesses first
        pump tax; Joint Engineering Reconnaissance Study report for San Gabriel
        River adjudication completed; principles of settlement signed by nego-
        tiating committees for Upper and Lower areas in San Gabriel River
        adjudication; Central Basin Water Association Board adopts resolution
        supporting an adjudication of water rights in Central Basin.

1962   Central and West Basin Water Replenishment District initiates adjudica-
        tion of Central Basin water rights; replenishment district engineer begins
        compiling production histories in Central Basin; Central Basin Water
        Association appoints settlement committee, which presents draft interim
        agreement to the association and the parties; signed interim agreement
        for Central Basin adjudication presented to the court, which enjoins
        signers to reduce pumping and appoints watermaster; referee's report
        (both volumes) of State Water Rights Board in *Los Angeles v. San Fernando*
        presented to court and parties; Los Angeles County Board of Supervisors
        authorizes Flood Control District to begin barrier project at Alamitos Gap
        using Zone I funds; Whittier Narrows Reclamation Plant begins supply-
        ing reclaimed wastewater to Central and West Basin Water Replenish-
        ment District.

1963   Third Santa Ana River adjudication begins, as Orange County Water
        District files complaint seeking adjudication of water rights of substan-
        tially all users in the Santa Ana River watershed tributary to Prado Dam;
        Mojave Water Agency enters contract with state of California for State
        Water Project entitlements; Mojave Water Agency receives report of
        Woodward, Clyde, Sherard and Associates, *Geological Study for the Pro-
        posed Mojave Water Agency*; Upper San Gabriel Valley Municipal Water
        District annexed to MWD.

1964   James Krieger retained as Special Legal Counsel to the Mojave Water Agency; public meeting held on issue of water rights determination in the Mojave River area; Hawthorne appeal of West Basin judgment ends unsuccessfully; Central Basin Water Association settlement committee completes draft of stipulated judgment for Central Basin adjudication; settlement agreement reached between negotiating committees in San Gabriel River adjudication; additional studies of ULARA subareas presented to the court.

1965   Stipulation among Central Basin parties presented to the court, Central Basin judgment entered; stipulated judgment in San Gabriel River adjudication presented to the court, judgment entered; city of Pasadena's suit against East Pasadena Water Company settled; Mojave Water Agency Special Committee on Water Development and Working Committee on Water Development formed to discuss water rights determination; program of verification of well records in the Mojave River area begins; Yucca Valley/Joshua Tree area annexed to Mojave Water Agency; Alamitos Gap Barrier Project begins operation; San Gabriel River Spreading Corporation dissolved.

1966   Mojave Water Agency files complaint initiating case of *Mojave Water Agency v. Clarence Abbey et al.*; MWA Working Committee on Water Development produces brochure titled "Mojave Water Agency Water Program"; trial of *Los Angeles v. San Fernando* case begins; stipulated judgment entered in second West Basin adjudication (American Plant Growers case).

1967   Trial of *Los Angeles v. San Fernando* completed; judge files memorandum of decision in the *Los Angeles v. San Fernando* case; construction of Orange County Coastal Barrier Project begins at Talbert Gap; Mojave Water Agency Law amended; California Department of Water Resources publishes its Bulletin no. 84, *Mojave River Ground Water Basins Investigation*; San Jose Creek Reclamation Plant begins supplying reclaimed waste water to Central and West Basin Water Replenishment District.

1968   Main San Gabriel Basin adjudication begins; findings of fact, conclusions of law, and judgment entered in the *Los Angeles v. San Fernando* case; settlement of the Orange County Water District action for adjudication of rights in the Santa Ana River watershed; Santa Ana River Watermaster created; Talbert Gap Unit of the Orange County Coastal Barrier Project operational; Orange County Water District Act amended by state legislature to give the district the authority to determine a basin production percentage and assess a basin equity assessment.

1969   City of Los Angeles files opening briefs on appeal in the *Los Angeles v. San Fernando* case; floods in the Mojave River area damage surface structures but recharge the underground water supply.

1970   Mojave Water Agency files a second complaint against additional defendants, cases consolidated as *Mojave Water Agency v. Abbey and Allison et al.*; demurrers overruled and defaults entered in Mojave River adjudication, motion for reference denied, notice of trial filed; Los Angeles completes second barrel of Los Angeles Aqueduct, increasing capacity to 565,000 acre-feet per year.

1971   Army Corps of Engineers completes Forksite Dam on Mojave River; Mojave Water Agency enters into contract with Southern California Edison Co.; Dominguez Gap Barrier Project begins operation; defendants file respondents' brief on appeal with the Court of Appeal in the *Los Angeles v. San Fernando* case.

1972   Construction of the Mojave Division of the State Water Project completed, water deliveries to Silverwood Lake begin; Court of Appeal holds hearing in *Los Angeles v. San Fernando*, and issues unanimous decision reversing the trial court judgment; Los Angeles County Flood Control District Conservation Zones expire, not renewed by County Board of Supervisors.

1973   Judgment entered in Main San Gabriel Basin adjudication; Main San Gabriel Basin Watermaster established; defendants file petitions for hearing in California Supreme Court in *Los Angeles v. San Fernando*, petitions granted; MWA enters into contract with Edison for pipeline construction and imported water sales; Carl Coleman removed as Mojave Water Agency Manager; Improvement District no. 1 formed within Mojave Water Agency, to raise funds for regional wastewater reclamation facility.

1974   Stetson Engineers issues *Report on Review of Overdraft of the Mojave River Basin*; two Mojave Water Agency Board members replaced in recall elections; Southern California Water Company requests and receives removal from Stipulation for Judgment in the Mojave River adjudication, and files an answer and cross-complaint; Mojave Water Agency Board votes to drop water rights adjudication; modification of Raymond Basin judgment allows parties credit for spreading and begins studies of pumping patterns; in Main San Gabriel Basin, first cyclic storage agreements between watermaster and San Gabriel Valley Municipal Water District, and between watermaster and Metropolitan Water District, executed; Upper San Gabriel Valley Municipal Water District and San Gabriel Valley Municipal Water District begin joint Area-Wide Water Quality Monitoring Program for the Main San Gabriel Basin.

1975   California Supreme Court holds hearing in *Los Angeles v. San Fernando*, and issues unanimous opinion; complaint filed beginning Chino Basin adjudication; Senate Bill 222 passes California Legislature, authorizing collection of pump tax to fund studies of groundwater basin overdraft and development of basin management plan for Chino Basin; Santa Ana Watershed Project Authority (SAWPA) established; Improvement District B formed within Mojave Water Agency to build extension water system to northwest Barstow; Hesperia Water District formed.

1976   Southern California Water Company withdraws cross-complaint; *Mojave Water Agency v. Abbey and Allison et al.* dismissed; Mojave Water Agency Board seeks declaratory relief from Edison contract.

1977   Deliveries of State Project water suspended due to severe statewide drought; stipulated agreements among parties on remand in *Los Angeles v. San Fernando* provide for continued extractions, continued watermaster service by Department of Water Resources, and temporary mining of groundwater to cope with drought; Mojave Water Agency and California

Department of Water Resources undertake development of a comprehensive general plan for water supply within the Agency.

1978   Chino Basin adjudication completed, with Chino Basin Municipal Water District named Watermaster; significant flooding in the Mojave River area again damages property but recharges underground water supplies; MWD institutes in-lieu replenishment program, which continues through 1981; Mojave Water Agency Board of Directors reduced to seven members, all elected from voting divisions within the agency; Mojave Water Agency purchases 22,500 acre-feet of State Water project surplus water for replenishment.

1979   Discovery of volatile organic contaminants in Main San Gabriel Basin; final judgment entered in *Los Angeles v. San Fernando*; ULARA Watermaster responsibilities transferred from Department of Water Resources to Melvin Blevins; Orange County Water District Act amended to allow greater funding flexibility as a result of reduced ad valorem revenue (due to Proposition 13 in 1978), allowing district operations to be funded with replenishment assessment collections.

1980   Los Angeles Department of Water and Power and California Department of Health Services discover TCE and PCE in water supply wells in ULARA.

1981   California Department of Water Resources publishes report, *Alternative Water Supply Plans for the Mojave Water Agency*; work begins on Groundwater Quality Management Plan for San Fernando Valley.

1982   MWD begins new, "interruptible" water-pricing program; Mojave Water Agency receives C M Engineers' *Report on Historic and Present Conditions in the Newberry Groundwater Basin*; city of Barstow initiates its program for growing crops with treated wastewater.

1983   Mojave Water Agency purchases 24,489 acre-feet of State Water Project surplus for replenishment, using a one-time acquisition charge on land; work completed on Groundwater Quality Management Plan for San Fernando Valley, with Interagency Coordinating Committee formed to oversee implementation; ULARA Watermaster reports to court that Sylmar Subarea is in overdraft condition; Mojave Water Agency receives C M Engineers' *Report on Historic and Present Conditions: Helendale Fault to Calico-Newberry Fault*.

1984   Modification of Raymond Basin Judgment assigns watermaster responsibilities to Raymond Basin Management Board; U.S. Environmental Protection Agency (EPA) designates superfund sites in Main San Gabriel Basin; SAWPA and the EPA contract for cleanup of Stringfellow toxic waste site; judge signs stipulated agreement between cities of Los Angeles and San Fernando restricting pumping in the Sylmar subarea; first year for transfer of unallocated safe yield water from agricultural pool to appropriative pool in Chino Basin; Mojave Water Agency receives report of John S. Murk Engineers, *Final Local Water Management Alternatives: Newberry Groundwater Basin*.

1985   Removal of contaminated wastewater at Stringfellow Acid Pits in Santa Ana River watershed begins; Mojave Water Agency receives report of

John S. Murk Engineers, *Final Local Water Management Alternatives: Barstow Area Groundwater Sub-Basins* and *Historic and Present Conditions: Upper Mojave River Basin.*

1986   Ron Barto and Associates issue report for San Bernardino County on water conditions in the Newberry Springs area; Mojave Water Agency receives report of John S. Murk Engineers, *Final Local Water Management Alternatives: Upper Mojave River Basin*; Mojave Water Agency issues *Report on Phase I Investigation: Morongo Basin Pipeline Project*; Army Corps of Engineers rejects plan to install gates in Forks Dam.

1987   *Morongo Basin Joint Powers Authority Project Consulting Report* issued; Mojave Water Agency indicates approval of plans to sell aqueduct water to Las Flores Ranch Group through a retailer; ULARA policies and procedures revised to allow for nonconsumptive pumping by nonparties for testing, cleanup, and long-term dewatering, without altering parties' pumping rights.

1988   Some Chino Basin water users begin legal proceedings for review of Chino Basin Watermaster's performance; Mojave Water Agency places Morongo Basin pipeline funding on ballot, then removes funding initiative from ballot before November election; Barstow city officials file suit against Mojave Water Agency to enjoin sale of water to Las Flores Ranch Group; Victorville City Council expresses support for an adjudication of water rights along the Mojave River.

1989   Ad hoc committee in Chino Basin begins work on socioeconomic and other studies toward development of an Optimum Basin Management Plan.

Bibliography

Alchian, Armen. 1950. "Uncertainty, Evolution, and Economic Theory." *Journal of Political Economy* 58, no. 3: 211–21.

Anderson, Jay M. 1977. "A Model of the Commons." In *Managing the Commons,* ed. Garrett Hardin and John Baden, 38–41. San Francisco: W. H. Freeman.

Anderson, Terry. 1983. "The Water Crisis and the New Resource Economics." In *Water Rights,* ed. Terry Anderson, 1–9. San Francisco: Pacific Institute for Public Policy Research.

———. 1983. *Water Crisis: Ending the Policy Drought.* Washington, D.C.: Cato Institute.

Anderson, Terry, Oscar Burt, and David Fractor. 1983. "Privatizing Groundwater Basins: A Model and Its Application." In *Water Rights,* ed. Terry Anderson, 233–48. San Francisco: Pacific Institute for Public Policy Research.

Anderson, Terry L., and Peter J. Hill. 1983. "Privatizing the Commons: An Improvement?" *Southern Economic Journal* 50, no. 2: 438–50.

Association of California Water Agencies. 1985. *ACWA's 75-Year History.* Sacramento.

Axelrod, Robert. 1970. *Conflict of Interest.* Chicago: Markham.

———. 1981. "The Emergence of Cooperation among Egoists." *American Political Science Review* 75, no. 2: 306–18.

Baden, John. 1977. "A Primer for the Management of Common Pool Resources." In *Managing the Commons,* ed. Garrett Hardin and John Baden, 137–46. San Francisco: W. H. Freeman.

Bader, J. S., and W. R. Moyle. 1958. *Data on Water Wells and Springs in Morongo Valley and Vicinity, San Bernardino and Riverside Counties, California.* Long Beach, Calif.: U.S. Geological Survey.

Bader, J. S., et al. 1958. *Data on Water Wells in the Upper Mojave Valley Area, San Bernardino County, California.* Long Beach, Calif.: U.S. Geological Survey.

Bain, Joe, S., Richard E. Caves, and Julius Margolis. 1966. *Northern California's Water Industry: The Comparative Efficiency of Public Enterprises in Developing a Scarce Natural Resource.* Baltimore: Johns Hopkins University Press.

Bancroft, Hubert Howe. 1890. *History of California.* Vol. 7: *1860–1890.* San Francisco: History Co.

Banks, Harvey. 1962. "Salt Water Intrusion in Ground Water Supplies." In *Ground Water Problems in California,* A11–A17. Sacramento: California Assembly Interim Committee on Water.

———. 1981. "Management of Interstate Aquifer Systems." *ASCE Journal of the Water Resources Planning and Management Division* 107, no. WR2: 563–77.

Beaver, J. A., and M. L. Frankel. 1969. "Significance of Ground-Water Management Strategy—A Systems Approach." *Ground Water* 7, no. 3: 22–26.

Bendor, Jonathan, and Dilip Mookherjee. 1985. "Institutional Structure and the Logic of Ongoing Collective Action." Stanford University Working Paper. Stanford University, Department of Economics. Stanford, Calif.

Berlien, Robert G. 1988. "An Early History of the Upper San Gabriel Valley Municipal Water District." El Monte, Calif.

Bickelmann, Christina, et al. 1987. *Mojave River Basin: Design for Desert Water Management.* Pomona: California State Polytechnic University, Department of Landscape Architecture.

Bird, John W. 1986a. "Water Resources and the Public Trust Doctrine." *Journal of Water Resources Planning and Management* 112, no. 1: 54–70.

———. 1986b. "Implications of Sporhase in Water-Resource Planning." *Journal of Water Resources Planning and Management* 112, no. 2: 198–204.

Birdlebough, Stephen C., and Alfred Wilkins. 1971. "Legal Aspects of Conjunctive Use in California." In *California Water: A Study in Resource Management,* ed. David Seckler, 263–70. Berkeley: University of California Press.

Bish, Robert. 1977. "Environmental Resource Management: Public or Private?" In *Managing the Commons,* ed. Garrett Hardin and John Baden, 217–28. San Francisco: W. H. Freeman.

Bish, Robert, and Vincent Ostrom. 1973. *Understanding Urban Government.* Washington, D.C.: American Enterprise Institute.

Blackburn, Duncan. 1961. "The Adjudication of the Raymond Basin." Paper presented at the Southern California Water Coordinating Conference, Pasadena, Calif.

Blevins, Melvin L. 1975. "*City of Los Angeles vs. City of San Fernando Et Al.*— Landmark Decision in California Water Law Annals." Paper presented at the Tenth Biennial Conference on Ground Water, Ventura, Calif.

———. 1978. "The Courts and Management of a Groundwater Basin." Paper presented at the Los Angeles Section of the American Society of Civil Engineers, Los Angeles, Calif.

Blomquist, William. 1987a. "Getting Out of the Trap: Changing an Endangered Commons to a Managed Commons." Ph.D. diss. Bloomington: Indiana University.

——. 1987b. *The Performance of Institutions for Groundwater Management*. Vol. 1: *Raymond Basin*. Bloomington, Ind.: Workshop in Political Theory and Policy Analysis.

——. 1988a. *The Performance of Institutions for Groundwater Management*. Vol. 2: *West Basin*. Bloomington, Ind.: Workshop in Political Theory and Policy Analysis.

——. 1988b. *The Performance of Institutions for Groundwater Management*. Vol. 3: *Central Basin*. Bloomington, Ind.: Workshop in Political Theory and Policy Analysis.

——. 1988c. *The Performance of Institutions for Groundwater Management*. Vol. 5: *Orange County*. Bloomington, Ind.: Workshop in Political Theory and Policy Analysis.

——. 1988d. *The Performance of Institutions for Groundwater Management*. Vol. 6: *The San Fernando Valley*. Bloomington, Ind.: Workshop in Political Theory and Policy Analysis.

——. 1989. *The Performance of Institutions for Groundwater Management*. Vol. 8: *The Mojave River Basin*. Bloomington, Ind.: Workshop in Political Theory and Policy Analysis.

——. 1990a. *The Performance of Institutions for Groundwater Management*. Vol. 4: *The San Gabriel Valley*. Bloomington, Ind.: Workshop in Political Theory and Policy Analysis.

——. 1990b. *The Performance of Institutions for Groundwater Management*. Vol. 7: *The Chino Basin*. Bloomington, Ind.: Workshop in Political Theory and Policy Analysis.

——. 1990c. "Groundwater Management Through Interjurisdictional Coordination." Paper presented at the Seventh Annual Donald G. Hagman Commemorative Conference, University of California at Los Angeles.

Blomquist, William, and Elinor Ostrom. 1985. "Institutional Capacity and the Resolution of a Commons Dilemma." *Policy Studies Review* 5, no. 2: 383–93.

Bowden, Gerald, Starhl Edmunds, and Norris Hundley. 1982. "Institutions: Customs, Laws and Organizations." In *Competition for California Water*, ed. Ernest A. Engelbert, 163–82. Berkeley: University of California Press.

Brajer, Victor, and Wade E. Martin. 1989. "Allocating a 'Scarce' Resource, Water in the West." *American Journal of Economics and Sociology* 48, no. 3: 259–71.

Bredehoeft, John D., and Robert A. Young. 1983. "Conjunctive Use of Groundwater and Surface Water for Irrigated Agriculture: Risk Aversion." *Water Resources Research* 19, no. 5: 1111–21.

Briggs, Philip C. 1983. "Ground-Water Management in Arizona." *Journal of Water Resources Planning and Management* 109, no. 3: 195–202.

Bromley, Daniel W. 1989. *Economic Interests and Institutions: The Conceptual Foundations of Public Policy*. New York: Basil Blackwell.

Bruington, A. E. 1969. "Control of Sea-Water Intrusion in a Ground-Water Aquifer." *Ground Water* 7, no. 3: 9–14.

Bruman, Henry J., and Clement W. Meighan. 1981. *Early California: Perception and Reality*. Los Angeles: William Andrews Clark Memorial Library.

Buchanan, James M. 1980. "Rent Seeking and Profit Seeking." In *Toward a Theory of the Rent Seeking Society*. ed. James M. Buchanan et al., 3–15. College Station: Texas A&M University Press.

Buchanan, James M., Robert D. Tollison, and Gordon Tullock, eds. 1980. *Toward a Theory of the Rent Seeking Society*. College Station: Texas A&M University Press.

Buono, Anthony, and David J. Lang. 1980. *Aquifer Recharge From the 1969 and 1978 Floods in the Mojave River Basin, California*. Water-Resource Investigations Report no. 80-207. Menlo Park, Calif.: U.S. Geological Survey.

Burges, Stephen J., and Reza Marnoon. 1975. *A Systematic Examination of Issues in Conjunctive Use of Ground and Surface Waters*. Water Resources Information System Technical Bulletin no. 7. Olympia: State of Washington Department of Ecology.

Burnham, W. L. 1955. *Data on Water Wells in Coyote, Cronise, Soda, and Silver Lake Valleys, San Bernardino County, California*. Long Beach, Calif.: U.S. Geological Survey.

Busby, Mark W. 1975. *Flood-Hazard Study—100-Year Flood Stage for Apple Valley Dry Lake, San Bernardino County, California*. Water-Resources Investigations Report no. 11-75. Menlo Park, Calif.: U.S. Geological Survey.

Busby, Mark W., and George T. Hirashima. 1972. *Generalized Streamflow Relations of the San Bernardino and Eastern San Gabriel Mountains, California*. U.S. Geological Survey Open-File Report. Menlo Park, Calif.: U.S. Geological Survey.

California Assembly Interim Committee on Water. 1962. *Ground Water Problems in California*. Sacramento: State Printing Office.

——— Assembly Office of Research. 1987. *California 2000: Paradise in Peril*. Sacramento: Joint Publications Office.

———, Department of Engineering. 1918. *Report on the Utilization of Mojave River for Irrigation in Victor Valley, California*. Bulletin no. 5. Sacramento: State Printing Office.

———, Department of Public Health, Bureau of Sanitary Engineering. 1970. *Barstow Groundwater Study*. Sacramento.

———, Department of Public Works (DPW), Division of Engineering and Irrigation. 1923. *Water Resources of California*. Bulletin no. 4. Sacramento: State Printing Office.

———, Department of Public Works (DPW), Division of Engineering and Irrigation. 1925. *Supplemental Report on the Water Resources of California*. Bulletin no. 9. Sacramento: State Printing Office.

———, Department of Public Works (DPW), Division of Engineering and Irrigation. 1927. *Summary Report on the Water Resources of California and a Coordinated Plan for Their Development*. Bulletin no. 12. Sacramento: State Printing Office.

————, Department of Public Works (DPW), Division of Engineering and Irrigation. 1928. *Santa Ana Investigation*. Sacramento: State Printing Office.

————, Department of Public Works (DPW), Division of Water Resources. 1929. *Water Resources Investigation, Southern California*. Report no. 171. Sacramento.

————, Department of Public Works (DPW), Division of Water Resources. 1930a. *Santa Ana River Basin*. Bulletin no. 31. Sacramento: State Printing Office.

————, Department of Public Works (DPW), Division of Water Resources. 1930b. *South Coastal Basin*. Bulletin no. 32. Sacramento: State Printing Office.

————, Department of Public Works (DPW), Division of Water Resources. 1930c. *Rainfall Penetration and Consumptive Use of Water in Santa Ana River Valley and Coastal Plain*. Bulletin no. 33. Sacramento: State Printing Office.

————, Department of Public Works (DPW), Division of Water Resources. 1932. *South Coastal Basin Investigation: Records of Ground Water Levels at Wells*. Bulletin no. 39. Sacramento: State Printing Office.

————, Department of Public Works (DPW), Division of Water Resources. 1934a. *South Coastal Basin Investigation*. Bulletin no. 45. Sacramento: State Printing Office.

————, Department of Public Works (DPW), Division of Water Resources. 1934b. *Mojave River Investigation*. Bulletin no. 47. Sacramento: State Printing Office.

————, Department of Public Works (DPW), Division of Water Resources. 1947. *South Coastal Basin Investigation: Overdraft on Ground Water Basins*. Bulletin no. 53. Sacramento: State Printing Office.

————, Department of Public Works (DPW), Division of Water Resources. 1952. *Report of Referee—West Coast Basin Reference*. Sacramento: State Printing Office.

————, Department of Public Works (DPW), Division of Water Resources. 1955. *Water Conditions in California*. Sacramento: State Printing Office.

————, Department of Water Resources (DWR). 1944–45 to 1988–89. *Annual Report on Watermaster Service in Raymond Basin Watermaster Service Area*. Los Angeles: Southern District Office.

————, Department of Water Resources (DWR). 1955–56 to 1988–89. *Annual Report on Watermaster Service in West Coast Basin Watermaster Service Area*. Los Angeles: Southern District Office.

————, Department of Water Resources (DWR). 1960–61 to 1988–89. *Annual Report on Watermaster Service in the Central Basin Watermaster Service Area*. Los Angeles: Southern District Office.

————, Department of Water Resources (DWR). 1968–69 to 1977–78. *Annual Report on Watermaster Service for the Upper Los Angeles River Watermaster Service Area*. Los Angeles: Southern District Office.

————, Department of Water Resources (DWR). 1957. *The California Water Plan*. Bulletin no. 3. Sacramento: State Printing Office.

————, Department of Water Resources (DWR). 1958. *Sea-Water Intrusion in California*. Bulletin no. 63. Sacramento: State Printing Office.

——, Department of Water Resources (DWR). 1959a. *Santa Ana River Investigation.* Bulletin no. 15. Sacramento: State Printing Office.

——, Department of Water Resources (DWR). 1959b. *Report on Proposed Central and West Basin Water Replenishment District.* Los Angeles: Southern District Office.

——, Department of Water Resources (DWR). 1960a. *Report on Hearing on Need for Functioning of Mojave Water Agency.* Los Angeles: Southern District Office.

——, Department of Water Resources (DWR). 1960b. *Data on Wells in the West Part of the Middle Mojave Valley Area, San Bernardino County, California.* Bulletin no. 91-1. Sacramento: State Printing Office.

——, Department of Water Resources (DWR). 1960c. *Data on Wells in the Eastern Part of the Middle Mojave Valley Area, San Bernardino County, California.* Bulletin no. 91-3. Sacramento: State Printing Office.

——, Department of Water Resources (DWR). 1961. *Water Conditions in California.* Special Report. Sacramento: State Printing Office.

——, Department of Water Resources (DWR). 1962. *Planned Utilization of the Ground Water Basins of the Coastal Plain of Los Angeles County.* Appendix B: *Safe Yield Determinations.* Bulletin no. 104. Sacramento: State Printing Office.

——, Department of Water Resources (DWR). 1963. *Wells and Springs in the Lower Mojave Valley Area, San Bernardino County, California.* Bulletin no. 91-10. Sacramento: State Printing Office.

——, Department of Water Resources (DWR). 1964a. *Coastal Los Angeles County Land and Water Use Survey, 1960.* Bulletin no. 24-60. Sacramento: State Printing Office.

——, Department of Water Resources (DWR). 1964b. *Water Supply Conditions in Southern California During 1961–62.* Bulletin no. 39-62. Sacramento: State Printing Office.

——, Department of Water Resources (DWR). 1964c. *Ground Water Occurrence and Quality: Lahontan Region.* Bulletin no. 106-1. Sacramento: State Printing Office.

——, Department of Water Resources (DWR). 1965. *Feasibility of Serving the Mojave Water Agency From the State Water Project.* Bulletin no. 119-12. Sacramento: State Printing Office.

——, Department of Water Resources (DWR). 1966a. *Planned Utilization of Ground Water Basins: Coastal Plain of Los Angeles County.* Appendix C: *Operation and Economics.* Bulletin no. 104. Sacramento: State Printing Office.

——, Department of Water Resources (DWR). 1966b. *Planned Utilization of Ground Water Basins, San Gabriel Valley.* Appendix A: *Geohydrology.* Bulletin no. 104-2. Sacramento: State Printing Office.

——, Department of Water Resources (DWR). 1967. *Mojave River Ground Water Basins Investigation.* Bulletin no. 84. Sacramento: State Printing Office.

——, Department of Water Resources (DWR). 1968. *Planned Utilization of Ground Water Basins: Coastal Plain of Los Angeles County.* Bulletin no. 104. Sacramento: State Printing Office.

———, Department of Water Resources (DWR). 1970. *Meeting Water Demands in the Chino-Riverside Area.* Appendix A: *Water Supply.* Bulletin no. 104-3. Sacramento: State Printing Office.

———, Department of Water Resources (DWR). 1971. *Meeting Water Demands in the Chino-Riverside Area.* Appendix B: *Operation and Economics.* Bulletin no. 104-3. Sacramento: State Printing Office.

———, Department of Water Resources (DWR). 1975. *California's Ground Water.* Bulletin no. 118. Sacramento: State Printing Office.

———, Department of Water Resources (DWR). 1980. *Ground Water Basins in California.* Bulletin no. 118-80. Sacramento: State Printing Office.

———, Department of Water Resources (DWR). 1981. *Alternative Water Supply Plans for the Mojave Water Agency.* Los Angeles: Southern District Office.

———, Department of Water Resources (DWR). 1982. *Recommended Water Management Plan for Solano County Flood Control and Water Conservation District.* Sacramento: State Printing Office.

———, Department of Water Resources (DWR). 1987. *California Water: Looking to the Future.* Bulletin no. 160-87. Sacramento: State Printing Office.

———, Joint Legislative Committee on Water Problems. 1947. *Water Problems of the State of California.* Sacramento: State Printing Office.

———, Joint Legislative Committee on Water Problems. 1949. *Water Problems of the State of California.* Sacramento: State Printing Office.

———, State Water Resources Board. 1952. *Central Basin Investigation.* Bulletin no. 8. Sacramento: State Printing Office.

———, State Water Resources Board. 1956. *Los Angeles County Land and Water Use Survey, 1955.* Bulletin no. 24. Sacramento: State Printing Office.

———, State Water Rights Board. 1959. *Determination of Rights to the Use of Water in California.* Sacramento: State Printing Office.

———, State Water Rights Board. 1961. *Report of Referee—West Coast Basin Reference Continuance.* Sacramento: State Printing Office.

Carruthers, Ian, and Roy Stoner. 1981. *Economic Aspects and Policy Issues in Groundwater Development.* World Bank Staff Working Paper no. 496. Washington, D.C.

Caulfield, Henry. 1983. "The Future of Local Water Districts and Agencies in Historical, Political Context." In *Special Water Districts: Challenge for the Future,* ed. James Corbridge, 103–11. Boulder, Colo.: Natural Resources Law Center.

Central and West Basin Water Replenishment District (CWBWRD). 1959–60 to 1989–90. *Annual Survey Report on Ground Water Replenishment.* Downey, Calif.

———. 1960. *Report on Ground Water Replenishment and Basin Management in the Central and West Basin Water Replenishment District.* Downey, Calif.

———. 1966. *Report on Renewal of Conservation Zones of the Los Angeles Flood Control District.* Downey, Calif.

———. 1986. *Evaluation of Saline Water Inland of West Coast Basin Barrier.* Downey, Calif.

Central Basin Water Association. 1961. "Adjudication of Water Rights in Central Basin." February. Downey, Calif.

Chino Basin Watermaster. 1977–78 to 1989–90. *Annual Report of the Chino Basin Watermaster.* Rancho Cucamonga, Calif.

Ciriacy-Wantrup, S. V. 1956. "Concepts Used as Economic Criteria for a System of Water Rights." *Land Economics* 32, no. 4: 295–312.

Clark, Alfred. 1970. "The San Gabriel River: A Century of Dividing the Waters." *Southern California Quarterly* 52, no. 2: 155–69.

Clark, Colin. 1980. "Restricted Access to Common-Property Fishery Resources: A Game-Theoretic Analysis." In *Dynamic Optimization and Mathematical Economics,* ed. Pan-Tai Liu, 117–32. New York: Plenum Press.

Clark, Ira G. 1988. *Water in New Mexico: A History of Its Management and Use.* Albuquerque: University of New Mexico Press.

Cleland, Robert G. 1951. *The Cattle on a Thousand Hills: Southern California, 1850–1880.* San Marino, Calif.: Huntington Library.

———. 1966. *From Wilderness to Empire: A History of California.* New York: Alfred A. Knopf.

C M Engineering Associates et al. 1982. *Historic and Present Conditions: Newberry Groundwater Basin.* Victorville, Calif.: Mojave Water Agency.

———. 1983. *Historic and Present Conditions: Helendale Fault to Calico-Newberry Fault.* Victorville, Calif.: Mojave Water Agency.

Coe, Jack J. 1983. "Responses to Some of the Adverse External Effects of Ground Water Withdrawals in California." Newport Beach, Calif.

———. 1986. "Conjunctive Use of Surface and Ground Waters—The California Experience." Paper presented at the United Nations Seminar on Conjunctive Use.

Coleman, James S. 1987. "Norms as Social Capital." In *Economic Imperialism: The Economic Approach Applied Outside the Field of Economics,* ed. G. Radnitzky and P. Bernholz. New York: Paragon House.

Commons, John R. 1968. *Legal Foundations of Capitalism.* Madison: University of Wisconsin Press. (Originally published by Macmillan, 1924.)

Coombs, Gary B. 1979. *The Archaeology of the Western Mojave.* Riverside, Calif.: Cultural Resources Publications.

Cooper, Erwin. 1968. *Aqueduct Empire.* Glendale, Calif.: Arthur H. Clark.

Corbridge, James. 1983. "An Overview of the Special Water District Workshop." In *Special Water Districts: Challenge for the Future,* ed. James Corbridge, 1–9. Boulder, Colo.: Natural Resources Law Center.

Corker, Charles E. 1957. "Water Rights and Federalism—The Western Water Rights Settlement Bill of 1957." *California Law Review* 45, no. 5: 604–37.

Coufal, Eugene, Melvin Blevins, and John Mann. 1986. *Management of the San Fernando Valley Groundwater Basin.* Los Angeles: Los Angeles Department of Water and Power.

Craig, Gavin. 1971. "California Water Law in Perspective." *West's Annotated California Water Code.*

Craine, Lyle E. 1959. "Intergovernmental Relations in Water Development and Management." Paper presented at the Southern Political Science Association annual meeting, Gatlinburg, Tennessee.

Crooke, Howard, and John Toups. 1961. "Ground Water Basin Management and Artificial Recharge in Orange County, California." Paper presented at the Biennial Conference on Ground Water Recharge, Berkeley, Calif.

Cross, John, and Melvin Guyer. 1980. *Social Traps.* Ann Arbor: University of Michigan Press.

Crouch, Winston W., Dean McHenry, John C. Bollens, and Stanley Scott. 1956. *California Government and Politics.* Englewood Cliffs, N.J.: Prentice-Hall.

Cuzan, Alfred G. 1979. "A Critique of Collectivist Water Resources Planning." *Western Political Quarterly* 32, no. 3: 320–26.

———. 1981. "Appropriators vs. Expropriators: The Political Economy of Water in the West." In *Water Rights,* ed. Terry Anderson. San Francisco: Pacific Institute for Public Policy Research.

Danskin, Wesley R. 1988. *Preliminary Evaluation of the Hydrogeologic System in Owens Valley, California.* Water Resources Investigations Report no. 88-4003. Sacramento, Calif.: U.S. Geological Survey.

Dawes, Robyn. 1973. "The Commons Dilemma Game: An N-Person Mixed-Motive Game with a Dominating Strategy for Defection." *Oregon Research Institute Bulletin* 13, no. 2.

Dawes, Robyn, Jeanne McTavish, and Harriet Shaklee. 1977. "Behavior, Communication, and Assumptions About Other People's Behavior in a Commons Dilemma Situation." *Journal of Personality and Social Psychology* 35, no. 1: 1–11.

Dawes, Robyn, John Orbell, Randy Simmons, and Alphons van de Kragt. 1986. "Organizing Groups for Collective Action." *American Political Science Review* 80, no. 4: 1171–85.

Demsetz, Harold. 1969. "Information and Efficiency: Another Viewpoint." *Journal of Law and Economics* 12, no. 1: 1–22.

DeYoung, Tim. 1983. "Discretion Versus Accountability: The Case of Special Water Districts." In *Special Water Districts: Challenge for the Future,* ed. James Corbridge, 31–50. Boulder, Colo.: Natural Resources Law Center.

Dickason, Clifford. 1988. "Improved Estimates of Groundwater-Mining Acreage." *Journal of Soil and Water Conservation* 43, no. 3: 239–40.

Dorfman, Robert. 1974. "The Technical Basis for Decision Making." In *The Governance of Common Property Resources,* ed. Edwin Haefele, 5–25. Baltimore: Johns Hopkins University Press.

Durbin, Timothy J., and William F. Hardt. 1974. *Hydrologic Analysis of the Mojave River, California Using a Mathematical Model.* Menlo Park, Calif.: U.S. Geological Survey.

Dutcher, Lee, and Lee Peterson. 1975. "Water Zoning—Tool for Ground-Water Basin Managers." *Ground Water* 13, no. 5: 395–99.

Eccles, Lawrence A. 1981. *Ground-Water Quality along the Mojave River Near Barstow, California, 1974–79.* Menlo Park, Calif.: U.S. Geological Survey.

Eggertsson, Thrainn. 1990. *Economic Behavior and Institutions.* New York: Cambridge University Press.

Ehrhardt, Robert, and Stephen Lemont. 1979. *Institutional Arrangements for Intrastate Groundwater Management: A Comparative Assessment Using Virginia as a Case Study.* Arlington, Va.: JBF Scientific Corporation.

El-Ashry, Mohamed, and Diana Gibbons. 1987. "Managing the West's Water." *Journal of Soil and Water Conservation* 42, no. 1: 8–13.

Elster, Jon. 1983. *Understanding Technical Change.* Cambridge, U.K.: Cambridge University Press.

Emel, Jacque. 1984. *Effectiveness and Equity of Groundwater Management Methods in the Western United States.* Arizona State University Center for Environmental Studies Working Paper no. 3. Tempe, Ariz.

Eucken, Walter. 1951. *The Foundations of Economics.* Chicago: University of Chicago Press.

Feazell, Larry. 1986. "Interstate Water Agencies." *The Book of the States.* 1986–87 ed. Lexington, Ky.: Council of State Governments.

Ferrier, Hugh. 1956. "Administration of Water Rights in California." *California Law Review* 44, no. 5: 833–52.

Ferris, Kathleen. 1986. "Arizona's Groundwater Code: Strength in Compromise." *Journal of the American Water Works Association* 78: 79–84.

Field, Alexander J. 1979. "On the Explanation of Rules Using Rational Choice Models." *Journal of Economic Issues* 13, no. 1: 49–72.

Field, Barry. 1986. *Induced Changes in Property Rights Institutions.* University of Massachusetts Department of Agricultural and Resource Economics Research Paper Series no. 86-1. Amherst, Mass.

Fife, Daniel. 1977. "Killing the Goose." In *Managing the Commons,* ed. Garrett Hardin and John Baden, 76–81. San Francisco: W. H. Freeman.

Fogelson, Robert M. 1967. *The Fragmented Metropolis: Los Angeles, 1850–1930.* Cambridge, Mass.: Harvard University Press.

Fossette, Carl F. 1961. "The Competition for Water Quantity: Industry." *Proceedings, Water Policy Conference,* 88–96. Davis, Calif.: University of California Water Resources Center.

———. 1986. *The Story of Water Development in Los Angeles County.* Downey, Calif.: Central Basin Municipal Water District.

Fox, Irving K. 1966. "We Can Solve Our Water Problems." *Water Resources Research* 2, no. 4: 617–23.

French, J. J. 1966. *Progress Report on Proposed Ground-Water Studies in the Lytle Creek-San Sevaine Area, Upper Santa Ana Valley, California.* U.S. Geological Survey Open-File Report. Menlo Park, Calif.: U.S. Geological Survey.

———. 1972. *Ground-Water Outflow From Chino Basin, Upper Santa Ana Valley, Southern California.* U.S. Geological Survey Water-Supply Paper no. 1099-G. Washington, D.C.: U.S. Government Printing Office.

———. 1978. *Ground-Water Storage in the Johnson Valley Area, San Bernardino County, California.* Water-Resources Investigations Report no. 77-130. Menlo Park, Calif.: U.S. Geological Survey.

Frohock, Fred M. 1987. *Rational Association.* Syracuse, N.Y.: Syracuse University Press.

Gaffney, Mason. 1961. "Diseconomies Inherent in Western Water Laws." Paper presented at the Western Agricultural Economics Research Council, Tucson, Ariz.

Gardner, B. Delworth. 1987. "Removing Impediments to Water Markets." *Journal of Soil and Water Conservation* 42, no. 6: 384–88.

Gensemer, Miriam, and Marianne Yamaguchi. 1985. "Successful Water Quality Planning: An Areawide Perspective." *Journal of Soil and Water Conservation* 40, no. 1: 76–78.

George, Ranjit Varkki. 1988. "Is Groundwater Regulation Blindman's Buff?" *Journal of Planning Literature* 3, no. 2: 231–43.

Getches, David H. 1991. *Water Allocation During Drought in Arizona and Southern California: Legal and Institutional Responses.* Research Report Series Paper. Boulder, Colo.: Natural Resources Law Center.

Gisser, Micha. 1983. "Groundwater: Focusing on the Real Issue." *Journal of Political Economy* 91, no. 6: 1001–27.

Goodall, Merrill, and John D. Sullivan. 1983. "Water System Entities in California: Social and Environmental Effects." In *Special Water Districts: Challenge for the Future*, ed. James Corbridge, 71–102. Boulder, Colo.: Natural Resources Law Center.

Goodcell, Rex B. 1961. "Ground Water Basin Management." Paper presented at the American Water Works Association meetings, Sacramento, Calif.

Grant, Douglas L. 1987. "The Complexities of Managing Hydrologically Connected Surface Water and Groundwater under the Appropriation Doctrine." *Land and Water Law Review* 22, no. 1: 63–95.

Green, Mary Ann. 1983. "Water Law—*Sporhase v. Nebraska.*" *Natural Resources Journal* 33, no. 4: 923–31.

Grigg, Neil S. 1985. *Water Resources Planning.* New York: McGraw-Hill.

———. 1987. "Appendix: Groundwater Systems." In *The Nation's Public Works: Report on Water Resources*, ed. Kyle Schilling et al. Washington, D.C.: National Council on Public Works Improvement.

———. 1989. "Regionalization in Water Supply Industry: Status and Needs." *Journal of Water Resources Planning and Management* 115, no. 3: 367–78.

Haefele, Edwin. 1974. "Introduction." In *The Governance of Common Property Resources*, ed. Edwin Haefele, 1–4. Baltimore: Johns Hopkins University Press.

Hampton, Nathan Eric. 1989. "Groundwater Management in California: Rent-Seeking Behavior under the Correlative Rights Doctrine." Ph.D. diss. Santa Barbara: University of California.

Hansen, Scott, and Floyd Marsh. 1982. "Arizona Ground-Water Reform: Innovations in State Water Policy." Ground Water 20, no. 1: 67–72.

Hardin, Garrett. 1968. "The Tragedy of the Commons." Science 162: 1243–48.

Hardin, Garrett, and John Baden. 1977. "Preface: The Evolution of Cultural Norms." In Managing the Commons, ed. Garrett Hardin and John Baden, ix–xii. San Francisco: W. H. Freeman.

Hardin, Russell. 1982. Collective Action. Baltimore: Johns Hopkins University Press.

Harding, Sidney T. 1960. Water in California. Palo Alto, Calif.: N-P Publications.

Hardt, William F. 1969. Mojave River Basin Ground-Water Recharge with Particular Reference to the California Floods of January and February 1969. Open-File Report. Menlo Park, Calif.: U.S. Geological Survey.

Hart, Henry C. 1974. "Toward a Political Science of Water Resources Decisions." In Man and Water, ed. L. Douglas James, 122–63. Lexington: University Press of Kentucky.

Hartman, L. M. 1965. "Economics and Ground-Water Development." Ground Water 3, no. 2: 4–8.

Hayek, F. A. 1945. "The Use of Knowledge in Society." American Economic Review 35, no. 4: 519–27.

Heath, Ralph C. 1985. "Introduction to State Summaries of Ground-Water Resources." National Water Summary 1984—Ground-Water Resources. Washington, D.C.: U.S. Government Printing Office.

Heckathorn, Douglas D., and Steven M. Maser. 1990. "The Contractual Architecture of Public Policy: A Critical Reconstruction of Lowi's Typology." Journal of Politics 52, no. 4: 1101–23.

Heiner, Ronald. 1983. "The Origin of Predictable Behavior." American Economic Review 73, no. 5: 560–95.

Henley, Albert. 1957. "The Evolution of Forms of Water Users Organizations in California." California Law Review 45, no. 5: 665–75.

Higdon, Philip R., and Terrence W. Thompson. 1980. "The 1980 Arizona Groundwater Management Code." Arizona State Law Journal 12: 621–68.

Hirschleifer, Jack. 1960. "Water Supply for Southern California—Rationalization or Expansion." Paper presented at the Western Economic Association Meetings, Stanford, Calif.

Hirschleifer, Jack, James DeHaven, and Jerome Milliman. 1960. Water Supply: Economics, Technology, and Policy. Chicago: University of Chicago Press.

Hobbs, Charles. 1979. The Water Districts of California. Sacramento: Association of California Water Agencies.

Hoese, William J. 1965. "Recapture of Reclamation Project Ground Water." California Law Review 53, no. 2: 541–58.

Holbert, Myron, Richard Atwater, and Timothy Quinn. 1988. "Water Marketing in Southern California." *American Water Works Association Journal* 80, no. 3: 38–45.

Howe, Charles W., and K. William Easter. 1971. *Interbasin Transfers of Water: Economic Issues and Impacts*. Baltimore: Johns Hopkins University Press.

Huckfeldt, Robert. 1989. "Structure, Indeterminacy, and Chaos: A Case for Sociological Law." Indiana University, Department of Political Science, Bloomington.

Hughes, Jerry L. 1975. *Evaluation of Ground-Water Degradation Resulting from Waste Disposal to Alluvium Near Barstow, California*. Professional Paper no. 878. Washington, D.C.: U.S. Geological Survey.

Hughes, Jerry L., and Dan L. Partridge. 1973. *Selected Data on Wells in the Barstow Area, Mojave River Basin, California*. Open-File Report. Menlo Park, Calif.: U.S. Geological Survey.

Hughes, Jerry L., and A. O. Waananen. 1972. *Effects of the January and February 1969 Floods on Ground Water in Central and Southern California*. Open-File Report. Menlo Park, Calif.: U.S. Geological Survey.

Hundley, Norris. 1975. *Water and the West*. Berkeley: University of California Press.

Hutchins, Wells A. 1956. *The California Law of Water Rights*. Sacramento: State of California Printing Division.

———. 1957. "California Ground Water: Legal Problems." *California Law Review* 45, no. 5: 688–97.

Ingram, Helen M., et al. 1984. "Guidelines for Improved Institutional Analysis in Water Resources Planning." *Water Resources Research* 20, no. 3: 323–34.

Institute of Public Administration. 1987. *Special Districts and Public Authorities in Public Works Provision: Report to the National Council on Public Works Improvement*. Washington, D.C.: Institute of Public Administration.

James, L. Douglas. 1974a. "The Challenge to the Social Sciences." In *Man and Water*, ed. L. Douglas James, 1–33. Lexington: University Press of Kentucky.

———. 1974b. "Reviews and Observations." In *Man and Water*, ed. L. Douglas James, 200–239. Lexington: University Press of Kentucky.

Jaquette, David L. 1978. *Efficient Water Use in California: Conjunctive Management of Ground and Surface Reservoirs*. RAND Corporation Report no. R-2389-CSA/RF. Santa Monica, Calif.

Jaquette, David L., and Nancy Y. Moore. 1978. *Efficient Water Use in California: Groundwater Use and Management*. RAND Corporation Report no. R-2387/1-CSA/RF. Santa Monica, Calif.

Jennings, Engstrand, and Henrikson. 1963. "Report to the City of Hawthorne on Status of Water Rights." Memo to city. Los Angeles, Calif.

Jensen, James H. 1966. "Governmental Responsibilities for Water Development." In *Strategies for Western Regional Water Development*, ed. Ernest Engelbert, 116–24. Los Angeles: Western Interstate Water Conference.

John S. Murk Engineers, Inc. 1984. *Final Local Water Management Alternatives: Newberry Groundwater Basin*. Report prepared for Mojave Water Agency, Victorville, Calif.

———. 1985a. *Final Local Water Management Alternatives: Barstow Area Groundwater Sub-Basins*. Victorville, Calif.: Mojave Water Agency.

———. 1985b. *Historic and Present Conditions: Upper Mojave River Basin*. Victorville, Calif.: Mojave Water Agency.

———. 1986. *Final Local Water Management Alternatives: Upper Mojave River Basin*. Victorville, Calif.: Mojave Water Agency.

Johnson, Ronald, Micha Gisser, and Michael Werner. 1981. "The Definition of a Surface Water Right and Transferability." *Journal of Law and Economics* 24, no. 2: 273–88.

Johnson, Thelma A., and Helen J. Peters. 1967. "Regional Integration of Surface and Ground Water Resources." Paper presented at the Symposium of the International Association of Scientific Hydrology, Haifa, Israel.

Jorgensen, Alfred W. 1967. "A New Approach to Solving Water Disputes: The Long Beach Case." Master's thesis. Los Angeles: University of Southern California.

Kahrl, William. 1981. *Water and Power*. Berkeley: University of California Press.

———. 1982, *Water and Power*. Berkeley: University of California Press.

Kiser, Larry, and Elinor Ostrom. 1982. "The Three Worlds of Action: A Meta-theoretical Synthesis of Institutional Approaches." In *Strategies of Political Inquiry*, ed. Elinor Ostrom, 179–222. Beverly Hills, Calif.: Sage.

Knapp, Keith, and H. J. Vaux. 1982. "Barriers to Effective Ground-Water Management: The California Case." *Ground Water* 20, no. 1: 61–66.

Koebig and Koebig, Inc. 1961. *The Need for Supplemental Water: A Report for Upper San Gabriel Valley Municipal Water District*. Los Angeles, Calif.

———. 1962. Mojave Water Agency Supplemental Water Report. San Diego, Calif.

Koehler, J. H. 1983. *Artificial Recharge in the Northern Part of Chino Ground-Water Basin, Upper Santa Ana Valley, California*. U.S. Geological Survey Water-Resources Investigations Report no. 82-4122. Sacramento: U.S. Geological Survey.

Krieger, James. 1955. "Progress in Ground Water Replenishment in Southern California." *Journal of the American Water Works Association* 47, no. 9: 909–13.

———. 1961. "Ground Water Regulation—State or Local." Paper presented at the American Water Works Association Meetings, Sacramento, Calif.

Krieger, James H., and Harvey O. Banks. 1962. "Ground Water Basin Management." *California Law Review* no. 50, 56–77.

Lachmann, Ludwig. 1978. *Capital and Its Structure*. Kansas City, Mo.: Andrews McMeel.

———. 1986. *The Market as an Economic Process*. New York: Blackwell.

Lamb, Karl. 1974. *As Orange Goes*. New York: W. W. Norton.

Lampe, Les K. 1987. "Recharge Saves Water for a Not-So-Rainy Day." *American City and County* 102, no. 6: 40–46.

Lantis, David W., Rodney Steiner, and Arthur Karinen. 1977. *California: Land of Contrast.* Dubuque, Iowa: Kendall/Hunt.

Lee, Dwight R. 1983. "Political Provision of Water: An Economic/Public Choice Perspective." In *Special Water Districts: Challenge for the Future,* ed. James Corbridge, 51–70. Boulder, Colo.: Natural Resources Law Center.

Lee, Eugene, and Harrison Dunning. 1982. "Political Dynamics and Decision Making." In *Competition for California Water,* ed. Ernest A. Engelbert, 183–98. Berkeley: University of California Press.

Lee, William Storrs. 1963. *The Great California Deserts.* New York: Putnam.

Leshy, John D. 1983. "Special Water Districts—The Historical Background." In *Special Water Districts: Challenge for the Future,* ed. James Corbridge, 11–30. Boulder, Colo.: Natural Resources Law Center.

Leshy, John D., and James Belanger. 1988. "Arizona Law: Where Ground and Surface Water Meet." *Arizona State Law Journal* 20, no. 3: 657–748.

Levi, Margaret. 1988. *Of Rule and Revenue.* Berkeley: University of California Press.

Lewis, R. E. 1972. *Ground-Water Resources of the Yucca Valley-Joshua Tree Area, San Bernardino County, California.* Menlo Park, Calif.: U.S. Geological Survey.

Lewis, Tracy, and James Cowens. 1982. *The Great Fish War: A Cooperative Solution.* California Institute of Technology Working Paper no. 448. Pasadena, Calif.

Lindblom, Charles E. 1990. *Inquiry and Change: The Troubled Attempt to Understand and Shape Society.* New Haven, Conn.: Yale University Press.

Liner, E. Blaine, et al. 1989. *State Management of Groundwater: Assessment of Practices and Progress.* Washington, D.C.: Urban Institute.

Lippert, Teressa. 1981. "*People v. Shirokow*: Abolishing Prescriptive Water Rights Against the State." *California Law Review* 69, no. 4: 1204–29.

Lipson, Albert J. 1978. *Efficient Water Use in California: The Evolution of Groundwater Management in Southern California.* RAND Corporation Report no. R-2387/2-CSA/RF. Santa Monica, Calif.

Lord, William B. 1979. "Conflict in Federal Water Resources Planning." *Water Resources Bulletin* 15, no. 5: 1226–35.

———. 1984. "Institutions and Technology: Keys to Better Water Management." *Water Resources Bulletin* 20, no. 5: 651–56.

Los Angeles, Area Chamber of Commerce, Water and Power Committee. 1968. *Report of Water and Power Committee, Los Angeles Chamber of Commerce, on Water Demands and Supplies for Southern California Coastal Area.* Los Angeles, Calif.

———, Board of Public Service Commissioners. 1916. *Construction of the Los Angeles Aqueduct: Final Report.* Los Angeles, Calif.

———, County Flood Control District. 1983. *Evaluation of Alternatives, South Reach West Coast Basin Barrier Project.* Special Report. Los Angeles, Calif.

————, County Flood Control District. 1984. *Report on the Groundwater Conditions in Los Angeles County for the Current Water Year, October 1, 1983 to June 30, 1984.* Los Angeles, Calif.

————, Department of Water and Power. 1986. "North Hollywood–Burbank Groundwater Cleanup." *DWP Backgrounder.* Los Angeles, Calif.

Luce, Charles. 1969. "Ground Water and Government." *Ground Water* 7, no. 6: 2–8.

McCay, Bonnie, and James M. Acheson. 1987. "The Human Ecology of the Commons." In *Capturing the Commons: The Culture and Ecology of Communal Resources,* ed. Bonnie McCay and James Acheson, 1–34. Tucson: University of Arizona Press.

McCleskey, George. 1972. "Problems and Benefits in Ground-Water Management." *Ground Water* 10, no. 2: 2–5.

McGuinness, C. L. 1969. "New Thrusts in Ground Water." *Ground Water* 7, no. 2: 7–10.

Main San Gabriel Basin Watermaster. 1972–73 to 1988–89. *Annual Report of the Main San Gabriel Basin Watermaster.* El Monte, Calif.

————. 1985. *Rules and Regulations of the Main San Gabriel Basin Watermaster.* El Monte, Calif.

Mallery, Michael. 1983. "Groundwater: A Call for a Comprehensive Management Program." *Pacific Law Journal* 14, no. 4: 1279–1307.

Maloney, Frank, and Richard Ausness. 1971. "A Modern Proposal for State Regulation of Consumptive Uses of Water." *Hastings Law Journal* 22, no. 3: 523–60.

Mann, John F. 1968. "Concepts in Ground Water Management." *Journal of the American Water Works Association* 60, no. 12: 1336–44.

————. 1975. "The San Fernando Case—Its Impact on Future Ground Water Management." Paper presented at the Tenth Biennial Conference on Ground Water, Ventura, Calif.

————. 1976. "Pueblo Water Rights of the City of Los Angeles." *California Geology*: 267–72.

————. 1983. "Ground Water Rights in California." *Proceedings of the National Water Well Association Western Regional Conference on Ground Water Management,* 181–86. San Diego, Calif.

Mann, John F., and Melvin Blevins. 1986. "Groundwater Management in the San Fernando Valley Basin." Paper presented at the Annual Meeting of the Cordilleran Section of the Geological Survey of America, Los Angeles, Calif.

Mansfield, Harvey C., Jr. 1991. *America's Constitutional Soul.* Baltimore: Johns Hopkins University Press.

March, James G., and Herbert A. Simon. 1958. *Organizations.* New York: John Wiley & Sons.

Metropolitan Water District of Southern California. 1962. *Water for People.* Los Angeles, Calif.

Metzger, Philip C. 1988. "Protecting Social Values in Western Water Transfers." *American Water Works Association Journal* 80, no. 3: 58–65.

Meyer, Carl. 1950. "Water Resources of the South Coastal Area in California." Paper presented at the American Water Works Association meetings, San Diego, Calif.

Meyers, Charles J., and A. Dan Tarlock. 1971. *Water Resource Management*. Minneola, N.Y.: Foundation Press.

Miller, R. E. 1971. *The Geological Survey and Water For Southern California*. Menlo Park, Calif.: U.S. Geological Survey.

Mojave Water Agency (MWA). 1964. *Annual Report 1964*. Victorville, Calif.

———. 1965. *Annual Report 1965*. Victorville, Calif.

———. 1966. *Annual Report 1966*. Victorville, Calif.

———. 1967. *Annual Report 1967*. Victorville, Calif.

———. 1968. *Annual Report 1968*. Victorville, Calif.

———. 1979. *Annual Report 1979*. Victorville, Calif.

———. 1986a. *Annual Report 1986*. Victorville, Calif.

———. 1986b. *Report on Phase I Investigation: Morongo Basin Pipeline Project*. Victorville, Calif.

Moore, Charles V. 1984. *Groundwater Overdraft Management: Some Suggested Guidelines*. Information Series no. 84-1, Davis, Calif.: Giannini Foundation.

Moreau, David. 1989. "New Federalism and Social and Environmental Goals." *Journal of Water Resources Planning and Management* 115, no. 1: 22–30.

Moreland, Joe A. 1972. *Artificial Recharge in the Upper Santa Ana Valley, Southern California*. U.S. Geological Survey Open-File Report. Menlo Park, Calif.

Mosher, Lawrence. 1986a. "Federal Water Development: Going, Going. . . ." *Journal of Soil and Water Conservation* 41, no. 3: 164–66.

———. 1986b. "What Role Water Markets?" *Journal of Soil and Water Conservation* 41, no. 6: 390–92.

Moskovitz, Adolphus. 1957. "Quality Control and Re-use of Water in California." *California Law Review* 45, no. 5: 586–603.

Muhsan, H. V. 1977. "An Algebraic Theory of the Commons." In *Managing the Commons*, ed. Garrett Hardin and John Baden, 34–37. San Francisco: W. H. Freeman.

National Council on Public Works Improvement. 1988. *Fragile Foundations: A Report on America's Public Works*. Washington, D.C.: U.S. Government Printing Office.

National Groundwater Policy Forum. 1986. *Groundwater: Saving the Unseen Resource*. Washington, D.C.: Conservation Foundation.

National Research Council, Committee on Water. 1966. *Alternatives in Water Management*. National Academy of Sciences Publication no. 1408. Washington, D.C.

———, Committee on Ground Water Quality Protection. 1986. *Ground Water Quality Protection: State and Local Strategies*. Washington, D.C.: National Academy Press.

National Water Commission. 1973. *Water Policies for the Future: Final Report to the President and to the Congress of the United States*. Port Washington, N.Y.: Water Information Center.

Nelson, Richard R. 1987. *Understanding Technical Change as an Evolutionary Process*. Amsterdam: North-Holland.

Nelson, Richard R., and Sidney G. Winter. 1982. *An Evolutionary Theory of Economic Change*. Cambridge, Mass.: Harvard University Press.

Nunn, Susan Christopher. 1986. "The Political Economy of Institutional Innovation: Coalitions and Strategy in the Development of Groundwater Law." Ph.D. diss. Madison: University of Wisconsin.

O'Flaherty, Joseph S. 1972. *An End and a Beginning: The South Coast and Los Angeles, 1850–1887*. New York: Exposition Press.

———. 1978. *Those Powerful Years: The South Coast and Los Angeles, 1887–1917*. Hicksville, N.Y.: Exposition Press.

Olsenius, Christine. 1987. "Tomorrow's Water Manager." *Journal of Soil and Water Conservation* 42, no. 5: 312–15.

Olson, Mancur. 1965. *The Logic of Collective Action*. Cambridge, Mass.: Harvard University Press.

Ophuls, William. 1973. "Leviathan or Oblivion." In *Toward a Steady State Economy*, ed. Herman Daley, 173–81. San Francisco: W. H. Freeman.

Orange County Water District (OCWD). n.d. *Orange County Water District Annual Report*. Annual Reports for Water Years 1970–71 to 1982–83. Fountain Valley, Calif.

Orbell, John, and L. A. Wilson. 1978. "Institutional Solutions to the N-Prisoner's Dilemma." *American Political Science Review* 72, no. 2: 411–21.

Ostrom, Elinor. 1965." Public Entrepreneurship: A Case Study in Ground Water Basin Management." Ph.D. diss. Los Angeles: University of California at Los Angeles.

———. 1977. "Collective Action and the Tragedy of the Commons." In *Managing the Commons*, ed. Garrett Hardin and John Baden, 173–81. San Francisco: W. H. Freeman.

———. 1982. *Systematic Analysis of Institutional Arrangements*. Workshop in Political Theory and Policy Analysis Working Paper no. W82-19. Bloomington, Ind.

———. 1985a. *Institutional Arrangements for Resolving the Commons Dilemma*. Workshop in Political Theory and Policy Analysis Working Paper no. W85-6. Bloomington, Ind.

———. 1985b. *The Rudiments of a Revised Theory of the Origins, Survival, and Performance of Institutions for Collective Action*. Workshop in Political Theory and Policy Analysis Working Paper no. W85-32. Bloomington, Ind.

———. 1986a. "How Inexorable Is the 'Tragedy of the Commons'?" Workshop in Political Theory and Policy Analysis Working Paper no. W86-8. Bloomington, Ind.

———. 1986b. "A Method of Institutional Analysis." In *Guidance, Control, and Performance Evaluation in the Public Sector*, ed. F. X. Kaufman, G. Majone, and V. Ostrom, 459–75. New York: Walter de Gruyter.

———. 1990. *Governing the Commons*. New York: Cambridge University Press.

———. 1991. "A Framework for Institutional Analysis." Workshop in Political Theory and Policy Analysis Working Paper no. 91-14. Bloomington, Ind.

———. 1992. *Crafting Institutions for Self-Governing Irrigation Systems*. San Francisco: ICS Press.

Ostrom, Vincent. 1953. *Water and Politics*. Newbury Park, Calif.: Haynes Foundation.

———. 1962. "The Political Economy of Water Development." *American Economic Review* 52, no. 2: 450–58.

———. 1963. "Property, Proprietorship, and Politics." Paper presented at the Western Section of the Regional Science Association, Eugene, Oreg.

———. 1971. *Institutional Arrangements for Water Resource Development*. Report to the National Water Commission. Washington, D.C.

———. 1980. "Artisanship and Artifact." *Public Administration Review* 40, no. 4: 309–17.

———. 1983. *Configurations of Relationships in Human Societies*. Workshop in Political Theory and Policy Analysis Working Paper no. 83-21. Bloomington, Ind.

———. 1991. *The Meaning of American Federalism*. San Francisco: ICS Press.

Ostrom, Vincent, Robert Bish, and Elinor Ostrom. 1988. *Local Government in the United States*. San Francisco: ICS Press.

Ostrom, Vincent, and Elinor Ostrom. 1965. "A Behavioral Approach to the Study of Intergovernmental Relations." *Annals of the American Academy of Political and Social Science* 359: 137–46.

———. 1977. "A Theory for Institutional Analysis of Common Pool Problems." In *Managing the Commons*, ed. Garrett Hardin and John Baden, 157–72. San Francisco: W. H. Freeman.

———. 1978. "Public Goods and Public Choices." In *Alternatives for Delivering Public Services*, ed. E. S. Savas, 7–49. Boulder, Colo.: Westview Press.

Ostrom, Vincent, Charles Tiebout, and Robert Warren. 1961. "The Organization of Government in Metropolitan Areas: A Theoretical Inquiry." *American Political Science Review* 55, no. 4: 831–42.

Peirson, Erma. 1970. *The Mojave River and Its Valley*. Glendale, Calif.: Arthur H. Clark.

Peters, Helen Joyce. 1972. "Groundwater Management." *Water Resources Bulletin* no. 8, 1: 188–97.

———. 1981. "Current Policies and Issues of Ground Water Basin Management." Presented at the California-Nevada Section of the American Water Works Association, Palm Springs, Calif.

———. 1982. "Ground Water Management in California." Presented at the American Society of Civil Engineers Conference, Las Vegas, Nev.

Phelps, Charles et al. 1978. *Efficient Water Use in California: Executive Summary.* RAND Corporation Report no. R-2385-CSA/RF. Santa Monica, Calif.

Powell, John Wesley. 1890. "Institutions for the Arid Lands." *Century Magazine* 40: 111–16.

Pratt, Kevin B. 1988. "Mitigating Third-Party Effects." *American Water Works Association Journal* 80, no. 3: 51–57.

Rausser, Gordon C., and Gerald W. Dean. 1971. "Uncertainty and Decision-Making in Water Resources." In *California Water: A Study in Resource Management*, ed. David Seckler, 233–50 . Berkeley: University of California Press.

Rayner, Frank. 1972. "Ground-Water Management—A Local Government Concern." *Ground Water* 10, no. 3: 2–5.

Reisner, Marc. 1986. *Cadillac Desert.* New York: Viking Penguin.

———. 1988–89. "The Next Water War: Cities Versus Agriculture." *Issues in Science and Technology* 5, no. 2: 98–102.

Riley, F. S. 1956. *Data on Water Wells in Lucerne, Johnson, Fry, and Means Valleys, San Bernardino County, California.* Long Beach, Calif.: U.S. Geological Survey.

Roberts, Rebecca, and Sally Gros. 1987. "The Politics of Ground-Water Management Reform in Oklahoma." *Ground Water* 25, no. 5: 535–44.

Robinson, W. W. 1961. *The Story of San Fernando Valley.* Los Angeles: Title Insurance and Trust.

Rogers, Harold, and Alan Nichols. 1967. *Water for California: Planning, Law and Practice, Finance.* 2 vols. San Francisco: Bancroft-Whitney.

Rolph, Elizabeth. 1982. "Government Allocation of Property Rights: Why and How." RAND Report no. R-2822-EPA. Santa Monica, Calif.

Rosenblum, Victor. 1974. "The Continuing Role of Courts in Allocating Common Property Resources." In *The Governance of Common Property Resources*, ed. Edwin Haefele, 119–43. Baltimore: Johns Hopkins University Press.

Rowe, Larry W. 1980. "Basin Management in the San Bernardino Basin Area." *Ground Water* 18, no. 6: 626–29.

Rubin, Harold. 1988. *The Solano Water Story.* Vacaville, Calif.: Solano Irrigation District.

Runge, C. Ford. 1981. "Common Property Externalities: Isolation, Assurance, and Resource Depletion in a Traditional Grazing Context." *American Journal of Agricultural Economics* 63, no. 4: 595–606.

———. 1983. "Common Property and Collective Action in Economic Development." Paper prepared for National Research Council Board on Science and Technology for International Development. Washington, D.C.

———. 1984. "Institutions and the Free Rider: The Assurance Problem in Collective Action." *Journal of Politics* 46, no. 1: 154–81.

Sacarto, Douglas, et al. 1989. *State Issues 1989: A Survey of Priority Issues for State Legislatures.* Denver, Colo.: National Conference of State Legislatures.

Samuelson, Charles, and David Messick. 1984. "Alternative Structural Solutions to Resource Dilemmas." University of California, Department of Psychology, Working Paper. Santa Barbara, Calif.

San Bernardino County Flood Control District. 1976. *Cucamonga Creek after 200 Years: 1776–1976.* San Bernardino, Calif.

San Gabriel River Watermaster. 1965–66 to 1988–89. *Annual Report of San Gabriel River Watermaster Service.* Glendale, Calif.

Sawyer, Frederic. 1949. "Water Law: Mutually Prescriptive Interests in Underground Water." *California Law Review* 37, no. 4: 713–18.

Schaefer, Donald H. 1979. *Ground-Water Conditions and Potential for Artificial Recharge in Lucerne Valley, San Bernardino County, California.* U.S. Geological Survey Water-Resources Investigations no. 78-118. Menlo Park, Calif.: U.S. Geological Survey.

Schaefer, Donald H., and James W. Warner. 1975. *Artificial Recharge in the Upper Santa Ana River Area, San Bernardino County, California.* U.S. Geological Survey Water-Resources Investigations no. 15-75. Menlo Park, Calif.: U.S. Geological Survey.

Schilling, Kyle, et al. 1987. *The Nation's Public Works: Report on Water Resources.* Report prepared for the National Council on Public Works Improvement. Washington, D.C.

Schlager, Edella, and Elinor Ostrom. 1987. "Common Property, Communal Property, and Natural Resources: Some Conceptual Clarifications." Workshop in Political Theory and Policy Analysis Working Paper no. W87-13. Bloomington, Ind.

Schmandt, Jurgen, Ernest Smerdon, and Judith Clarkson. 1988. *State Water Policies.* New York: Praeger.

Schneider, Anne J. 1977. *Groundwater Rights in California: Background and Issues.* Governor's Commission to Review California Water Rights Law, Staff Paper no. 2. Sacramento.

Scott, M. B. 1977. *Development of Water Facilities in the Santa Ana River Basin, 1810–1968.* U.S. Geological Survey Open-File Report no. 77-398. Menlo Park, Calif.: U.S. Geological Survey.

Seckler, David, and L. M. Hartman. 1971. "On the Political Economy of Water Resources Evaluation." In *California Water: A Study in Resource Management,* ed. David Seckler, 285–309. Berkeley: University of California Press.

Setmire, James G. 1985. *A Conceptual Ground-Water-Quality Monitoring Network for San Fernando Valley, California.* Water Resources Investigations Report no. 84-4128. Sacramento: U.S. Geological Survey.

Shupe, Steven J. 1990. *Water Rights Decisions in the Western States: Upgrading the System for the 21st Century.* Western Water Policy Discussion Series Paper no. 4. Boulder, Colo.: Natural Resources Law Center.

Simmons, Malcolm M. 1981. *California Water.* Congressional Research Service Report no. 81-108 ENR. Washington, D.C.

Simon, Herbert A. 1985. "Human Nature in Politics: The Dialogue of Psychology with Political Science." *American Political Science Review* 79, no. 2: 293–304.

Skrove, Tim. 1989a. "Babysitting That Morning Cup of Coffee." *Aqueduct* 55, no. 1: 2–4.

———. 1989b. "The Wonders, Wages and Woes of Wellwater." *Aqueduct* 55, no. 1: 5–8.

Smith, Robert J. 1981. "Resolving the Tragedy of the Commons by Creating Private Property Rights in Wildlife." *Cato Journal* 1, no. 2: 439–68.

Smith, Rodney. 1988a. "The Changing Role of Water Policy in California's Economic Development." Paper prepared for the California Economic Development Corporation. Claremont-McKenna College, Claremont, Calif.

———. 1988b. *Trading Water: An Economic and Legal Framework for Water Marketing.* Washington, D.C.: Council of State Policy and Planning Agencies.

Smith, Stephen C. 1956. "Problems in the Use of the Public District for Ground-Water Management." *Land Economics* 32, no. 3: 259–69.

———. 1974. "Economics and Economists in Water Resources Development." In *Man and Water*, ed. L. Douglas James, 82–101. Lexington: University Press of Kentucky.

Smith, Zachary. 1984. "Rewriting California Groundwater Law: Past Attempts and Prerequisites to Reform." *California Western Law Review* 20, no. 2: 223–57.

———. 1985. "Federal Intervention in the Management of Groundwater Resources: Past Efforts and Future Prospects." *Publius* 15, no. 1: 145–59.

———. 1986a. "Competition for Water Resources: Issues in Federalism." *Journal of Land Use and Environmental Law* 2, no. 2: 177–93.

———. 1986b. "Stability amid Change in Federal-State Water Relations." *Capital University Law Review* 15, no. 3: 479–91.

———. 1987. "Interstate and International Competition for Water Resources." *Water Resources Bulletin* 23, no. 5: 873–77.

———. 1989a. *Groundwater in the West.* San Diego: Academic Press.

———. 1989b. "The Policy Environment." In *Water and the Future of the Southwest*, ed. Zachary Smith, 9–18. Albuquerque: University of New Mexico Press.

Solley, Wayne, Charles Merk, and Robert Pierce. 1988. *Estimated Use of Water in the United States, 1985.* U.S. Geological Survey Circular no. 1004. Washington, D.C.

Sopp, C. W. 1943. "Adjudication of Water Rights in the Raymond Basin." *Journal of the American Water Works Association* 35: 429–38.

Sproule-Jones, Mark. 1989. *Governments at Work.* Bloomington, Ind.: Workshop in Political Theory and Political Analysis.

Starr, Kevin. 1985. *Inventing the Dream: California through the Progressive Era.* New York: Oxford University Press.

———. 1990. *Material Dreams: Southern California through the 1920s.* New York: Oxford University Press.

Steiner, Wesley E. 1982. "Public Water Policy in Arizona." *State Government* 55, no. 4: 133–35.

Stetson, Thomas. 1966. "Management Plan for San Gabriel Valley Ground Water Basin." Report to the Upper San Gabriel Valley Water Association.

———. 1966–1973. *Engineering Survey and Report on Ground Water Supplies of the Upper San Gabriel Valley Municipal Water District.* Annual Reports for Water Years 1965–66 through 1972–73. El Monte, Calif.: Upper San Gabriel Valley Municipal Water District.

———. 1976. *Report on Nitrate Investigation in the Easterly Portion of the Main San Gabriel Basin.* Report to the Upper San Gabriel Valley Municipal Water District and the San Gabriel Valley Municipal Water District. El Monte, Calif.

———. 1982. "Ground Water Basin Management." Paper presented to the San Francisco Section of the American Society of Civil Engineers.

———. 1985. "Relationship of the Los Angeles County Flood Control District to the Management of the Waters of the San Gabriel River System." Paper presented to the Upper San Gabriel Valley Water Association. El Monte, Calif.

———. 1986a. "Main San Gabriel Basin Ground-Water Management." Paper presented at the 82nd Annual Meeting of the Cordilleran Section of the Geological Society of America. In *Hydrogeology of Southern California: Vol. and Guidebook,* ed. Prem K. Saint, 5–10. Los Angeles: Geological Society of America.

———. 1986b. "Water Quality of the Main San Gabriel Basin." Paper presented at the 82nd Annual Meeting of the Cordilleran Section of the Geological Society of America. In *Hydrogeology of Southern California: Vol. and Guidebook,* ed. Prem K. Saint, 11–15. Los Angeles: Geological Society of America.

Stetson, Strauss, and Dresselhaus, Inc. 1962a. *Compendium of Report on a Supplemental Water Supply for Upper San Gabriel Valley Municipal Water District.* Los Angeles.

———. 1962b. *Final Report on a Supplemental Water Supply for Upper San Gabriel Valley Municipal Water District.* Los Angeles.

Stetson Engineers. 1974. "Report on Review of Overdraft of the Mojave River Basin." West Covina, Calif.

———. 1975. "Possible Physical Solutions to Water Supply and Water Rights Problems of the Mojave River Basin." West Covina, Calif.

Stickel, E. Gary, et al. 1980. *An Overview of the Cultural Resources of the Western Mojave Desert.* Riverside, Calif.: Cultural Resources Publications.

Sutherland, Lorenz, and John A. Knapp. 1988. "The Impacts of Limited Water: A Colorado Case Study." *Journal of Soil and Water Conservation* 43, no. 4: 294–98.

Tang, Shui Yan. 1992. *Institutions and Collective Action: Self-Governance in Irrigation.* San Francisco: ICS Press.

Taylor, Edward F. 1967. "*Arizona v. California*—Landmark on the Colorado River." *Ground Water* 5, no. 2: 5–12.

Taylor, Paul S. 1971. "The 160-Acre Law." In *California Water: A Study in Resource Management*, ed. David Seckler, 251-62. Berkeley: University of California Press.

Teerink, John. 1974. "Impact of Water Pollution Control Legislation on Meeting Future Water Needs in California." *Ground Water* 12, no. 2: 102-5.

Thompson, David G. 1929. *The Mohave Desert Region, California: A Geographic, Geologic, and Hydrologic Reconnaissance.* U.S. Geological Survey Water-Supply Paper no. 578. Washington, D.C.

Thompson, Grant P. 1972. *Courts and Water: The Role of the Judicial Process.* National Water Commission Background Report. Arlington, Va.

Tocqueville, Alexis de. 1945. *Democracy in America.* Phillips Bradley, ed. New York: Vintage Books.

Todd, David Keith. 1971. "Groundwater Utilization." In *California Water: A Study in Resource Management*, ed. David Seckler, 174-89. Berkeley: University of California Press.

———. 1983. *Ground-Water Resources of the United States.* Berkeley: Premier Press.

Tollison, Robert. 1982. "Rent Seeking: A Survey." *Kyklos* 35, no. 4, 575-602.

Trager, Susan M. 1988. "Emerging Forums for Groundwater Dispute Resolution in California: A Glimpse at the Second Generation of Groundwater Issues and How Agencies Work Towards Resolution." *Pacific Law Journal* 20, no. 1: 31-74.

Trelease, Frank J. 1966. "States Rights Versus National Powers for Water Development." In *Strategies for Western Regional Water Development*, ed. Ernest Engelbert, 99-115. Los Angeles: Western Interstate Water Conference.

———. 1980. "Legal Solutions to Groundwater Problems—A General Overview." *Pacific Law Journal* 11, no. 4: 863-75.

Tripp, James T. B., and Adam B. Jaffe. 1979. "Preventing Groundwater Pollution: Toward a Coordinated Strategy to Protect Critical Recharge Zones." *Harvard Environmental Law Review* 3, no. 1: 1-47.

Troxell, Harold C. 1957. *Water Resources of Southern California, With Special Reference to the Drought of 1944-51.* U.S. Geological Survey Water-Supply Paper no. 1366. Washington, D.C.

UINTEX Engineering Consultants. 1985. *Review of Water Resources within the Los Angeles County Drainage Area.* Final Report to L.A. District, U.S. Army Corps of Engineers, Los Angeles, Calif.

Uphoff, Norman. 1986. *Local Institutional Development: An Analytical Sourcebook with Cases.* West Hartford, Conn.: Kumarian Press.

U.S. Advisory Commission on Intergovernmental Relations. 1964. *The Problem of Special Districts in American Government.* Report no. A-22. Washington, D.C.

———. 1987. *The Organization of Local Public Economies.* Report no. A-109. Washington, D.C.

———. 1988. *Metropolitan Organization: The St. Louis Case.* Report no. M-158. Washington, D.C.

———. 1991. *Coordinating Water Resources in the Federal System: The Groundwater-Surface Water Connection.* Report no. A-118. Washington, D.C.

U.S. Environmental Protection Agency, Region IX. 1986. *San Gabriel Basin Sites.* Issue 1.

———. 1987a. *San Gabriel Basin Sites.* Issue 2.

———. 1987b. *San Gabriel Valley Superfund Sites.* Issue 4.

———. 1989a. *San Gabriel Valley Sites.* Fact Sheet no. 6.

———. 1989b. *San Gabriel Valley Superfund Sites.* Fact Sheet no. 7.

U.S. Geological Survey. 1984. *National Water Summary 1983.* Water-Supply Paper no. 2250. Washington, D.C.

———. 1985. *National Water Summary 1984.* Water-Supply Paper no. 2275. Washington, D.C.

———. 1987. *National Water Summary 1986.* Water-Supply Paper no. 2325. Washington, D.C.

Utton, Albert E. 1983. "The El Paso Case: Reconciling *Sporhase* and *Vermejo.*" *Natural Resources Journal* 23, no. 1: ix–xv.

van Parijs, Philippe. 1981. *Evolutionary Explanation in the Social Sciences: An Emerging Paradigm.* Totowa, N.J.: Rowman and Littlefield.

Viessman, Warren. 1990. "Water Management: Challenge and Opportunity." *Journal of Water Resources Planning and Management*: 155–69.

Viessman, Warren, and Claire Welty. 1985. *Water Management: Technology and Institutions.* New York: Harper and Row.

Wade, Robert. 1987. "Managing Water Managers: Deterring Expropriation, or Equity as a Control Mechanism." In *Water and Water Policy in World Food Supplies,* ed. Wayne R. Jordan, 177–83. College Station: Texas A&M University Press.

Wade Miller Associates. 1987. *The Nation's Public Works: Report on Water Supply. Report for the National Council on Public Works Improvement.* Washington, D.C.: U.S. Government Printing Office.

Wallace, L. T., Charles Moore, and Raymond Coppock. 1982. "An Overview: The Conflicts and the Questions." In *Competition for California Water,* ed. Ernest Engelbert, 199–208. Berkeley: University of California Press.

Walters, E. H., Ira R. Calvert, and Max A. Bengel. 1961. *History of the San Gabriel River Water Committee, The San Gabriel Spreading Corporation, The San Gabriel Protective Association.* El Monte, Calif.: Upper San Gabriel Valley Water Association.

Ward, C. H., N. N. Durham, and L. W. Canter. 1984. "Ground Water—A National Issue." *Ground Water* 22, no. 2: 138–40.

Weatherford, Gary. 1990. *From Basin to "Hydrocommons": Integrated Water Management without Regional Governance.* Western Water Policy Discussion Series Paper no. 5. Boulder, Colo.: Natural Resources Law Center.

Weatherford, Gary, et al. 1982. *Acquiring Water for Energy: Institutional Aspects.* Littleton, Colo.: Water Resources Publications.

Welch, W. 1983. "The Political Feasibility of Full-Ownership Property Rights." *Policy Science* 16, no. 2: 165–80.

Welsh, Frank. 1985. *How to Create a Water Crisis.* Boulder, Colo.: Johnson Books.

Weschler, Louis. 1968. *Water Resources Management: The Orange County Experience.* California Government Series no. 14. Davis, Calif.: Institute of Governmental Affairs.

Westphal, Joseph. 1982. "The Potential for Ground-Water Management in the West." *Ground Water* 20, no. 1: 59–60.

Williams, Stephen F. 1983. "The Requirement of Beneficial Use as a Cause of Waste in Water Resource Development." *Natural Resources Journal* 23, no. 1: 7–23.

Wilm, Harold. 1969. "Intergovernmental Planning of Water Resources." *Ground Water* 7, no. 2: 15–17.

Woodward, Clyde, Sherard, and Associates. 1963. *Geological Study for the Proposed Mojave Water Agency.* San Diego, Calif.

Worster, Donald. 1985. *Rivers of Empire: Water, Aridity, and the Growth of the American West.* New York: Pantheon.

Wright, Kenneth K. 1952. "Underground Water Problems in California." *Journal of the American Water Works Association* 44, no. 8: 662–68.

Young, Robert A. 1970. "Safe Yield of Aquifers: An Economic Reformulation." *Journal of the ASCE Irrigation and Drainage Division* 96, no. IR4: 377–85.

———. 1987. "Market Versus Nonmarket Management of Irrigation Water: A Review of the Issues." In *Water and Water Policy in World Food Supplies,* ed. Wayne R. Jordan, 205–11. College Station: Texas A&M University Press.

Zeiger, Richard. 1988. "Water, Water." *California Journal* 19, no. 3: 104–9.

Index

Abbey case. *See Mojave Water Agency v. Clarence L. Abbey et al.*
Adaptability, 11, 315–17
Adjudication
  Central Basin, 132, 135–41, 146–50, 353–54
  Chino Basin, 278–81, 292, 312
  Main San Gabriel Basin, 163–71, 277–78
  Mojave River, 225–36, 354–55
  San Gabriel River case, 132, 135–41, 163–67
  Santa Ana River, 261–64
  West Basin, 105–10
  See also specific court cases
Adjudication costs
  Central Basin, 141
  Chino Basin, 295
  derivation of, 306–8
  Main San Gabriel Basin, 171
  San Fernando Valley, 200
Administrative efficiency, 11, 305–9
Agricultural land, 23. *See also* Irrigation
Airola, Virgil, 136, 141, 195
Alamitos Gap, 32, 34, 39, 129, 150
Alamitos Gap Barrier Project, 265–66, 268
Alhambra (city), 76, 135, 164–65, 171, 186

Alhambra Cooperative Water Exchange Agreement, 185–86
Anaheim (city), 247, 250
Anaheim Union Water Company, 254
Anderson, Dick, 240
Annual safe yield, 15
Appropriative rights, 64–65
Aquifers, 13, 21–23
Arcadia (city), 81, 91, 135
Arizona v. California, 261
Arroyo Seco (stream), 29
Artesian wells, 15, 245, 247
Assurance, 347
Ayala, Ruben S., 278
Azusa (city), 135, 164–65, 171, 177

Baldwin, E. J. "Lucky," 47
Baldwin Park Key Well, 162, 167, 173, 180, 183–84
Ballona Creek, 33
Ballona Gap, 33
Banks, Harvey, 24–25, 324
Barstow (city), 237, 240
Basin equity assessment, 266–67
Basins, 13–26
  common threats to, 16–17
  general characteristics of, 13–16
  need for management of, 17–20
  overlying area of, 23

Basins (*continued*)
particular characteristics of, 20–23
significance of time-and-place-
specific information and, 24–26
See also specific basins
Baumann, Paul, 102, 115
Best, Best, and Krieger (law firm),
225, 227, 231
Blackburn, Duncan, 324
Blevins, Melvin, 205, 324
*Board of Water Commissioners of the
City of Long Beach et al. v. San Gabriel
Valley Water Company et al.*, 136
Bookman, Edmonston, and Gianelli
(law firm), 136, 140
Bookman, Max, 136–37, 140, 142,
152, 324
Bookman-Edmonston Engineering,
142, 147
Bowen, Marshall, 136
Brommenschenkel, Frank, 285
Burbank and *Glendale* cases, 192–94
Burbank (city), 192–94, 200–201, 204,
206, 208, 211, 213
Burns-Porter Act (1959), 337
Burris and Lagerlof (law firm), 136
Busch, Henry, 235–36

Caldwell, Terry, 239
California Administrative Code, 175
California Aqueduct, 222, 236–37
California Civil Code, 64, 84, 202,
215–16, 279–80
California Constitution, 63, 65
California Department of Health
Services, 118, 175, 178, 207
California Department of Water
Resources, 6, 89–91, 93, 110–11,
113, 120, 148, 188n10, 199–200, 237
California Division of Engineering
and Irrigation, 18, 59
California Division of Water
Resources, 58–59, 60, 75, 77, 80,
85, 92, 247, 273
West Basin adjudication and, 106–7
California-Michigan Land and Water
Company, 79–80, 82–83
California Supreme Court, 49, 52,
65–69, 79, 83–84, 109, 192–94,
201–4, 212, 216, 279, 354
California Water Code, 107, 121

California Water Resources Control
Board, 6, 115, 131, 208–10
California Water Service Company,
103, 106
*California Water Service Company et al.
v. City of Compton et al.*, 106–10
Calvert, Ira, 137
Carbon tetrachloride, 177–78
Carter, Johnathan, 234–35
Caruso, Rick, 210
CBMWD. *See* Central Basin Municipal
Water District; Chino Basin
Municipal Water District
CBWA. *See* Chino Basin Water
Association
Central and West Basin Water
Replenishment District
(CWBWRD), 113, 117–19, 121,
146–47, 154, 305, 316, 356
*Central and West Basin Water
Replenishment District v. Charles E.
Adams et al.*, 147–48
Central Basin, 31–32, 110, 112–13,
115, 127–57, 305, 316, 340–41
adjudication, 146–50, 353–54
assessment of management of,
151–57
first organizational attempts, 129–31
initial groundwater problems, 127,
129
judgment, 148–50
saltwater intrusion, 150–51
San Gabriel River adjudication,
132, 135–41
San Gabriel River judgment, 141–46
supplemental supplies and artificial replenishment, 131–32
Central Basin Municipal Water
District (CBMWD), 131–32, 153
*Central Basin Municipal Water District
v. Fossette*, 141
Central Basin Water Association
(CWBA), 112, 130–31
Cerritos (city), 157
Chapman, A. B., 47
Chino Basin, 37–38, 44, 90, 216,
271–96, 316
adjudication, 278–81, 312
assessment of management in,
289–96
creation of water districts in, 274–75

designing of management
program, 275–78
initial problems, 271, 273–74
judgment, 281–86
management costs, 308–9
storage, 286–88
watermaster's role, 286–89
water-quality problems in, 288–89
Chino Basin Municipal Water District
(CBMWD), 262, 264, 274–79, 284
*Chino Basin Municipal Water District
v. City of Chino et al.*, 278
Chino Basin Protective Association,
271, 273–74, 290–91
Chino Basin Water Association
(CBWA), 135, 146–48, 275–78,
286, 290, 291
Chino Basin Water Conservation
District, 291
Chino (city), 289
Citizens for Accountable Water
Management, 239
Cleminson, J. Ercel, 137
Climate, 45–46
Coastal Municipal Water District, 252
Code, William, 189
Coleman, Carl, 226, 235
Collective problem solving, 327–28,
330, 344–48
Collier, Frank, 76–80, 82–83, 192–93
Colorado River Aqueduct, 4, 61–62
Colorado River water, 75–76, 88,
105, 194, 252–53
Commons, John R., 9
Communication, 328
"Competitive equilibrium" argu-
ment, 18–20
Compliance, 346–48
Central Basin, 154
Chino Basin, 292, 294
Main San Gabriel Basin, 182–83
measurement of, 302
Orange County basin management
program, 269
Raymond Basin, 93
San Fernando Valley, 213
West Basin, 122
Compton (city), 130, 131–32
Cone, 14
Conjunctive use, 191–93
Conrock Company, 286

Conservation zones (West Basin
Water Association), 111–13
Constraints, 324–31
Contamination, 17
Chino Basin, 288–89
Main San Gabriel Basin, 176–80
San Fernando Valley, 207–8
See also Saltwater intrusion
Costs. *See* Adjudication costs;
Management costs
Court Reference Procedure (California
Water Code), 77
Court settlements
advantages of, 76–77
decision-making process and, 345
Covina (city), 135
Craig, Ted, 249
Crescenta Valley County Water
District, 200–201, 206, 213
Cucamonga County Water District,
287
Cucamonga Creek, 38
CWBA. *See* Central Basin Water
Association
CWBRWD. *See* Central and West Basin
Water Replenishment District

Dalton, Henry, 49–50
Dalton Ditch dispute, 49–50
Dams
San Fernando Valley, 191–92
See also specific dams
Darby, Raymond, 104
Decreed rights, 80
Deep-well turbine pump, 58
Dellman, Milo, 136
Democracy in America (Alexis de
Tocqueville), 7, 346
Desert Well Owners Association,
232–33, 234–35
Devil's Gate dam, 89
Distribution, equity in, 314–15
Dominguez Gap, 33
Dominguez Gap Barrier Project, 116
Droughts
Great Drought of 1863–64, 46, 49
Main San Gabriel Basin, 163, 166,
167–68
Raymond Basin, 85
San Fernando Valley, 195
Duarte (city), 135

Eagle Rock Basin, 36
East Pasadena Water Company, 95n2
East Valleys Organization, 179
Eaton, E. C., 55
Edwards, N. T., 249
Edward Sidebotham and Son, Inc., 109
Effectiveness
  defined, 10
  evaluation of, 302–5
Efficiency
  administrative, 305–9
  defined, 10–11
  resource use, 309–13
El Monte (city), 135
El Segundo (city), 105
Elster, Jon, 322, 330
Entrepreneurship, 348–52, 358–59
Environmental Protection Agency
  (EPA), 178–79, 208
EPA. See Environmental Protection
  Agency
Equity, 11, 313–15
Equity jurisprudence, 76–77
Evaluation of performance, 301–17
  adaptability, 315–17
  administrative efficiency, 305–9
  compliance, 302
  effectiveness, 302–5
  equity, 313–15
  resource use, 309–13
  See also specific basins
Exchange pool arrangement, 87–88
Extraction of groundwater, 14

Fairness in Bonding (citizens'
  group), 237
Federalism, 7
Federal Reclamation Service, 53
Feedback, 329
Feliz v. City of Los Angeles, 67–68
Fiscal equivalence, 313–14
Fiscus, David, 137
Flood Control District Act, 121
Floods, 46, 55
  Mojave River, 230
  San Fernando Valley, 193–94
Flowing well. See Artesian well
Foothill Municipal Water District, 88
Fossette, Carl, 130, 138–39, 151–52,
  164, 166, 168, 324

Francis, George, 108–9
Fullerton (city), 247, 250
Furlong, Robert J., 135

Garces, Franciso, 44
Gardena aquifer, 33
Gardena (city), 105
Gaspur aquifer, 33
General knowledge, scientific
  knowledge versus, 24
Gierlach, O. A., 102, 115
Glassell, Andrew, 47
Glendale (city), 192–94, 200–201,
  204, 206, 211, 213
Great Drought of 1863–64, 46, 49

Haggott, Ben, 324
Haile, Howard, 142
Hamlin, Homer, 189
Harris, Hilton, 136
Harsh, Howard, 233
Hartman, Glenn R. "Dick," 235
Hawthorne (city), 105, 109
Hayek, F. A., 325, 344
Heiner, Ronald, 325
Helm, Ralph, 139, 166, 168, 171,
  174, 178
Hermosa Beach (city), 105
Hesperia Land and Water
  Company, 48
High Plains aquifer. See Ogallala aquifer
History of water use, 43–69
  beginnings of organized water use,
  43–45
  law of water rights, 63–69
  nineteenth and early twentieth
  centuries, 45–54
  urbanization, 54–63
  See also specific basins
Human factor in institutional
  development, 319–38
  coping with contraints, 328–31
  importance of facilitative political
  regime, 335–38
  intentional problem solving under
  constraint, 322–28
  levels of action and, 333–35
  social capital and, 331–33
Hupp, Harry, 204–6, 218n8
Hydraulic gradient, 14

Hyperion Treatment Plant (Los Angeles), 119

Ideal models, 320–21
Importation of water, costs of, 17
Indeterminacy, human interaction and, 328–29
Information, computation and, 343–44
Inglewood (city), 105
Injection/intrusion barriers
Orange County, 265–66
West Basin, 115–17, 119
Innovation, 358–63
Institutional development, human factor in. *See* Human factor in institutional development
Intentionality, problem solving and, 323–24
Investigative reports
Central Basin, 130–31, 137–38, 147, 152
Main San Gabriel Basin, 166, 167
Orange County, 247
Raymond Basin, 77–78
San Fernando Valley, 195
West Basin, 103, 106, 108
Inyo County, 208–9
Irrigation
beginnings of, 45
late nineteenth century, 53
Mojave River basins, 221–22
Orange County, 245, 247, 259
postwar growth and, 63
Irvine, James, 47
Irvine Co. v. Fontana Union Water Company et al., 248
Irvine Company, 248–49
Irwindale (city), 177

Johnstone, William J., 222
Jorgensen, Alfred W., 137
Jorgensen, Alfred W., 324
"Judge-made" law, 214–16
Judgments
Central Basin, 141–46, 148–50
Chino Basin, 281–86
Main San Gabriel Basin, 172–75, 184–85
San Fernando Valley, 204–7

San Gabriel River, 141–46, 169
Santa Ana River, 275–78
See also specific court cases

Karst aquifers, 21
Katz v. Walkinshaw, 66, 84
Kemper-Campbell Company, 229
King, Jess, 235
K-Line Ranch, 229
Koebig and Koebig, Inc., 166
Krieger, James H., 24–25, 225–26, 228–29, 231, 324

La Canada Irrigation District, 79
LACFCD. *See* Los Angeles County Flood Control District
Lachmann, Ludwig, 323, 359
LADWP. *See* Los Angeles Department of Water and Power
Lagerlof, Stanley, 136
Lankershim, Isaac, 47
La Puente (city), 135
Leichter, Maxine, 179–80
Levels of action, 333–35
Levi, Margaret, 347
Lindblom, Charles, 325
Lippincott, J. B., 53, 247–48
Lipson, Albert, 350
Littleworth, Arthur, 231, 233, 235–36, 324
Local Agency Formation Commission, 278
Long Beach (city), 130, 131
Long Beach judgment. *See* San Gabriel River case
Long-term accounting, 144–46
Los Angeles Aqueduct, 54–55, 189, 194, 208–10, 213
Los Angeles Board of Water Commissioners, 189
Los Angeles (city), 119, 131, 211–13
Burbank and *Glendale* cases and, 192–94
conjunctive use program, 191–93
early water management in, 53–54
pueblo water rights, 189, 192–93, 196–97, 201, 205–6, 216
urbanization of, 55–57
See also Los Angeles v. City of San Fernando et al.

Los Angeles County Department of
Public Works, 89, 151
Los Angeles County Flood Control
District (LACFCD), 55, 75, 102,
111, 115–17, 121, 132, 151, 162,
191–93, 274
Los Angeles Department of Water
and Power (LADWP), 191–92,
205, 207–13
Los Angeles Narrows, 36
Los Angeles-Owens Valley
Aqueduct, 4
Los Angeles River, 34–36, 43, 189,
191, 211
Los Angeles Times, 3–4, 62
Los Angeles v. A.E. Pomeroy et al., 68
Los Angeles v. Buffington et al., 68
Los Angeles v. City of San Fernando et al.
appeal, 200–204
case, 195–200
Chino Basin and, 279–80
"judge-made" law and, 214–17
judgment (1979), 204–7
mutual-prescription doctrine and,
353–54
Los Angeles v. Hunter et al., 68
Lower Mojave River Basin, 42
Lowry, Beverly, 233
Lux v. Haggin, 217n2
Lynwood aquifer, 32

Maclay, Charles, 47
Main San Gabriel Basin, 29–31, 90,
110, 135, 159–87, 316, 354
adjudication, 167–71, 277–78
assessment of management of,
180–86
initial groundwater problems, 159,
162–63
judgment, 172–75
management costs, 308–9
recent challenges, 175–80
San Gabriel River adjudication
and, 163–67
Main San Gabriel Basin Water
Quality Authority, 180
Makeup water, 144
Management costs
administration, 305–9, 342–43
equity and, 313–14
Manhattan Beach (city), 105, 115

Mann, John F., Jr., 136, 198, 216,
226–27, 231, 324
Marliave, Elmer, 136
Metropolitan Water District of
Southern California (MWD), 61–62,
125n1, 247, 303, 339, 359–60
administrative efficiency, 306
Central Basin and, 131–32, 135,
146, 153
Chino Basin and, 287
Main San Gabriel Basin and, 135,
164–67, 179, 184–86
Orange County and, 252–53, 259,
261, 264, 269
Raymond Basin and, 75–76, 85,
87–88, 93
San Fernando Valley and, 194, 213
Santa Ana River system and, 274–75
West Basin and, 104–5, 111, 115–19
Mexican-American war, 45
Middle Mojave River Basin, 41–42
Mining, 48
Mission San Gabriel, 44
Models, 320
Mojave River, 39–42
Mojave River basins, 219–42, 322, 354
Abbey case, 229–36
adjudication, 354–55
assessment of management of,
240–42
development and population
growth, 221–22
initial problems, 222, 224–25
recent developments, 239–40
State Water Project and, 236–38
supply-demand imbalance in, 238–39
water rights determination in
1950s and early 1960s, 225–29
Mojave River County Water District,
232
Mojave Water Agency Law, 222, 224
Mojave Water Agency (MWA), 219,
221–22, 224–42, 354
Mojave Water Agency v. Clarence L.
Abbey et al., 229–36
Monk Hill subarea, 29, 77, 87–88
Mono Lake, 209–10
Monrovia (city), 135
Montebello Forebay, 32, 111, 132–34
Monterey Park (city), 135, 164–65, 171
Montgomery Engineers, 287

Moor, Edmund, 147–48, 195–203, 216
Moseley, M. E., 137
Mulholland, William, 61, 189
Municipal Water District Act, 140, 169, 274
Municipal Water District of Orange County, 252
Murdy, John A., Jr., 251
Mutual prescription doctrine, 80, 84–85, 197–99, 202, 216, 353–54
MWA. *See* Mojave Water Agency
MWD. *See* Metropolitan Water District of Southern California

National Audubon Society, 210
Negit Island, 210
Nelson, Richard, 360–61
Nitrates, 176–77, 288
Nonconsumptive water rights, 117
Norco (city), 289
Norms, reliance on, 328–29
Nunn, Susan Christopher, 350

Oakes, George, 242n1
OCWD. *See* Orange County Water District
Ogallala (High Plains) aquifer, 21
Ontario (city), 287
Orange County, 38–39, 111–12, 230–31, 245–70, 315
    assessment of groundwater management in, 267–70
    augmentation of water supplies in, 304–5
    establishment of water district, 248–50
    history of supply problems in, 245, 247–48
    management costs, 308
    replenishment program of 1950s, 257, 259, 261
    supply-management program (1933–1948), 250–51
    supply-management program (1949–1964), 251–55
    supply-management program (1965–1991), 261–67
Orange County Farm Bureau, 248–49
Orange County Flood Control District, 55, 247, 249–51
Orange County Water Basin Conservation Committee, 253–54

Orange County Water District Act, 249–50, 254
Orange County Water District (OCWD), 151, 249–57, 259, 261–70, 275, 304–5, 310, 356
Orange County Water District v. City of Chino et al., 262
Orange County Water District v. City of Riverside et al., 255–57
Orange Grove wells, 91
Orange growing, 48
Orchard, William, 233, 235
Ostrom, Elinor, 7, 335, 344
Ostrom, Vincent, 8–9, 26, 349
Overdraft, 16–17
    Central Basin, 129
    Mojave River basins, 221, 225, 227
    Pasadena v. Alhambra, 82–83
    precedent and definition of, 216
    San Fernando Valley, 198–99, 201–2, 212
    West Basin, 99, 101–3
Overlying rights, 64, 281–82
Owens Valley, 208–10

Palos Verdes Estates (city), 105
Palos Verdes Sand and Gravel Company, 109
Palos Verdes Water Company, 106
Pasadena (city), 57–58, 61, 73, 75, 87–91, 93, 162. *See also Pasadena v. Alhambra*
Pasadena subarea, 29, 77
Pasadena v. Alhambra, 75–81, 198, 201–3
Peralta, Juan Pablo, 44
Percolation, 13–14
Performance, assessment of, 10–11
Peters, Donald, 285
Pickard, Florence T., 180, 185
Pickens Canyon, 35–36
Piezometric level, 15
Poland, J. F., 115
Political regime, importance of facilitative, 335–38
Pollution. *See* Contamination
Polycentric basin management, 8–9, 339–48
    Central Basin, 151, 153
    innovation and, 358–63
    West Basin, 120
Pomona Valley Municipal Water District, 275

Pomona Valley Water Company, 276
Population growth. *See* Urbanization
    and population growth
Porter, Carley V., 337
Porter, George K., 47
Porter, William, 235
Porter-Cologne Water Quality
    Control Act (1969), 337
Porter-Dolwig Ground Water Basin
    Protection Law (1961), 337
Portola, Gaspar de, 43–44
Prado Dam, 36, 251–52, 262–64
Praeger, Arnold, 106–7
Precipitation, 45–46
Prescriptive rights, 68
    Burbank and *Glendale* cases, 193
    Main San Gabriel Basin, 172
    Raymond Basin, 107–9
    San Fernando Valley, 197–99
    West Basin, 107–8
Problem solving, 322–31
Public economies, 9
Pueblo water rights, 67–68, 189,
    192–93, 196–97, 201, 205–6, 216
Puente Basin Water Agency, 187n3
Pulling water, 14
Pumping trough, 14
Pump tax, 112–15, 140, 253–55,
    270n1, 275–76, 278, 283–84, 355–57

Quasi-voluntary compliance, 347
Quinton, John, 189

Railroads, 48, 50
Rainfall. *See* Precipitation
RAND Corporation, 6
Raymond Basin, 28–29, 73–95, 202,
    310–11, 316
    assessment of self-management of,
        91–95
    Central Basin and, 129
    governance and management since
        Pasadena, 85, 87–91
    initial groundwater problems, 73, 75
    management costs, 308
    Pasadena v. Alhambra, 75–85
Raymond Basin Advisory Board, 90
Raymond Basin Management Board,
    90–91, 93
Raymond Fault, 28–29
Reasonable-use doctrine, 65–66

Recordation Act, 226, 229
Redondo Beach (city), 105
Rent seeking, 350–51
Replenishment
    artificial, 14
    Central Basin, 132
    Orange County, 251–55, 257–61,
        264–65
    Raymond Basin, 88–89
    urbanized areas, 23
    West Basin, 110–15, 117–18
Reports, investigative. *See*
    Investigative reports
Resource use, efficiency in, 11, 309–13
Return flows, 23
Rhone, Richard, 142
Rio Hondo, 30
Riparian rights, 64
Rising water, 15
Robinson, Hamilton, 136
Ross, Albert F., 256
Rules and norms, reliance on, 328–29
Runge, Ford, 347

Safe yield, 15, 356–57
    Chino Basin, 280–82
    Main San Gabriel Basin, 172–73
    Raymond Basin, 85–87
Salinity, 22
Salsbury, M. E., 142
Saltwater intrusion, 22, 59, 305
    Central Basin, 129, 130, 150–51
    Orange County, 252
    Orange County basin, 265–66
    West Basin, 97, 99, 101–3, 115–17
San Antonio Creek, 38
San Bernardino County Flood
    Control District, 274, 291
San Bernardino v. Riverside, 69
San Bernardino Valley Municipal
    Water District (SBVMWD), 262
San Bernardino Valley Water Con-
    servation District, 248
San Fernando (city), 47, 200–201,
    206, 211, 213
San Fernando Farm Homestead
    Association, 47
San Fernando subarea, 197, 199,
    201, 203–4, 205–6
San Fernando Valley, 34–36, 35,
    189–217, 316

adjudication, 321–22
assessment of management in,
  211–14
early conjunctive use program in,
  191–92
Glendale and *Burbank* cases, 192–94
Los Angeles v. San Fernando,
  195–200, 214–17
management costs, 308
during 1940s and early 1950s, 194–95
recent challenges and problems,
  207–10
San Fernando appeal, 200–204
San Fernando judgment (1979), 204–7
San Gabriel River, 27–34, 75–76
  Central Basin, 31–32
  Main San Gabriel Basin, 29–31
  Raymond Basin, 28–29
  West Basin, 32–34
San Gabriel River case
  adjudication, 132, 135–41, 163–67, 268
  judgment, 141–46, 169
San Gabriel Valley Municipal Water
  District (SGVMWD), 88, 93, 164–65,
  174–76, 179–80, 182, 186, 354
San Gabriel Valley Protective
  Association, 75, 162
San Jose Creek Reclamation Project,
  118
San Jose Fault, 37
San Pedro aquifer, 33
Santa Ana Canyon, 36
Santa Ana (city), 247, 250
Santa Ana River, 250–51
  adjudication, 261–64
  judgment, 275–78
  watershed, 36–39
Santa Ana Valley Irrigation
  Company, 254
Santa Ana Watershed Project Authority
  (SAWPA), 263, 268–69, 289
Santa Anita subarea, 29, 77
Santa Fe railroad, 50
Saturated zone, 14
SAWPA. *See* Santa Ana Watershed
  Project Authority
SBVMWD. *See* San Bernardino
  Valley Municipal Water District
Schneider, Anne, 25
Scientific knowledge, general
  knowledge versus, 24

Scott, LeRoy, 234
Search activity, 327
Seawater intrusion. *See* Saltwater
  intrusion
Self-conscious social behavior, 323–24
Self-governing groundwater
  systems, 339–43
Serra, Junipero, 43–44
SGVMWD. *See* San Gabriel Valley
  Municipal Water District
Shafer, Ross, 252
Shape, basin, 20–21
Shaw, Stanford C., 222, 231, 233,
  234–35
Shea, John, 171
Sierra Club, 179–80
Sierra Madre (city), 88, 91, 93, 135,
  164–65, 186
Silverado aquifer, 32, 33
Silver Lakes Ranch, 229
Smith, Zachary, 350
Social capital, 331–33
Southern California Edison
  Company, 58, 99, 229–32, 236
Southern California Water
  Company, 229, 234–35, 240
Southwest Water Fact-Finding
  Committee, 104
Spanish colonists, 43–44
Springs, 15
Spurgeon, William, 47, 49
Stark, Donald, 234–35, 324
State control, 6
State officials, 336
State Water Project, 3–4, 88, 93, 165–67,
  166–67, 222, 224–25, 236–37, 264
Stetson, Strauss, and Dresselhaus
  (engineering firm), 167
Stetson, Thomas, 25, 136–37, 140,
  141–42, 152, 167–71, 174, 181,
  188n10, 324
Stevens v. Oakdale Irrigation District, 192
Storage
  agreements, 286–88
  capacity, 4
  groundwater basins, 310–13
  surface, 18
  underground, 17–18
Subsidization, 355
Sunnyside aquifer, 32
Superfund, 178, 208

Surface storage, 18
Surplus water, 65, 68–69, 193
Surr, John B., 136–37, 139
Sylmar Basin, 35
Sylmar subarea, 197, 199, 201, 203, 207

Talbert Gap, 39, 265–66
Taxation
  Central and West basins, 112–15
  Chino Basin, 275–76, 278, 282–84
  Main San Gabriel Basin, 169
  Mojave Water Agency, 222, 224
  Orange County, 112, 252–55, 266–67
  pump tax, 112–15, 140, 253–55,
    270n1, 275–76, 278, 355–57
  San Gabriel River adjudication, 140
  West Basin, 122
Taylor, Ed, 232–33, 236
Tetrachloroethylene, 177–78, 207–8
Thirty-Fifth Parallel Association, 48
Thomas, Brennan, 135–37, 139, 165
Thomas, Franklin, 125n1
Three Valleys Municipal Water
  District, 274, 317n3
Time-and-place-specific information,
  24–25
Tocqueville, Alexis de, 7–8, 346, 349, 362
Torrance (city), 106, 119
Torres, Art, 179
Torres, Esteban, 179
Trager, Susan, 324
Transaction costs, 326
Transaction resource frontier, 333
Transmissivity rate, 14
Trichloroethylene, 177–78, 207–8
Tri-Counties Reforestation
  Committee, 54
Tri-Counties Water Conservation
  Association, 54, 247–48
Turner, Don A., 289

ULARA. See Upper Los Angeles
  River Area
Underground storage, 17–18
Upper Los Angeles River Area
  (ULARA), 34–36, 195–97, 199,
  204–5, 207–14, 303–5, 312, 316
Upper Mojave River Basin, 41
Upper San Gabriel Valley Municipal
  Water District (USGVMWD), 93,
  138–40, 165–71, 174–82, 184, 186

Upper San Gabriel Valley Municipal
  Water District v. City of Alhambra
  et al., 171
Upper San Gabriel Valley Water
  Association (USGVWA), 135–37,
  164–70
Urbanization and population growth
  Central Basin, 127, 129
  late nineteenth century, 51–53
  Los Angeles, 55–56
  Main San Gabriel Basin, 163
  Mojave River basins, 221–22, 238
  postwar period, 62–63
U.S. Army Corps of Engineers, 6,
  36, 55, 191, 211, 263
U.S. Forest Service, 210
U.S. Geological Survey, 97, 99,
  101–2, 162
U.S. Supreme Court, 261
USGVMWD. See Upper San Gabriel
  Valley Municipal Water District
USGVWA. See Upper San Gabriel
  Valley Water Association
Usufructuary rights, 63–64

Vadose zone, 14
Van Nuys, Isaac, 47
Verdugo Basin, 35
Verdugo subarea, 197, 199, 201, 203,
  206–7
Victorville (city), 239
Victorville County Water District,
  232–33
Volatile organic contamination
  Main San Gabriel Basin, 177–80

WATER. See Water Association to
  Establish Rights
Water and Politics (Vincent Ostrom), 26
Water Association to Establish
  Rights (WATER), 235, 238
Water Exchange Agreement, 80–81,
  87, 89
Watermaster
  Chino Basin, 284–86
  expenditures for, 306
  Main San Gabriel Basin, 174
  San Gabriel River, 141, 142, 143
  Upper Los Angeles River Area, 205
Water quality monitoring program
  (Main San Gabriel Basin), 175–76

Water Recordation Act (1955), 112,
  120-21, 147, 164, 170-71, 290
Water Replenishment District Act
  (1955), 112, 121, 278
Water rights, 63-69
  appropriative rights, 64-65
  prescriptive rights, 68-69
  pueblo water rights, 67-68
  "reasonable use" and correlative
    rights, 65-66
  riparian and overlying rights, 64
Watersheds
  Los Angeles River, 34-36
  Mojave River, 39-42
  San Gabriel River, 27-34
  Santa Ana River, 36-39
Water table, 14
WBMWD. *See* West Basin Municipal
  Water District
WBWA. *See* West Basin Water
  Association
Weatherford, Gary, 25
Weber Aircraft, 208
Weiner, Howard B., 280-81
Wells, 14, 16. *See also specific wells*
West Basin, 32-34, 97-125, 305, 316,
  340-41
  adjudication of rights in, 105-10
  assessment of management of, 119-25
  formation of municipal water
    district, 104-5
  information gathering, 102-4
  initial groundwater problems, 97,
    99, 101-2

  modifications to management
    program, 117-19
  replenishment problems, 110-15
  saltwater intrusion, 115-17
West Basin Campaign Committee, 104
West Basin Ground Water Conser-
  vation Group, 103, 115, 120-21
West Basin Municipal Water District
  (WBMWD), 104-6, 111
West Basin Survey Committee,
  102-3, 120-21
West Basin Water Association (WBWA),
  103-13, 115-16, 120-21, 130
West Basin Water Replenishment
  District, 153-54
Western Municipal Water District
  of Riverside County (WMWD),
  262, 274
Western Unit (Raymond Basin), 77
Weymouth, Frank E., 61
Whelan, Martin, Jr., 231-34
Whittier Narrows, 29-32, 113, 138, 144
Whittier Narrows Dam, 132
Whittier Narrows Reclamation
  Project, 118
Winter, Sidney, 360
WMWD. *See* Western Municipal
  Water District of Riverside County
Wright, Donald, 201-2
Wright, Kenneth, 78, 103, 106, 130,
  192-93, 324
Wright Act (1889), 53

Yorba, Jose Antonio, 44

About the Author

William Blomquist has been studying water resource issues and institutions for ten years. He is the author of several articles on these topics and the 1991 U.S. Advisory Commission on Intergovernmental Relations report *Coordinating Water Resources in the Federal System.*

Blomquist received his Ph.D. in political science from Indiana University in Bloomington in 1987. Since then, he has been a member of the political science faculty at Indiana University in Indianapolis, teaching state and local government, constitutional law, and political analysis. He lives in Indianapolis with his wife, Kerry.